To my parents

SOVIET HELICOPTERS

Design, Development and Tactics

John Everett-Heath

JANE'S INFORMATION GROUP

Published in the United Kingdom in 1983 and 1988 by
Jane's Information Group,
163 Brighton Road
Coulsdon
Surrey CR3 2NX United Kingdom

ISBN 0 7106 0572 2

Distributed in the Philippines and the USA and its
dependencies by Jane's Information Group Inc

Computer Typesetting by Tameside Filmsetting Ltd, Ashton-under-Lyne, Lancs

Printed and bound in the United Kingdom by
Biddles Ltd, Guildford and King's Lynn

Contents

Preface

It is over 50 years since the first Soviet rotary-wing aircraft flew. Giant strides have been made in the intervening years. The Russians have not only built the four largest helicopter types in the world but also have in service the two most heavily armed battlefield helicopters. For 35 years they have had machines with co-axial, contra-rotating rotor systems; this configuration is still being pursued and a new type has just entered service. Soviet books and articles for some years now have emphasized the value of helicopters both in war and for civil use. These words are backed by action: the continuing development of advanced types, a high production rate and innovative use. As the *Soviet Military Review* put it in April 1979: "A helicopter is an irreplaceable labourer in the sky."

The aim of this book is to trace the historical development of Soviet rotary-wing aircraft, including autogiros, and to describe their characteristics and employment. A short chapter is devoted to Soviet design philosophy. It is, however, a limited aim; a discussion of the relative merits and demerits of Soviet designs, techniques, procedures or tactical doctrine has been deliberately avoided. The intention has been to provide a balanced and impartial survey of the Soviet helicopter scene. The book is for the interested layman and I hope that I have therefore succeeded in eliminating all but the most essential technical terms. I have included a simple Glossary.

I am in debt to a number of people who have kindly provided me with help: Colonel Michael Badger, Professor Christopher Donnelly, Frank McGuire, Sergei Sikorsky and Kenneth Munson. I have also received help and advice from many others, notably Mrs Felicity Cave for checking translations from the Russian, Mr P. W. Welsh of the FAI for providing details of all rotary-wing records, and Christy Campbell and Alex Vanags-Baginskis of Jane's. I must also express my gratitude to my wife and children for their patience and encouragement.

I am very grateful to Mr John R. Taylor, editor of *Jane's All the World's Aircraft*, for permission to extract relevant specifications from his annual publications. For specific detail they are unequalled in their comprehensive coverage and accuracy. I am also indebted to the International Institute for Strategic Studies for permission to quote from the *Military Balance 1982/83*.

I have used many other references. I have relied on a number of books and pamphlets by Russian authors including Mikhail Mil, Boris Yuriev and the naturalised American, Igor Sikorsky. I have also drawn on Aleksandr Yakovlev's *Tsel Zhizni* (The Aim of a Lifetime) and Aleksandr Izakson's *Sovetskoe Vertoletostroenie* (Soviet Helicopter Construction) which is particularly useful in describing developments up to the end of the 1940s. Two excellent works of reference are Václav Němeček's book *Sovetska Letadla* (Soviet Aircraft) and Jean Alexander's *Russian Aircraft Since 1940*. All these sources have been supplemented by Western and Communist aviation magazines, some unfortunately now defunct. As far as Soviet publications are concerned I have made use of Aviaexport brochures and articles in *Aviatsiya i Kosmonavtika* (Aviation and Cosmonautics), *Krasneya Zvezda* (Red Star), *Voennyi Vestnik* (Military Herald), the English-language *Soviet Military Review* and various texts published separately.

J. E-H.   London, December 1982

Preface to Second Edition

Since the publication of the First Edition in 1983 the Soviet investment in helicopters, both civil and military, has not slackened. Indeed, a number of new types has been under development and new roles given to older types; experimentation with new tactics, techniques and procedures has been continuous. Much has therefore happened during the last five years and a considerable amount of new information has become available from a variety of sources. This Second Edition has been completely reviewed, revised and brought up-to-date with much new material added. I have included a select bibliography this time.

This revision could not have been undertaken without the help of Charles Dick and Christopher Donnelly to whom I am most grateful for their advice on the tactical use of helicopters. Once again, of course, I must thank Alex Vanags-Baginskis for all the help that he has provided in so many ways; to Carolynn Lawrie go my admiration and thanks for converting many of my drafts into typescript. I am indebted, as before, to John Taylor, editor of Jane's *All the World's Aircraft* and to Jane's Information Group, for permission to extract relevant specifications and to John Cross for permission to quote from the International Institute for Strategic Studies' *Military Balance 1987/88*. Finally, my wife and children have been no less patient or encouraging, even with the distraction of a move back to the United Kingdom after living abroad for three years; to them I owe a great deal.

J.E.H.   May 1988

Introduction

This book is entitled *Soviet Helicopters* but because the Soviet leadership gives to the development of its Armed Forces a very high priority it has a distinctly military flavour. Only one helicopter, the Ka-26 Hoodlum, has entered production which was not originally designed for military service. Many of the others, it is true, have been used both for military purposes and in support of the civil economy. However, some 2,000 helicopters from the Soviet Union's only civil airline, Aeroflot, are available at very short notice to support the military forces; and it is no quirk of fate that Aeroflot is 'commanded' by a Colonel General of Aviation, a former commander of Transport Aviation.

The development of the Soviet Military Air Forces since the end of the Great Patriotic War (1941–45) has not by any means followed a smooth course. At the end of that war the Red Air Force was accused of exaggerating its contribution to the victory and sharply reminded that the Ground Forces remained pre-eminent. Soviet political and military leaders still considered that the role of air power was merely to support ground operations. This view prevailed until after Stalin's death when, in the mid-1950s, the value of nuclear weapons was recognised. The Strategic Rocket Forces assumed the primary position in the Armed Forces with the Ground Forces being relegated to a secondary role. Nevertheless, the principal aim in war was to defeat the enemy's military forces and capture his territory – a feat that only the Ground Forces could achieve. Strategic air operations, however, were now believed to be more effective but still only of lesser importance.

During the Krushchev era (1957–64) strategic and tactical air power declined in favour of missiles and an upsurge in air defence forces. But even before Krushchev was deposed the marshals, rather than the air marshals, were beginning to express their dissatisfaction with the low priority accorded to the tactical air forces. They made their point convincingly enough to generate a modernisation of these forces in the mid-1960s. There was little doubt that many of the roles undertaken in support of the Ground Forces could well be discharged by helicopters, the production of which gathered pace significantly towards the end of the 1960s. It was then only a matter of time before the appearance of an attack helicopter and the establishment of a helicopter force structure to meet the needs of the ground forces. Towards the end of the 1970s the Soviet Military Air Forces began a major reorganisation. In February 1979 a contributor to *Voennyi Vestnik* had noted that ". . . today already more than 50% of the destructive firepower potential in the tactical zone belongs to aviation. Operations from the air have ceased being auxiliary and have been transferred into a component, organic part of combined arms combat." This view was given expression by commanders of Groups of Forces and Military Districts being allocated their own air assets. The helicopter element became known as Army Aviation, with some machines being subordinated to armies and even divisions.

During the last decade the procurement of an increasing number of helicopters and greater mechanisation have given the Soviet Ground Forces a mobility that they have never previously enjoyed. Together with technological developments in weaponry, this new-found mobility has opened up possibilities for dynamic new operational concepts.

The pace and scope of Soviet military modernisation during the last decade has been impressive, embracing both nuclear and conventional forces. Not only has a wide spectrum of new land, sea, air and strategic weapons been deployed but the numbers held have been increased in line with the Soviet view that victory will go to the side that has the determination and sheer numbers to maintain its effort, irrespective of human and materiel losses. But even more important is the realisation that Soviet Super Power status rests largely on Soviet military strength. Continual expansion and modernisation are the goals therefore and they are made possible by the positive willingness of the Soviet leaders to allocate between 12% and 17% as the estimated share of the Gross Domestic Product devoted to defence. For the sake of comparison in 1985 the USA allocated 6.9% and Great Britain 5.2%. For the last decade Soviet annual defence expenditure is thought to have grown in real terms at an average rate of about 3%. Spending on defence-related research and development has held steady at about 20% of total defence expenditure for the last decade while spending on equipment procurement is estimated to have risen by 3% to 5% each year from 1981–86.

The Communist Party runs the Soviet Union according to the tenets of Marxism-Leninism. This ideology and the experience of the Russian and Soviet nation are the two most influential factors in Soviet policy-making. The Party claims the right to control every facet of Soviet society, including and particularly the Armed Forces since they are one of the main instruments with which the party ensures its policies are carried out. These Forces are organised, equipped and trained to undertake any actions demanded of them within and beyond the borders of the USSR; war, in the Soviet view, is merely an extension of the political process.

The relationship between the Armed Forces and their controlling authority, the Communist Party and not the Soviet government, is totally unlike that which prevails between the non-partisan military forces and their governments in the Western democracies. Soviet political control is pervasive and is achieved simply by the necessity for Party approval for all promotions. The Party has laid down four principal roles for its Armed Forces:

- Deter capitalist-imperialist aggression against the USSR; if deterrence fails, defend the USSR as the socialist homeland and ensure the decisive and complete defeat of any enemy who dares attack the Soviet nation.
- Ensure favourable international conditions for the building of socialism and communism.
- Ensure, together with other socialist countries, the reliable defence and security of the entire socialist camp against external attack or counter-revolution.
- Provide support and military assistance to national liberation movements.

NATO, as a defensive alliance, does not need to match the Warsaw Pact man for man or weapon for weapon. But as the British Foreign Secretary asked in January 1987: "Why do (Soviet) weapons and military doctrine match so closely what is needed for a swift offensive strike against Western Europe? Why do the forces of the Soviet Union go so far beyond the needs of a purely defensive strategy?"

A factor that Soviet planners cannot escape is the geography of their country and its climate. The Soviet Union traverses 11 time zones, extending over 9,650 km (6,000 miles) from west to east and 4,825 km (3,000 miles) from north to south. It has a population of some 280 million compared to that of the United States of around 240 million. Siberia alone comprises over 50% of the Soviet land mass. Its size is mind-numbing: it comprises one-sixth of the land area of the world (except Antarctica). The whole of the USA and half Canada would fit into Siberia comfortably. The flatness of the terrain is another important consideration. Between the Ural Mountains and the United Kingdom, a distance of about 3,700 km (2,300 miles), there is no land higher than 500 m (1,640 ft). The huge but flat expanse of the European part of the USSR, larger than Western Europe, has had a major influence on Soviet battle doctrine, tactics and the design of equipment. The lack of terrain features encourages speed of action but makes more difficult concealment; thus surprise must be achieved by other means such as speed, deception, camouflage and so on. But this harsh and forbidding land, the northern section of which suffers from eternal winter, is rich in natural resources. It was Mikhail Lomonosov, who first awakened Russian interest in rotary craft in the 18th century, who predicted that Siberia's natural resources, once tapped, would become the source of Russian power. But the climate must also be taken into account, particularly in the vastness of Siberia where it can range from 38° C (100° F) in the summer to −51°C (−60° F) in winter. Despite bonus payments and other inducements the majority of Russians are not keen to work in climatically harsh and geographically remote regions and it is therefore by no means easy to exploit the potential of Siberia.

It is easy to appreciate how these realities of nature – distance and climate – have limited the speed of development and how aircraft can help. Where there are no airfields recourse to helicopters must be made if the riches are to be tapped in the quickest and most economical way. It is believed, for example, that some 600 Aeroflot helicopters are working in the Tyumen gas and oil fields, just east of the Ural Mountains to the north-east of Sverdlovsk. So the requirement for large numbers of helicopters of different types is easily understood: the build-up of armed might and the conquest of the remoter regions of the country.

In the two decades after the Second World War the rapid progress of Soviet helicopter development astonished many Western observers. Few remembered that the intricacies of rotary-wing flight had been under study, if intermittently, in Russia as far back as 1754. The spasmodic flow of information ever since had made it difficult to appreciate the true situation and this led to a tendency, at least until quite recently, to underestimate Soviet capabilities. Hopefully Stalin's comment to a Western leader in 1945 is a thing of the past: "Even though the Russians are a simple people, the West often makes the mistake of regarding them as fools." With the appearance of the Mi-24 Hind and the Mi-26 Halo that particular failing may now have been dispelled. The assessment of Soviet research and development is a notoriously difficult task and one that is fraught with pitfalls; little more than educated guesses can usually be made. Even when a piece of equipment is eventually revealed in public it is rarely possible to get a completely accurate technical description and an idea of performance capabilities unless the machine is offered for export. The legendary Tsarist and Communist obsession with secrecy does not make historical and technical evaluations easy; and any efforts are clouded by propaganda, unverified claims of success, paucity of published data and the overriding Soviet unwillingness to admit failure. Accident statistics, for example, are never published and, while there has been a greater willingness to report aircraft crashes since Mikhail Gorbachev became the General Secretary of the Communist Party, such openness has not extended to military aircraft.

The United States has always led the Soviet Union in the number of military helicopters in service. The *Military Balance 1987/88*, for example, credits the US Army alone with virtually 9,000 while the Soviet Armed Forces total about 5,000. The gap is slowly closing but since it is much easier for Aeroflot helicopters to be pressed into military service the US Army probably has a lesser overall capability. There is an approximate balance between armed helicopters; the Soviet Union has the edge in heavy lift and electronic warfare helicopters while the USA is undoubtedly superior in reconnaissance and utility helicopters and at sea with her anti-submarine warfare and Marine Corps helicopters.

This introduction would not be complete without mentioning Mikhail Mil and Nikolai Kamov, both now dead. Mil, of course, has no rival as the leading Soviet helicopter designer and he eclipsed Kamov in the number of different types he designed that entered production and in sheer numbers of machines built. His textbook is still standard reading for Soviet aeronautical students. Kamov was less successful but he consistently designed small helicopters that found favour with the Soviet Navy. Both men were pragmatic, intent on designing helicopters that were rugged, reliable and able to do the job, wherever it might be, for which they were designed. Both were showered with honours.

Mikhail Mil (1909–1970), Chief of the leading helicopter design bureau, standing in front of one of his Mi-6 Hooks. (Novosti)

Nikolai Kamov (1902–1973). His compact co-axial, contra-rotating designs have been seen around the world in operation with the Soviet Navy. (Novosti)

The Soviet helicopter industry is experienced and well established. Tishchenko and Mikheyev, who now preside over the Mil and Kamov design bureaux respectively, can be expected to maintain a flow of sophisticated, yet unfussy, designs to meet the future needs of the Soviet Armed Forces and Aeroflot. No doubt some surprises are in store for the West as some of these designs enter production in the next few years.

The Union of Soviet Socialist Republics, usually known as the Soviet Union, came into being on 1 January 1923 and comprises 15 Republics. While only the inhabitants of the Russian Soviet Federated Socialist Republic call themselves Russians I have referred to all inhabitants of the Soviet Union as Russians for the sake of convenience.

The performance figures given at the end of each chapter are taken in the main from *Jane's All the World's Aircraft* with kind permission of the publishers. Maximum speed is taken as straight and level at maximum take-off weight; range with standard fuel and a 5% reserve. It should be understood that in general terms payload and range are directly connected: the greater the useful load lifted, the less distance it can be taken because less weight is available for fuel. Conversely, with maximum fuel on board the full useful load cannot always be carried although the full range is achieved.

The date of the first flight always refers to that of the first prototype of a new helicopter and not the first flight date of a later version whose characteristics may be described. Contemporary Western aircraft are included for comparative purposes.

NATO has a system of codenaming Soviet aircraft: bombers begin with the letter B, transports with C, fighters with F, helicopters with H, etc. Subsequent versions are identified by a further letter in sequence, eg. Hind-A, -B, -C, -D, -E, -F and -G.

Russian is a phonetic language and the Cyrillic alphabet has 30 letters and two symbols. The method of transliterating into the Latin alphabet varies. The system used in this book is based on that known as the Library of Congress modified. No use, however, has been made of the symbol ´ for the soft sign ь which has been ignored. Similarly, the hard sign ъ has been ignored. The third and final exception is that I have used 'ya' for я rather than 'ia'. In this system ё is shown as e and not 'yo'. As far as combinations of letters are concerned these have been transliterated as follows:

ый	:	y	in names only. Otherwise	ый	:	yi
ий	:	y		ий	:	ii
ье	:	ie				
ьи	:	yi				
х	:	kh				

Familiar Russian names, eg. Sikorsky, Yuriev, *Ogonyok* etc, have been spelled in accordance with common English usage.

The Beginning
1754–1940

Soviet Academician Boris Yuriev, called by some Soviet writers 'The Grand Old Man of Soviet Helicopter Development', wrote in his book *The Aerodynamic Design of Helicopters*: "Our country is rightfully called the birthplace of the helicopter. Not only was its design developed here, but also the first real flight of such a machine took place here. All this was not done by us by the method of 'sheer inventiveness', but through the growth of the theory of such craft and by conducting a multitude of experiments." This opinion, which might be vigorously challenged in certain quarters, is based on the work of Lomonosov from 1754 and others since, and the belief that Soviet helicopters were the first to fly, in the 1930s, rather than merely to jump.

It was Mikhail Lomonosov who designed and built the first self-propelled model of a lifting airscrew in 1754. Also rejoicing in an unofficial title, that of 'The Father of Russian Science', he was among other things, a physicist, chemist, astronomer and geologist. In 1745 he had been the first Russian to be elected to the Russian Academy of Sciences. The Russian claim that Lomonosov's design was built in complete ignorance of Leonardo da Vinci's work three hundred years earlier. Be that as it may, the purpose of the apparatus was to lift thermometers and other light scientific instruments into the air. The proceedings of the meeting of the Academy on 1 July, 1754 at which details of the device were presented read: "The Honourable Adviser Lomonosov demonstrated his invention called *Aerodynamic* to be used for the purpose of depressing the air by means of wings rotated horizontally in the opposite directions by the agency of a spring of the type used in clocks in order to lift the machine into the upper layers of the air." (1) The device 'promised desirable results' but was not developed further because of the excessive weight of the springs.

Matters rested there for over a hundred years until, in 1869, another scientist, A. N. Lodygin, presented a design for a helicopter, which he called an 'Electroflier', to the Central Engineering Agency. It was of an unusual shape with a propeller at one end for propulsion and control, and a crude rotor above for lifting purposes. Powered by a 300 hp electric motor, the craft would have weighed about 1,630 kg (3,600 lb). An ambitious project – and one with which the members of the Agency were not impressed. Lodygin did not help his case by omitting to describe the storage batteries which were to provide the energy for the electric motor. After closely examining the design the members concluded that it was "entirely inapplicable in practice". Attempts to control an 'aerostat' by means of propellers, sails and wings had been made before, they observed, and no useful results had come from them. They did not expect to hear from Lodygin again. Nor did they for another 44 years. This time, just after the outbreak of the First World War in 1914, Lodygin asked the Russian government for 5,000 roubles to subsidise his work on a one-man ornithopter with four paddle wheels, each driven by a separate motor. The machine had no rudders or elevators, control being obtained by varying the power to the paddles. Simultaneously hopeful and doubtful, an Army Technical Board scrutinised Lodygin's design in November 1914. In due course it delivered its considered opinion that Lodygin had made no errors in his calculations and concluded that: 'If successfully realised, a flying apparatus of the type proposed by the electrical engineer, Lodygin, could be of certain use to the cause of military aviation." Nevertheless, the Board could not bring itself to recommend the grant of 5,000 roubles – or even a lesser amount – to the luckless inventor. Just before the Revolution overtook Russia Lodygin emigrated to the USA where he died in 1923.

While Lodygin was otherwise engaged between 1869 and 1914 others were examining the use of airscrews for flying machines. In 1871 M. A. Rykachev, a member of the Academy of Sciences and Director of the Central Physics Laboratory, made a study of lifting rotors, measuring their thrust and power by means of a small device driven by a clock spring. A metallurgist, D. K. Chernov, developed the theory of wings and propellers, based, according to Yuriev, "on the wholly correct idea of the need for repulsing a mass of the surrounding air downwards to obtain lift." Tests with a propeller actuated by a clock spring were conducted between 1888 and 1893. Chernov presented his work to the Russian Technical Society in 1893 and begged for financial help. He even offered to put 5,000 roubles of his own towards further research. His appeals fell on deaf ears; in the words of Yuriev, not wishing to miss the opportunity to take a dig at the previous regime: "He received no assistance; neither private individuals nor Tsarist institutions wished to render aid to this outstanding scientist to complete his remarkable works."

In 1897 I. Bykov suggested a monocycle, supported by an airscrew and propelled by pedalling. This was greeted by the Aviation Division of the Electrotechnical Committee with a distinct lack of enthusiasm; such a design presupposed a certain level of physical fitness. In September 1899 a peasant artisan, one Nikita Mitreikin, presented his 'aviation bicycle' which was driven by two rotors worked by the pilot's feet. Mitreikin claimed that he had successfully tested it, lifting it one *arshin* (71 cm, 28 in) and flown it forward five *sazhens* (10.67 m, 35 ft). He offered it to the 'learned gentlemen' of the Ministry of War as an aerial ambulance. Since no records exist of aviation bicycles entering service with the Russian Army in the early days of this century we can only conclude that the 'learned gentlemen' politely declined Mitreikin's offer. Nonetheless, in the accounts of his flights, Mitreikin described the problems of torque: ". . . it can lift into the air, fly forward; but in this it puzzled me that, having risen even half an *arshin* into the air, it turned me too, though slowly, in the opposite direction of the wings . . ." Mitreikin went on persuasively: "Although I never rose up into the air higher than one *arshin*, nor flew forward more than five *sazhens*, still I was convinced of the full practicability. Therefore, if my labours are lost, it will only be in case the learned gentlemen pay no attention to my model . . ."

In 1899 Nikolai Ye. Zhukovsky had established the first aerodynamic laboratory in Russia as part of Moscow University. In 1902 a wind tunnel was added. Zhukovsky came to be hailed as the 'Father of Russian Aviation'. Over the next few years he conducted a number of studies devoted to helicopter theory. In 1904 he published a paper *On the Useful Load Lifted by a Helicopter* in which he wrote that ". . . given the present proportionate weight of the engine, a twin-propeller helicopter cannot lift into the air more than a definite useful load . . ." Multi-propeller helicopters on the other hand, he believed, could lift any load. In 1909 he investigated the effect of forward speed on a helicopter's rotor and showed that three forces and three tilting moments act on it.

In that year Zhukovsky began to lecture at the Moscow Technical Institute on the

Theoretical Principles of Aeronautics and five years later a special aeronautical section was formed. Three of Zhukovsky's most famous students were G. Kh. Sabinin, Vladimir P. Vetchinkin and Boris N. Yuriev. These three envisaged a helicopter with the rotor mast tilted slightly forwards, thus permitting vertical ascent and forward flight.

During this period helicopter projects were proceeding elsewhere in Russia. Konstantin Antonov designed a co-axial, twin multi-bladed rotor helicopter in 1907 which was subsequently built at the Lessner Works in St. Petersburg (now Leningrad) and called the *Helikoplan*. A 35 hp engine was installed, also to drive a tractor propeller for forward propulsion. Lifting tests were far from successful and Antonov, suffering hugely from disappointment, destroyed the machine.

N. I. Sorokin and V. V. Tatarinov also built helicopters. Tatarinov's device was called an *Aeromobile* and consisted of four lifting propellers and a five-bladed 'centrifugal propeller', all driven by a 25 hp water-cooled engine, and a frame. Progress was so slow that the Minister of War, Sukhomlinov, and his technical advisers visited Tatarinov in August 1909 and told him that no more funds would be forthcoming. Tatarinov took this decision badly but continued without official help until 4 November, 1910 when "hounded by the Press (for failing to justify the hopes placed in him), I suffered a psychic disturbance under the influence of which I personally set fire to my aerodynamic laboratory, hangar and shed, destroying all the apparatus contained therein." Yuriev was unsympathetic, archly judging Tatarinov and the others: "But all of these helicopters were also unable to leave the ground since their designers attempted to dispense with theory and preliminary tests. Their failure, thus, was perfectly normal", that is to say, to be expected.

Having returned to Kiev after spending four months in Paris, the cradle of European aviation, Igor I. Sikorsky set about building his first flying machine in May 1909. Not yet 20 years old, he was to experience failure initially as a helicopter designer. He turned to fixed-wing flight and not for some 30 years did he return to his first great interest, vertical flight. His first helicopter took just three months to build and another three months to realise that it was a failure. Although it could not fly Sikorsky derived considerable experience and engineering information from his experiment. A co-axial design with two sets of two-bladed rotors turning in opposite directions, the upper with a diameter of 4.57 m (15 ft), the lower with one of 5.03 m (16 ft 6 in), the 25 hp Anzani engine lacked sufficient power even to lift the empty machine, which weighed 204 kg (450 lb), off the ground, let alone with a pilot in it.

In February 1910 Sikorsky began to build concurrently his second helicopter and his first aeroplane, the S-1. This second version had larger (5.8 m, 19 ft) diameter, three-bladed rotors but weighed some 24 kg (53 lb) less than the first model. In early spring it was ready. In the words of Sikorsky himself: "It was a graceful, although strange-looking machine. With its slender propellers in motion, it resembled a huge butterfly. Results were somewhat better and the helicopter lifted almost its whole weight of about 180 kg (397 lb). The first tests indicated that it could not carry the additional weight of an operator." Sikorsky turned his attention to his S-1. While devoting his main energies in this direction he still found time to experiment further with his second helicopter but gradually came to realise that it would never fly (2). Russia was to benefit instead from his successes as a fixed-wing designer but never as the builder of helicopters.

While listening to Zhukovsky, Yuriev proposed at the end of 1910 that theory should be converted into practice in the shape of a co-axial design. A 70 hp engine would drive two two-bladed rotors, the upper 9 m (29 ft 6 in) in diameter, and the lower 3 m (9 ft 10 in). A variable pitch 'steering propeller' would be used for directional control. Sparing a thought for the hapless pilot, Yuriev allowed for a parachute in the event of an engine failure. Weight of the machine was some 320 kg (705 lb). In 1911 he designed a second version. Yuriev now estimated that 50 hp would be required for take-off but, since no engine that could produce this power was available locally, the craft was never built. In this year Yuriev claimed that he invented cyclic control "which finally solved the problem of helicopter control." (3)

Unlike most of his contemporaries, Yuriev based his next design on a single main rotor. In 1912 he built such a helicopter with a rotor diameter of 8 m (26 ft 3 in) and powered by the same type of 25 hp Anzani engine used by Sikorsky. The machine had a small tail rotor. The 'aeronautical section' of the Society for the Promotion of Inventors helped Yuriev in this venture but, through a severe shortage of funds, decided to build it without cyclic control and carry out the first tests with the machine captive. It was first put on display at the 1912 International Aeronautical and Automobile Exposition in Moscow. For his design Yuriev was presented with an Exposition Gold Medal "for the excellent theoretical development of a helicopter project." During the ground tests which followed the Exposition the main rotor drive shaft failed due to the uneven running of the engine. The project was abandoned because no more funds were available and because of the outbreak of war. Yuriev was one of the first to comprehend the principle of autorotation, likening it to the benefits derived from a fully reliable parachute. This technique "with the blades of a large rotor revolving in the air, with the motor idle" he called 'rotor gliding'. The credit for the discovery that a helicopter could land safely, however, goes to another of Zhukovsky's students, G. V. Sorokovmovsky, who was the first to investigate the possibility during the early months of 1910.

Zhukovsky, Yuriev and others have written of their disgust at the low priority accorded to aviation by the Tsarist government which apparently considered its development a "matter of private initiative". Continuing this theme, Yuriev wrote: "The Tsarist government, bowing before everything that came from abroad but cold to its own researchers, showed no inclination to aid in this work." Indeed, it was believed that the government thought aviation a threat to its own survival and a representative of the *Duma* was quoted as saying: "Before the man in the street is allowed to fly, one must teach the police how to fly." As far as the designers were concerned – writing at a time after the Revolution when dissent of any kind was simply not tolerated by the Communist leaders – the picture changed dramatically for the better once the Revolution and Civil War had run their courses.

The 1910/11 edition of *Jane's All the World's Aircraft* gives a brief description only of two hitherto unknown helicopter designs. The first is a Baranovsky monoplane-helicopter with a 'bird-shaped body', a wing on either side of the engine and a propeller 'mounted behind the planes'. The same edition describes the Loutzky biplane-helicopter with the comment: "Does not seem to have come up to expectations. Probably scrapped ere this." Both were designed to rise vertically although no mention is made of the means to achieve this.

As the storm clouds gathered for the First World War even the optimistic and hard-working Yuriev could not claim that any of his designs were worthy of production. The war itself and the subsequent Revolution tended to cramp the style of men such as Yuriev and effectively prevented any further helicopter development while Russia sorted out her internal affairs.

Some enthusiasts, however, did continue with their projects although none succeeded in even completing construction. A. S. Korzinshchikov, who had taken out patent No. 21,232 in 1912, at least inspired the Vice-Governor of Nizhny-Novgorod and the Chief of the local artillery forces to take an interest in his design but, though impressed, they were unable to obtain any funds for its construction. K. Ye. Moroz almost completed his machine in September 1915. It was an amphibian and had removable wings but lacked sufficiently high quality cylinders and pistons for the engine. Despite his efforts Moroz was not able to overcome this problem and the aircraft was never completed. Another amphibian was proposed in the same month by F. S. Buryan to the War Minister but he declined to provide support since he was not convinced that Buryan had explored all the technical problems in sufficient depth. A large helicopter, capable of carrying up to 20 passengers, was proposed by A. P. Fedotov. Its sheer size attracted interest but again it came to nothing.

By 1919 *Jane's* had almost lost touch with aviation developments inside Russia. After a mere three short paragraphs it concluded that: "All this information is merely of historical value, for since the deposition of his Imperial Majesty the Tsar by his rebellious subjects Russia has ceased to exist. The Bolshevik armies apparently possess a few aircraft manned and maintained by traitors to the Emperor." By 1922 *Jane's* had an even less complimentary view of Russia: "The ideals of Bolshevism, which were apparently 'Everyone for himself' ... were not in keeping with industrial prosperity and development with the result that popular interest palled and production fell off." Helicopter development was impossible in such circumstances. Indeed, *Jane's* believed that "So long as the Red Regime exists Russia can never hope to reorganise its aircraft industry. ... According to those who know, the Russian is temperamentally unfit to fly, and will never make a mechanic."

In December 1918, however, unbeknownst to the editors of *Jane's*, Russia's leading aeronautical laboratory was re-established as the Central Aero- and Hydrodynamic Institute (*Tsentralnyi Aero-gidrodinamicheskii Institut* – TsAGI). TsAGI's purpose was to undertake the development of new aircraft or configurations and the building of prototypes. Thus all its aircraft were to be experimental. Once accepted for production actual manufacture was to be undertaken by plants throughout the country. It was not until 1925, however, that TsAGI began helicopter research in earnest under the direction of its vertical flight section leader, the ubiquitous Yuriev (4). For the next three years painstaking research into the theoretical problems associated with rotor systems, flying controls and torque was conducted. Two models were built as a result of this research, both to be powered by the French 110 hp Gnome-Rhône engine, licence built as the M-2 (5). This engine was favoured for helicopters because it did not require a radiator for cooling purposes yet had sufficient power to drive the rotor. The first model was of a single-engined machine with two contra-rotating rotors on outriggers on either side of the fuselage; the second, a huge eight-engined affair with eight rotors, envisaged as a combat machine with a machine gun.

The third line of development proved the most successful and in 1928 a decision was taken to build an experimental helicopter. This culminated in the first Soviet helicopter to fly, the TsAGI 1-EA (*Eksperimentalnyi Apparat*, Experimental Apparatus). The group was strengthened and renamed the Section of Special Constructions (*Otdel Osobykh Konstruktsii* – OOK). Almost immediately, however, TsAGI lost Yuriev when he left to join the Academy of Sciences, his place being taken by his old pre-Revolutionary associate, G. Kh. Sabinin. Despite the move Yuriev remained the inspiration behind helicopter development, maintaining a great personal interest. But before following this line we should go back again to 1928 and examine another branch of rotary-wing development.

KaSkr-I and II

The first Soviet rotary-wing craft to fly was actually an autogiro, the KaSkr-1. Inspired by the success achieved by the Spaniard, Juan de la Cierva, with his autogiros, Nikolai I. Kamov, later to become a successful helicopter designer, and Nikolai K. Skrzhinsky built a machine which took its name from the initial letters of its designers' names; it was popularly called the *Krasnyi Inzhener* (Red Engineer). Constructed in 1929, it made its maiden flight in September of that year and was then flown for the next two years from Moscow Central Airport by I. V. Mikheyev, father of the present Head of the Kamov OKB. The KaSkr-I was in fact little more than a conversion of the U-1 trainer, a Soviet-built copy of the Avro-504K, with a wider track and, latterly, a larger rudder. The four-bladed, 12 m (39 ft 4½ in) diameter rotor was pylon-mounted above the fuselage and spun up to take-off rpm by the engine by means of a clutch. Power was supplied by a 110 hp Gnome-Rhône radial engine which regrettably proved to be inadequate for its task. The machine was thus re-engined with a five cylinder 230 hp Gnome-Rhône Titan radial engine in 1930, given a different rudder, and redesignated KaSkr-II. This more powerful engine confirmed the decision to undertake the modification and the test pilot, D. A. Koshits, made some 90 flights. He reached a height of 450 m (1,476 ft) and a maximum speed of 110 kph (68 mph); an endurance of 28 minutes was achieved.

These bald facts hide a series of incidents which do not normally come the way of the average pilot. Koshits could be forgiven for any periods of doubt that he may have had as to the qualifications of the designers when "... sometimes during the flight tests bolts, fasteners and aileron controls broke loose. ..." His courage and dedication were undeniable. Gross weight of this two-seater was 1,100 kg (2,425 lb).

TsAGI 2-EA

Vyacheslav A. Kuznetsov took over the mantle of leading autogiro designer in the early 1930s and he was assisted, among others, by Mikhail L. Mil. His first venture was the 2-EA, another two-seater autogiro with bent-up wing tips and a twin fin and rudder assembly. It was a direct copy of the British Cierva C.19 Mk 3. It had a wire-braced four-bladed rotor, spun up through a clutch, by the same Gnome-Rhône Titan engine as in the KaSkr-II. The engine drove a conventional propeller. Test pilot K. A. Korzinshchikov made the maiden flight in 1931, design work having started in the autumn of 1930. Despite many difficulties, including serious rotor vibrations, which were slowly overcome, an excellent performance was claimed for this autogiro: a speed range of 58–160 kph (36–99 mph), a ceiling of 4,200 m (13,780 ft) and an endurance of 1¾ hrs. In 1933 it was assigned to the prestigious Maksim Gorky squadron (6) once the research and development tests for which it was really built were complete. Here, it turned out to be little more than a showpiece and in 1934 it was retired to a museum when the engine wore out.

TsAGI 4-EA

The success of the 2-EA encouraged further development. The intention now was to have a Soviet-designed engine and use the machine for military pilot training; furthermore, series production was to be ordered before the prototype had even explored the full flight envelope. The prototype of the 4-EA (better known as the A-4) was designed by Aleksei Cheremukhin and flew for the first time on 6 November 1932; although construction had started in June the first production model flew only 24 days later. The credit for this achievement was claimed by Pyotr I. Baranov who rejoiced in the appointment of Head of the Chief Directorate of the Military Air Forces of the Workers' and Peasants' Red Army – the Red Air Fleet's new title. The most obvious design departures from the 2-EA were a larger 300 hp M-26 engine, a Soviet licence-built variant of the American Wright Whirlwind nine cylinder radial, enclosed in a

From left, the TsAGI 2-EA, the 4-EA and the A-6 autogiros.

formidable Townend ring cowling and a conventional tail unit, dual controls and mechanical, rather than aerodynamic, rotor starting.

It was quite difficult to tell in the early days whether the test pilot Korzinshchikov was testing the aircraft or whether the aircraft was testing him. On 9 November, 1932 during the second flight he identified serious rotor vibrations: suddenly he lost all lift and the machine fell to earth. Fortunately Korzinshchikov was not hurt and was able to help in the frantic efforts to pinpoint the cause or causes of the accident. On speedy fault-finding hung the fate of the series production beginning on time. Several rotor configurations and sizes were built and tested until a satisfactory solution was found in late 1933. Ten production machines were delivered during 1934. Perhaps 30 or 40 A-4s eventually found their way into military service.

TsAGI A-6

Shortly after the A-4 entered production Kuznetsov's group turned its attention to the development of a lighter but more sophisticated version of the A-4, designated the A-6. A two-seater, it had a 100 hp M-11 five cylinder radial engine, designed by Arkadi D. Shvetsov, but without a Townend ring. Both the wings and 11 m (36 ft 1 in) diameter three-bladed rotor could be folded. Because the A-6's specific weight per hp was 8.4 kg (18.5 lb) rather than the more usual 4–5 kg (8.8–11 lb) its take-off run was long. Despite this it had admirable characteristics which even allowed 'hands-off' flight. Korzinshchikov made the first flight in early 1933. Nevertheless it was considered unwise to pursue series production in competition with the A-4. Instead, from the summer of 1933, the single A-6 was used to explore further problems connected with stability, control and ground resonance, a phenomenon met for the first time. Mil was particularly active in its study and elimination. Two more examples were begun but ended up as one A-8 and one A-14.

TsAGI A-8/A-9/A-13/A-14

The A-8 flew for the first time on 29 June, 1934. It was still basically an A-6 incorporating both conventional aeroplane and rotary-wing controls, and for the first time hydraulic shock absorbers. The wings, instead of having upturned tips, had 5° of dihedral. What was particularly interesting about the A-8 was that the pilot could fly the aircraft by tilting the rotor head in the direction in which he wanted to go or by using his conventional fixed-wing (aileron) controls. Rotor tilting was considered to be much more effective, particularly at low speed when aileron control was poor. For the A-14, therefore, the wings were removed and a massive butterfuly tail installed. The purpose of this autogiro was to test and evaluate the peculiarities of wingless autogiros with direct control of the rotor hub and of course no aileron control. The first flight took place on 17 September, 1935. During the course of flight trials by Korzinshchikov, Koshits, Kozyrev, Chernavsky and Popov a lack of lateral stability was revealed but otherwise the test programme was remarkably troublefree. The A-14 represented the peak of Kuznetsov's achievements as an autogiro designer although he continued working on a number of different designs. None entered production but Kuznetsov remained forever optimistic. The A-8 reappeared in another guise as the A-13, also with a direct control rotor and folding wings and blades; it began flying on 13 March, 1936. The intention was to make the A-13 75 kg (165 lb) lighter than the A-8 but only 39 kg (86 lb) were actually achieved; and when the fuselage had to be strengthened in an effort to eliminate tailplane vibration even less weight was saved. Other modifications led to a performance so disappointing that the machine was quietly scrapped after a few months. The A-9, a development of the A-13, never got beyond the drawing board.

While Kuznetsov had been leading the second Brigade, five other Brigades within TsAGI had been wrestling with autogiro development. Kamov and Skrzhinsky had been involved with design and Mil with aerodynamics; the other two with stability and structures.

TsAGI A-7

Even as he was contemplating work on the KaSkr-II, Kamov was considering a response to the Red Air Force's need for a communications autogiro and one that could be used for reconnaissance and spotting for the artillery. By 1931 he had already brought out a design for a military autogiro, subsequently to be designated the TsAGI 7-EA and later still the A-7. Its maiden flight with Korzinshchikov at the controls was on 20 September, 1934. It was a strong and robust machine, made of metal, and featuring two open seats in tandem. The radial engine was the nine cylinder 480 hp M-22, a Gnome-Rhône Jupiter 9ASB, licence-built since 1930 at Zaporozhe. Following the pioneer work of Cierva in Britain, the rotor had a mechanical drive. As soon as take-off rpm were reached the pilot de-clutched the rotor, the angle of attack of the blades increased and, using the kinetic energy stored in the rotor, the autogiro leapt into the air.

The three-bladed rotor had a diameter of 15.2 m (49 ft 10 in) and an rpm of 195. The wooden wings had a span of 10.4 m (34 ft 1½ in). Given its strength it is not surprising that the gross weight was some 2,300 kg (5,071 lb). Speed ranged between 53 and 221 kph (33 and 137 mph).

The A-7 was unusual in that it had a tricycle undercarriage with a steerable nosewheel and with fairings for the wheels. It could also claim the distinction of being the first rotary-wing aircraft in the world to be equipped with weapons. Armament consisted of a fixed, synchronized forward-firing 7.62 mm ShKAS machine gun and a second, flexibly-mounted machine gun for the observer. Although the A-7 proved to be something of a sensation at the Tushino Air Display (7) in August 1935, serious rotor vibration had prevented completion of the test programme by then. Eventually in

December 1935 it was handed over for State tests. These ran quite smoothly although, because of a certain lack of directional stability, it was decided to add two vertical tail fins. This slightly modified version was designated the A-7*bis*. Testing of the prototype started in May 1937 and proceeded somewhat desultorily until late 1938. In the first half of 1940 five pre-production A-7*bis* were built and handed over to the Red Air Force.

In February 1941 one of these five was taken on an expedition to the Tyan-Shan mountains, one of the great mountain chains in Central Asia. In June 1941 the Germans invaded the Soviet Union and all five A-7*bis* autogiros were quickly rushed to the area of Smolensk where they were used for close reconnaissance at night and leaflet dropping. They were not popular machines to fly, being cast rather in the role of Soviet lambs to the German slaughter. The unit was almost as quickly rushed eastwards again and then disbanded. Only seven A-7s were ever built.

AK

The AK autogiro barely qualifies for inclusion here. In 1939 Kamov had left TsAGI to become chief designer in the A-7 production plant. Here he designed the AK in 1940 as a wingless two-seat machine with a 220 hp MV-6 engine. Progress was slow and when the plant was evacuated in 1941 the partially-completed prototype was taken east as well and rebuilt. At this juncture, to the chagrin of the designers, the Red Air Force lost interest in autogiros and development came to a halt.

When Kamov had turned his attention from the KaSkr-II to the A-7 so had Skrzhinsky and his Sixth Brigade started on a design for a six-seat wingless transport autogiro, the A-10, powered by an M-22 engine. Very shortly afterwards he moved onto more important matters and work on the A-10 was abandoned.

TsAGI A-12

Skrzhinsky's more important matters encompased in particular the A-12 single-seat wingless autogiro-fighter. The performance required was ambitious: a speed of between 45 and 300 kph (28 and 186 mph), a service ceiling of 7,010 m (23,000 ft) and a ground roll of no more than 48 m (50 yds). Skrzhinsky paid particular attention to the aerodynamic qualities of the machine which used the stubby 6.7 m (22 ft) long fuselage of an I-16 fighter with a twin-finned tailplane and which was fitted with the most powerful engine yet to be put into an autogiro: a nine cylinder 670 hp Wright Cyclone, designated the M-25 and later to be built at GAZ No. 19 (8) in Perm. The direct control three-bladed rotor had a diameter of 14 m (45 ft 11 in). Gross weight of the A-12 was 1,687 kg (3,719 lb). Construction began in 1935 but the flying programme was to be dogged by misfortune, culminating in a fatal accident. On 10 May, 1936 test pilot Chernavsky began flying with a series of ground runs and short hops but found the machine to be disconcertingly unstable. The cause was traced to the rotor head which was quickly modified. On 27 May he tried again and all was well. After three flights he had been airborne for just under an hour and had reached a height of 2,000 m (6,560 ft).

A year later Chernavsky and Kozyrev had achieved the rather unimpressive total of 43 flights and 18 flying hours. If this progress was less than invigorating then a true disaster was still to come on 23 May, 1937 when the A-12 crashed, killing Kozyrev. The cause was never made public but it was generally held to have been a fatigue fracture in a rotor blade spar. It was decided not to proceed with the A-12. This crash was a tragic outcome for a project which at one time appeared to be going comparatively well: a speed of 245 kph (152 mph) had been reached.

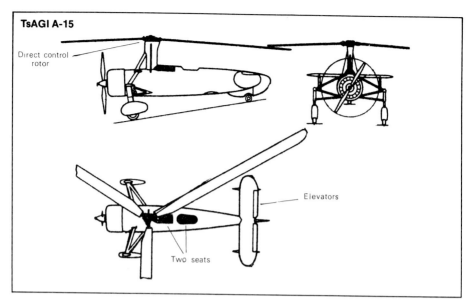

TsAGI A-15

Direct control rotor

Elevators

Two seats

TsAGI A-15

In 1936 Mikhail Mil began to work on the A-15, a two-seater, wingless autogiro powered by a 750 hp M-25V engine. It was the largest Soviet autogiro built with an 18 m (59 ft 1 in) diameter main rotor and it was intended to be the fastest. The pilot was equipped with a synchronized ShKAS machine gun while the observer had twin guns and a camera.

The A-15 was ready for flight tests in April 1937 but at the time of the A-12's crash test pilots Chernavsky and Ivanov had only managed a few ground runs. Tests were halted until February 1938 when the drive to the rotor was found to be inadequate. Modifications were not authorised and the A-15 was put into store – never to fly.

So ended interest in autogiros, at least until the 1960s. Even then they made no headway against helicopters. In the 1930s, however, Soviet efforts had not been rewarded with much success in a tangible sense but at least knowledge and experience of the machinations of rotary-wing craft had been gained. No more than about 40 autogiros, mainly A-4s, entered military service with only a handful of A-7s being used during the early stages of the German invasion of the Soviet Union in 1941.

TsAGI 1-EA

The first TsAGI helicopter, the 1-EA, was built in the spring of 1930 and completed in August. Boris Yuriev had started on the design of the 1-EA in 1928 and Sabinin had taken it on when Yuriev departed. It was a great moment, however, for Yuriev, Sabinin, Izakson, Cheremukhin who had been the chief designer and who was to fly it, and many others from the factory as the machine was rolled out. When, for the first time, the machine was started up, although still tethered, and the blades began to turn, Yuriev and his erstwhile colleagues must have felt that at last their dreams had been realised. Because high speed was not a requirement the 1-EA featured an open framework fuselage of steel tubes, tapering at front and rear. At the centre of gravity were installed two vertically-mounted M-2 120 hp engines which drove the 11 m (36 ft 1 in) diameter four-bladed rotor. A pair of 1.8 m (5 ft 10 in) two-bladed, contra-rotating steering rotors was fitted at both ends of the fuselage, one on each side. Rpm of the main rotor were 153 with the steering rotors turning at 1,200 rpm. The pilot sat just in front of the engines. The undercarriage was somewhat unusual, having two main wheels, a tail wheel and a front skid. Gross weight of the 1-EA was about 1,150 kg (2,535 lb).

The TsAGI 1-EA, the first experimental Soviet helicopter, left the ground for the first time one night late in 1930.

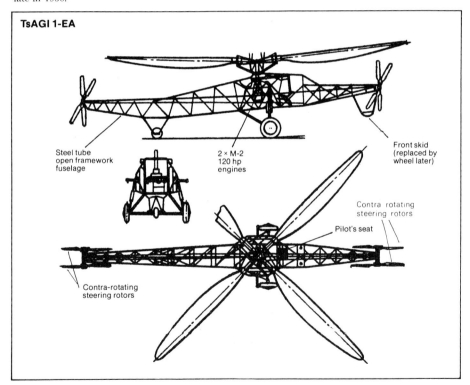

Eventually at the end of 1930, after repeated ground testing, the first flight took place – at night. The machine lurched into the air and wobbled between 1 and 3 m (3 and 10 ft). Slowly it edged up to about 9 m (30 ft) before descending to land.

Despite being difficult to control – the pilot's control was an overhanging stick connected directly to the swashplate – and suffering from excessive vibration,

11

Cheremukhin slowly began to master the idiosyncracies of the machine, surviving two crashes in 1932. A year earlier, however, the forward steering rotors had been removed and Cheremukin had climbed to over 90 m (300 ft). In August 1932 he broke his altitude record four times, reaching 605 m (1,985 ft) on the 14th. This height has never been verified and indeed was not even known about for a long time since the USSR was not a member of the FAI. This altitude should be compared with the world record at the time of 18 m (59.05 ft) established on 19 October, 1930 by the Italian d'Ascanio helicopter flown by Marienello Nelli.

Perhaps elated at having reached nearly 610 m (2,000 ft) on the 14th, Cheremukhin inadvertently exceeded the critical rotor speed on the way down which resulted in a loss of control and a heavy landing; the helicopter was severely damaged. It was rebuilt and flown again with Cheremukhin setting an endurance record of 14 minutes on 15 June, 1933; a maximum speed of 29.93 kph (18.6 mph) was also reached. Cheremukhin's achievements should not be underrated. The first flight of the first Soviet helicopter was also Cheremukhin's first flight: he had to teach himself to fly and thus was obviously the first Soviet helicopter test pilot.

TsAGI 3-EA

As soon as the 1-EA had got airborne the construction of a new version, the 3-EA, with a similar layout was begun. Some design features were different from the 1-EA as a result of experience gained from flying that helicopter. A number of sources believe that numerous short flights up to a distance of 3 km (2 miles) were made in 1933. On the contrary, Izakson writes authoritatively: "This apparatus passed manifold ground tests, and on it pilot training on a free tether was conducted but it was not tested in free flight."

In January 1933 rotary-wing development within TsAGI was radically changed. The somewhat ad hoc organisation was formally established as OOK-TsAGI with proper scientific support. Aleksandr M. Izakson became the Chief with Cheremukhin and D. I. Antonov as his deputies. Helicopter Construction Brigade-A, led by V. P. Lapisov, became responsible for experimental work and flight tests while Ivan P. Bratukhin, in charge of Brigade-B, actually designed and built the prototypes. At the end of 1933 Izakson's and Cheremukhin's efforts were recognised with the award of the Order of the Red Star while Bunkin, the leading transmission expert, Antonov and Yuriev received Certificates from the Central Executive Committee.

TsAGI 5-EA

It was Bratukhin who developed the 5-EA and began tethered testing of it in 1933. This machine had an unusual rotor system consisting of three rigidly attached blades with a diameter of 12.00 m (39 ft 4 in) for lift and three shorter blades with a diameter of 7.8 m (25 ft 7 in), mounted between the larger blades, which were attached to the hub by feathering hinges to provide control. The two anti-torque rotors at each end of the fuselage were retained. Cheremukhin flew the 5-EA for over three years but, although the rotor system was considered a success, the machine's weight was 1,210 kg (2,667 lb) – rather too heavy for the two aged M-2 engines which suffered from frequent unserviceability. Furthermore, the 5-EA's performance was uninspiring: a maximum altitude of 39.9 m (131 ft), a maximum speed of 19 kph (12 mph), an endurance of 13 minutes and a greatest distance covered in a straight line of 700 metres (765 yards) – all achieved in September and October 1934. The most interesting innovation of the 5-EA was the replacement of the engines with two electric motors, each giving 200 hp. Test pilot Koshits made a few tethered flights in 1941 when the modification was completed but the outbreak of war soon put an end to these trials for good.

TsAGI 11-EA

It was clear to the designers of Brigade-B that to better the performance of the 5-EA presented little of a challenge. A more powerful and reliable engine with a streamlined fuselage would certainly achieve better results. In 1934 work had begun on an unusual design for a tandem, two-seat helicopter powered by a 630 hp Curtiss Conqueror water-cooled engine. The rotor system was similar to that of the 5-EA although the larger blade diameter had been stretched to 15.4 m (50 ft $6\frac{2}{3}$ in) and the smaller to 9.2 m (30 ft 2 in). Small three-bladed anti-torque rotors were mounted towards the tips of a fixed wing, 11.24 m² (121 ft²) in area. A traditional tail configuration of fin, rudder, tailplane and elevators was provided and a means to operate the differential pitch change via cyclic pitch control was incorporated.

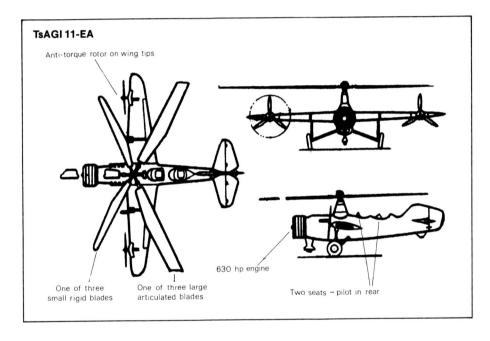

TsAGI 11-EA

Anti-torque rotor on wing tips

One of three small rigid blades

One of three large articulated blades

630 hp engine

Two seats – pilot in rear

Designated the 11-EA, this aircraft was completed in mid-1936 with the intention of flying it as a pure helicopter, that is to say, with a direct drive to the rotor and with a vertical take-off capability. The small propellers on the wings were to be used simply to equalise torque. These propellers could, however, in theory also be employed for propulsion, thus making the machine a compound helicopter. The technical skills needed to synchronise the two modes of employment were however lacking in the design team.

Tethered testing began but it was soon decided to replace the wood and fabric-covered rotor blades with all-metal ones. But this was not to be; the Stalinist purges were at their height by now and many members of the Section were arrested, including Cheremukhin and Izakson (9). Others were 're-located' and the remainder dismissed. Bratukhin survived and was able to carry on slowly with development of the 11-EA. As

13

he did so he came to realise eventually that his machine in fact suffered from a number of perplexing problems, most of which stemmed from the sharp increase in gross weight to 2,600 kg (5,732 lb) and to the fact that the anti-torque rotors consumed too much power. Due to the numbing fear that any mistakes, however minor, would almost certainly be construed as sabotage serious progress in rotary-wing work was understandably slow.

TsAGI 11-EA PV

In 1938 Bratukhin received permission to recruit design staff and increase the pace of development. The 11-EA underwent radical changes, perhaps the most important among them being the replacement of the wings by steel tube outriggers, each of which had at the tip two anti-torque rotors in tandem. These new rotors, 10.97 m (36 ft) apart, provided some thrust and thus the 11-EA became the 11-EA PV (*Propulsivnyi Variant*, Propulsive Variant), a form of compound helicopter. As envisaged earlier the main rotor had all-metal blades. With these modifications it was possible to reduce the gross weight to 2,250 kg (4,960 lb). In early 1940 tethered testing with D. I. Saveliev at the controls began. He was able to complete the first free flight in October of that year. Principally because of lack of spare parts for the Curtiss Conqueror engine the test programme was halted in the spring of 1941. By that time the 11-EA PV, with two crew on board, had reached a height of 50 m (164 ft), a maximum speed of 60 kph (37 mph) and an endurance of almost one hour. The 11-EA PV was to be the forerunner of Bratukhin's later Omega helicopters.

So ended an era. (10) No true helicopter had yet reached the production stage, either in the Soviet Union or anywhere else. The 1940s were to see the resurgence of Soviet helicopter development and the appearance of the first successful Soviet helicopter.

Notes

1. Four documents concerning Lomonosov's 'helicopter' work survive: the minutes of two meetings of the Academy, a report by the historian I. S. Gagen, and Lomonosov's own description of his tests in 1754.

2. In November 1964 Sikorsky said of his experiments in 1910: ". . . by that time I had learned enough to recognize that with the existing state of the art, engines, materials and . . . lack of experience . . . I would not be able to produce a successful helicopter at that time."

3. On the other hand, an Italian, G. A. Crocco, thought that he had patented cyclic pitch control five years earlier in 1906!

4. Also in 1925 the Central Design Bureau (*Tsentralnoe Konstruktorskoe Biuro* – TsKB) was established to develop, according to Aleksandr Yakovlev, light military aircraft. The aim was to take some of the pressure off TsAGI and Andrei Tupolev's Aviation, Hydroaviation and Experimental Design Section (*Aviatsiya, Gidroaviatsiya i Opytnoe Stroitelstvo* – AGOS) which had been formed in 1922 and been concerned with all-metal aircraft.

5. Soviet aeroengines were designated by the letter M (*Motor*) until 1944 when a new system incorporating the designer's initials was adopted.

6. In 1932 the Union of Soviet Writers and Editors, with government approval, decided to raise funds for the construction of a Maksim Gorky Propaganda Squadron. The squadron was publicised in the Soviet press and was used to visit selected places throughout the USSR to give displays and lectures in support of government policies. Some 30 aircraft were involved in this political propaganda campaign.

7. The first Red Air Force Display was held at Moscow Central Aerodrome on 18 August, 1933, the first Aviation Day. It was opened by Yakov I. Alksnis, Head of the Chief Directorate of the Red Air Force, and Aleksandr I. Yegorov, then Chief of Staff of the Red Army. The next and subsequent displays were held at Tushino. The 1937 parade, at the height of the Stalin purges, was spectacular for its 'political' formation flying. Again and again large numbers of aircraft flew over the enraptured crowd in formation spelling out LENIN, STALIN and SSSR (USSR).

8.   Almost within days of seizing power Lenin decreed that aircraft factories should be nationalised and known individually as a State Aviation Factory (*Gosudarstvennyi Aviatsionnyi Zavod* – GAZ) with a number. Sikorsky's design bureau within the Russo-Baltic Railway Carriage Plant in St. Petersburg, for example, became GAZ No. 3 in renamed Petrograd (later Leningrad). The Gnome-Rhône engine factory in Moscow became GAZ No. 2.

9.   Other leading designers arrested by the NKVD were Tupolev (unbelievably accused of having sold the plans of the Messerschmitt Bf 109 and Bf 110 fighters to Germany), Petlyakov, Polikarpov and Myasishchev. While in an NKVD prison in Moscow Petlyakov designed the VI-100 high-altitude interceptor, subsequently reworked as a dive bomber and redesignated Pe-2 when it entered production in 1940. Tupolev was not released until 1943.

10.   A brief mention of the I-4 should be made. Also called the Isacco-4 and *Gelikogyr*, this helicopter was designed in the USSR by an Italian, Vittorio Isacco. Work began in 1932. The helicopter had a cabin for a pilot and five passengers. What was unusual was that the four-bladed rotor was driven by four separate 120 hp de Havilland Gipsy III engines mounted one at each blade tip. In addition a 300 hp Wright J-5 radial engine was in the nose to drive a propeller. Construction was not completed until 1935 and subsequent ground tests proved unsatisfactory. The I-4 never flew.

CHARACTERISTICS

	KaSkr-1	KaSkr-II	TsAGI 2-EA	TsAGI 4-EA (A-4)	TsAGI A-6
Designation					
Engine	Gnome-Rhône 110 hp	Gnome-Rhône Titan 230 hp	Gnome-Rhône Titan 230 hp	M-26 300 hp	M-11 100 hp
Rotor diameter	12 m (39 ft 4½ in)	12 m (39 ft 4½ in)	12 m (39 ft 4½ in)	13 m (42 ft 8 in)	11 m (36 ft 1 in)
Fuselage length	8.8 m (28 ft 10¼ in)	9 m (29 ft 6¼ in)	6.5 m (21 ft 4 in)	7.2 m (23 ft 7½ in)	6.3 m (20 ft 8 in)
Empty weight	750 kg (1,653 lb)	865 kg (1,907 lb)	756 kg (1,687 lb)	1,065 kg (2,348 lb)	562 kg (1,239 lb)
Max gross weight	950 kg (2,094 lb)	1,100 kg (2,425 lb)	1,032 kg (2,275 lb)	1,365 kg (3,009 lb)	815 kg (1,797 lb)
Max speed	90 kph (56 mph)	110 kph (68 mph)	160 kph (99 mph)	176 kph (109 mph)	142 kph (88 mph)
Range	?	?	?	185 km (115 mls)	?
Service ceiling	?	450 m (1,476 ft)	4,200 m (13,780 ft)	4,100 m (13,451 ft)	2,000 m (6,562 ft)
First flight	1929	1930	1931	1932	1933

CHARACTERISTICS

	TsAGI A-13	TsAGI A-14	TsAGI A-7	TsAGI AK	TsAGI A-12
Designation					
Engine	M-11 100 hp	M-11 100 hp	M-22 480 hp	MV-6 220 hp	M-25 (Wright Cyclone) 670 hp
Rotor diameter	11.5 m (37 ft 8½ in)	11 m (36 ft 1 in)	15.2 m (49 ft 10 in)	13.5 m (44 ft 3½ in)	14 m (45 ft 11 in)
Fuselage length	?	6.3 m (20 ft 8 in)	?	?	6.3 m (20 ft 8 in)
Empty weight	540 kg (1,190 lb)	576 kg (1,270 lb)	1,225 kg (2,701 lb)	1,026 kg (2,262 lb)	1,343 kg (2,961 lb)
Max gross weight	802 kg (1,768 lb)	815 kg (1,797 lb)	2,300 kg (5,071 lb)	1,317 kg (2,903 lb)	1,687 kg (3,719 lb)
Max speed	151 kph (94 mph)	167 kph (104 mph)	221 kph (137 mph)		245 kph (152 mph)
Range	250 km (155 mls)	?	400 km (249 mls)		?
Service ceiling	3,000 m (9,843 ft)	?	4,700 m (15,400 ft)		5,570 m (18,275 ft)
First flight	1936	1935	1934	Did not fly	1936

CHARACTERISTICS

Designation	TsAGI A-15	TsAGI 1-EA	TsAGI 5-EA	TsAGI 11-EA PV
Engine	M-25V	2 × M-2	2 × M-2	Curtiss Conqueror
	730 hp	2 × 120 hp	2 × 120 hp	630 hp
Rotor diameter (Large blades)	18 m (59 ft 1 in)	11 m (36 ft 1 in)	12 m (39 ft 4½ in)	15.4 m (50 ft 6½ in)
Rotor diameter (Small blades)	—	—	7.8 m (25 ft 7 in)	9.2 m (30 ft 2 in)
Fuselage length	8.6 m (28 ft 2½ in)	12.8 m (42 ft)	11 m (36 ft 1 in)	8.3 m (27 ft 2¾ in)
Empty weight	1,695 kg (3,737 lb)	982 kg (2,165 lb)	1,047 kg (2,308 lb)	?
Max gross weight	2,560 kg (5,644 lb)	1,150 kg (2,535 lb)	1,210 kg (2,668 lb)	2,250 kg (4,960 lb)
Max speed		30 kph (19 mph)	20 kph (12 mph)	60 kph (37 mph)
Range		?	?	?
Service ceiling		605 m (1,985 ft)	?	?
First flight	Did not fly	1930	1933	1940

The Dawn
of the Helicopter Age:
1941–1950

In Western Europe the 1930s had seen strenuous efforts to build a truly practical helicopter. The first was probably the *Gyroplane Laboratoire* built by Louis Bréguet and René Dorand and flown for the first time in June 1935. Within 18 months it had set new world records for speed, altitude, distance and endurance. And it made use of the latest step in technology: the employment of fully articulated rotors (co-axially mounted) capable of permitting safe 'engine-off' autorotative landings. This helicopter was however eclipsed by the Focke-Achgelis Fa 61 which first flew exactly a year later. Twelve months after this Ewald Rohlfs shattered the Bréguet-Dorand records, proving the Fa 61 to be a vastly superior machine. Six weeks before these feats and even before the Bréguet-Dorand had achieved it, the Fa 61 had made its first autorotative landing.

But what really captured world-wide publicity was the flight by Hanna Reitsch before a large Nazi audience inside the Deutschlandhalle in Berlin in February 1938. The Fa 61's remarkable controllability was admirably demonstrated. With the outbreak of the Second World War work ceased on the two prototypes but by this time the Fa 61 had set a world speed record of 122 kph (76 mph), an altitude record of 3,427 m (11,243 ft), a distance record of 230 kilometres (143 miles) and an endurance record of one hour, 20 minutes, 49 seconds.

The USA was a little behind these developments. Although patenting a design for a helicopter in 1931 Igor Sikorsky had been too busy with his fixed-wing aircraft to have much time actually to build a helicopter. Eventually he was permitted to embark on a helicopter by the management of the United Aircraft Corporation for whom he was working as the Engineering Manager of the Vought-Sikorsky Division. During the summer of 1939 he built his historic VS-300 and himself took it off the ground, though still tethered, for the first time on 14 September, 1939. On 13 May, 1940, now with two subsidiary rotors on either side of the fuselage in addition to the main and tail rotors, it made its first full free flight; and on 6 May, 1941 it set a world endurance record of one hour, 32 minutes, 26.1 seconds. The VS-300 indicated that the helicopter had the potential to carry out a useful job and prompted the US Army Air Force to order an experimental two-seater. From the VS-300 was developed the R-4 which, in 1944, was the first helicopter in the world to be mass-produced.

On 23 August, 1939, to the amazement of the Western Powers, the German-Soviet pact was signed. By signing this treaty with Hitler, Stalin gained not only strategically important territory but also, more vital, time to rearm. For the defence of the Soviet Union TsAGI's priority now clearly lay with fixed-wing aircraft. It was decided to hive off helicopter development and form instead, in January 1940, an experimental design bureau, the OKB-3 (*Opytno Konstruktorskoe Biuro*-3), as part of the Moscow Aviation

Institute. It was staffed principally by ex-members of the defunct Section of Special Constructions. The indefatigable and persistent Yuriev was initially in charge but within three months Bratukhin had replaced him. While development tests of the 11-EA PV continued, Bratukhin began to contemplate a new project.

Mightily impressed by the exploits of the Fa 61, Bratukhin could not conceive of any other configuration that might be more successful: two fully articulated rotors mounted on lateral outriggers. Every subsequent design of his used this layout. Unlike the Fa 61, which had its single engine mounted at the nose, the 2 MG (*Motor Gelikopter*, twin-engined helicopter) Omega, as Bratukhin's new machine was called, had two 220 hp in-line engines also on outriggers.

2 MG Omega

The welded, steel-tube, fabric-covered fuselage permitted a two-man crew seated in tandem. The outriggers consisted of an open, welded, steel-tube framework at the ends of which was a large podded engine. A long pylon protruded from the top of each engine and supported the 7 m (23 ft) diameter, three-bladed rotor. The rotor shaft had a reduction gear at either end. A synchronising gear ran between the two engines to allow the drive of both rotors from a single engine should the other fail, and to maintain equal rotor rpm. These were high: 577 rpm. The aircraft could not, however, fly on one engine alone. The synchronising gear was only adjusted after both engines had been started. A conventional tail fin and rudder were used. The variable tailplane, whose angle was altered by the pilot by means of a wheel in the cockpit, was really a form of trim. It was atop the fin and had no elevator. A fixed nosewheel, a very small tailwheel and single main wheels protruding below the engines and attached to the ends of the outriggers, comprised the undercarriage.

The OKB-3 received approval to go ahead with the 2 MG Omega on 27 July, 1940 and it was completed just after the German invasion in June 1941. By August it was ready for tethered testing. It was taken off successfully and initial tests of the controls begun. Difficulties with the drive system soon surfaced and it was quickly appreciated that the outriggers were not sufficiently rigid. At an engine speed of between 1,700 and 1,800 rpm they started to twist and the helicopter to lurch in a most disconcerting manner. But now there was not time for modifications. The rapid advance of the Germans brought everything to a halt while the OKB-3, and indeed the Moscow Aviation Institute, removed themselves some 1,610 km (1,000 miles) to the east. Stalin's top priorities at this time were the production of fighters and ground attack aircraft and Yakovlev experienced a hiatus of only three weeks before his aircraft factory restarted production. It took Bratukhin six months to get going again so low a priority was his OKB. Eventually tethered testing began once more while Bratukhin worked on the much needed modifications. The twisting of the outriggers was cured by the simple remedy of fitting dampers to the flapping hinges and strengthening the outriggers themselves. But nothing could be done about the unreliability of the aircooled MV-6 six cylinder engines which seriously vibrated, overheated and ran rough. The excessively hot summer of 1943 when temperatures reached 55° C (131° F) no doubt contributed to the overheating. Progress was slow. Finally, in mid-summer, the first free flight took place. The test pilot, K. I. Ponomarev, made a number of vertical take-offs and landings and in subsequent flights hovering turns and autorotations. He did not dare, however, to make any flights exceeding 15 minutes in duration because of the engine problems. Nevertheless the machine was declared a success and, with more powerful and reliable engines, was thought to have considerable potential in both civil and military versions.

G-2 Omega II

A decision was thus made in late 1943 to build a new model, to be known as the G-2 Omega II, with two pre-war MG-31F 350 hp nine cylinder radial engines, bracing struts for the outriggers rather than wires, and other more minor structural modifications. With the Red Army (1) about to drive the last German soldier from Soviet territory, the Moscow Aviation Institute judged Moscow to be safe and so the OKB-3 returned there in 1944. In September the Omega II began tethered testing. The long-suffering Ponomarev conducted these and the flight tests which were completed in January 1945. Modifications and further testing were needed. By reducing the transmission ratio from 0.32 to 0.283 and rotor rpm from a dizzy 595 to 526, Ponomarev was eventually able to reach nearly 3,050 m (10,000 ft). Maximum speed was 150 mph (93 mph) and payload 420 kg (906 lb).

Formal testing ended in July 1945 and at the end of the year Bratukhin and Ponomarev were able to convince the authorities that the helicopter was safe enough for others to fly and it was turned over for pilot training. M. K. Baikalov, later to be associated with the testing of the Mi-1, demonstrated the Omega II before the public and Stalin at the first post-war Tushino Air Display on Soviet Aviation Day, 18 August, 1946. The lack of spare engine parts, however, soon became an insurmountable problem and the machine was perforce grounded.

G-3

As the testing of the Omega II proceeded the Red Army began to show an interest in using Bratukhin's helicopters for artillery spotting. The British and Americans had pioneered the use of fixed-wing aircraft in this role in 1942 but the Russians were keen to take this a step further with helicopters. Work was thus begun on two new prototypes. Designated the G-3, they only differed from the Omega II in having two 450 hp Pratt and Whitney R-985-AN-1 Wasp Junior nine cylinder radial engines with minor modifications to the engine installation. Maximum speed was 170 kph (106 mph), the service ceiling 2,500 m (8,200 ft), but maximum gross weight had increased from the Omega II's 2,300 kg (5,070 lb) to 2,600 kg (5,732 lb). The prototypes were ready for flight in early 1945 and the initial flight tests showed such promise that a decision to build ten pre-production aircraft was made. Work began at Plant 82 at Tushino but in fact only five were completed during 1945 and 1946. Of these five only two may actually have flown.

This shortfall was largely due to the shortage of Pratt and Whitney engines. A more obscure and profound reason was the failure of the senior commanders in the Red Air Force to appreciate the advantages offered by this new breed of flying machines. This comparative lack of interest resulted in little encouragement for Bratukhin, a shortage of funds and a consequent lack of urgency within the production programme. Nevertheless, in company with the single Omega II, two G-3s were flown at the 1946 Tushino Display, with Ponomarev piloting one of them. They generated considerable uninformed interest. Of the five completed models four were subsequently diverted to further research and one was given to an unsuspecting Army in 1948 or 1949 for pilot training.

G-4

As disagreements between the Allies grew more frequent it became obvious to the Russians that to put themselves in a position where they had to rely on Pratt and

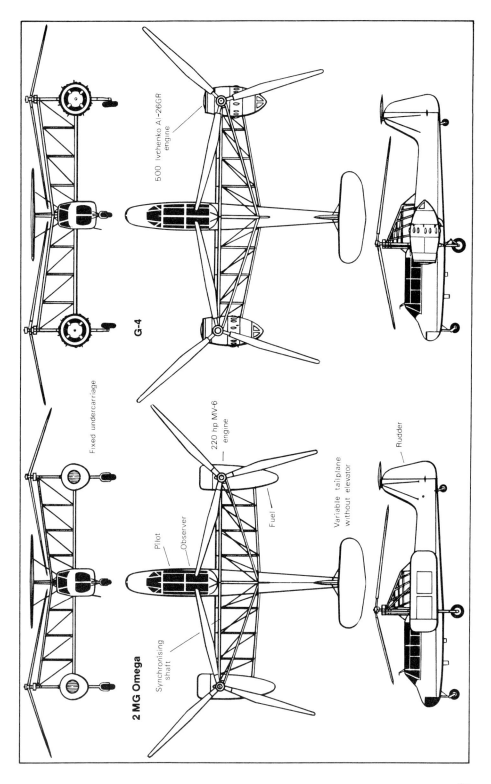

G-4

500 Ivchenko AI-26GR engine

Fixed undercarriage

2 MG Omega

220 hp MV-6 engine

Pilot

Observer

Fuel

Synchronising shaft

Variable tailplane without elevator

Rudder

Whitney engines in the 400–500 hp range was not sensible. They should rather, for technical and political reasons, build their own. An aero-engine designer, Aleksandr G. Ivchenko, in co-operation with Bratukhin, had thus turned his attention to this problem and produced the AI-26GR, a seven cylinder radial engine developing 500 hp for take-off. Built-in was a reduction gear linked vertically to the upper reduction gear and rotor, and laterally to the synchronising gear. The AI-26GR was the first Soviet engine designed specifically for helicopter use. Four engines were available by the end of 1946 and so Bratukhin agreed to use two in a modified G-3, to be called the G-4. Rotor diameter was a little greater at just 7.7 m (25 ft 3 in), small for a machine with a gross weight of 3,000 kg (6,614 lb). Rotor blade construction itself was similar to Bratukhin's earlier efforts: the leading edge was made from a continuous duralumin aerofoil-shaped beam which was of circular section at the root while the trailing edge was constructed of folded duralumin sheet.

The first prototype was rolled out in October 1947 but, without the experienced Ponomarev at the controls, crashed due to pilot error in January 1948. Ponomarev was entrusted with the second prototype which had fortunately begun flight testing in November. As a result of the accident this prototype was grounded and modifications carried out: in particular, the rotor blades were given a few degrees of twist. In the subsequent flight tests much valuable information was obtained on single-engine flight, vortex ring and autorotative characteristics in the most comprehensive test programme yet devised for any Soviet helicopter. Autorotations proved quite simple and harmless: with rotor pitch at 5°45′, the rate of descent was 716 m (2,350 ft)/min at an optimum speed of 155–159 kph (96–99 mph). The quality of component engineering was improving and for the first time such items as the rotor blades, transmission and gears, exceeded the required life of 100 hours. Nonetheless, only ten production machines were planned and of these only four were built before production was abandoned in late 1948.

It was reported that the first prototype and two G-3s participated in the Tushino Display in 1947 but this is hard to believe since the G-4 was not ready for its maiden flight until October 1947. Perhaps it was on static display only.

B-5

Back in 1945 Bratukhin's design team had appreciated that their open framework and fabric-covered helicopters presented a somewhat crude and even then unfashionable appearance. Stub wings, for example, besides looking more refined, could also help to offload the rotors. The first of a new breed of aerodynamically-shaped helicopters was designated the B-5, although it incorporated the same transmission and dynamic parts as the G-4. It was larger than its predecessors, being designed to carry a crew of two and six passengers in four rows of seats.

Rotor diameter was increased to 10 m (32 ft 10 in). Empty weight rose only to 2,932 kg (6,464 lb) whereas maximum take-off weight was 4,032 kg (8,889 lb). It was calculated that the stub wings would effectively unload the rotors by about 25% at the maximum speed of 235 kph (146 mph). Take-off power was boosted to 550 hp from each of the two AI-26GR(F) engines. Actual construction of the first prototype was held up as Bratukhin awaited the more powerful engines. It was not until 1947 that the B-5 was finally ready for flight. It proved a disappointment, the stub wings vibrating excessively and restricting flight to a few spasmodic hops. Modifications failed to conquer the problems.

B-9

The B-9 followed closely on the heels of the B-5 and was specifically designed as an air ambulance to take a crew of two, four stretcher cases and an attendant. It was identical to its predecessor apart from its fuselage which was slightly stretched and of duralumin monocoque structure. The B-9, in the shadow of the B-5 and its problems, never reached the stage of flight trials. Construction was completed, however, in 1947.

B-10

As if two helicopters in a single year were not enough a third, the B-10, dubbed the VNP (*Vozdushnyi Nabliudatelnyi Punkt*, Air Observation Post) in military circles, was also completed in 1947. It was specifically designed for artillery observation with a crew consisting of a pilot, navigator and observer. A huge transparent nose was topped by a large glazed dome. The observer's position was in a smaller dome at the tail, perhaps some 9 m (29 ft 6 in) behind the pilot although the actual length of the fuselage is not known. Because of his position the variable incidence tailplane was mounted above the fuselage and had a fin at either end. A small cabin was available for freight or up to three passengers. To reduce the wing flexing experienced with the B-5 which had a cantilever wing, the B-10 had twin bracing struts from the base of the fuselage to approximately half-way along the wing; single struts also connected the upper surface at mid-span to the rotor pylons. Slightly more powerful 575 hp AI-26GVF engines were mounted at the end of the high-mounted stub wings. While the empty weight of the B-10, at 3,185 kg (7,020 lb), was 253 kg (556 lb) more than that of the B-5, maximum gross weight at 3,900 kg (8,598 lb) was 132 kg (291 lb) less. It was reported that a machine gun was flexibly mounted both in the nose and the tail. It is not known how far ground and flight tests progressed but it was estimated that the B-10 might reach a top speed of 220 kph (137 mph) and have a service ceiling of 6,400 m (20,995 ft).

It was at about this time, however, that with the failures of the B-5 and B-9, the configuration of side-by-side, non-intermeshing rotors lost the support of the Air Force. The West had long since abandoned any such designs. Indeed, the highly successful Bell Model 47 had already entered large-scale production in 1946. Nevertheless, a Soviet Information Bulletin proudly claimed that: "The first flying helicopters were devised in the Soviet Union by Yuriev and his students. Yuriev and Bratukhin have found the correct forms of the helicopter and have elaborated the theory of rotors, which hitherto have been faulty and, therefore, unable to hold the machine in the air." In an article in *Ogonyok*, a widely-distributed Soviet magazine, Yuriev proclaimed that: "All that American technology can boast in the field of helicopter design is a long-forgotten stage in our research."

No helicopter had yet completely proved itself: defects were rife, all helicopters were treated with distrust, and an inability to comprehend the rudimentary state of the art prevailed. Far too early Bratukhin was told to arm them and install special equipment. Consequently he was unable to concentrate his efforts on ironing out the basic airframe and engine problems that kept recurring. Towards the end of 1947 the authorities realised that they had overloaded Bratukhin. He was ordered to terminate all work on the B-5, B-9 and B-10 and to compete with the OKBs of Mikhail Mil and Aleksandr Yakovlev to produce a two/three-seat communications helicopter, capable of night and all-weather operations and suitable for both civil and military use. So the OKB-3 was given another chance to demonstrate the efficacy of its configuration in competition against two single rotor types.

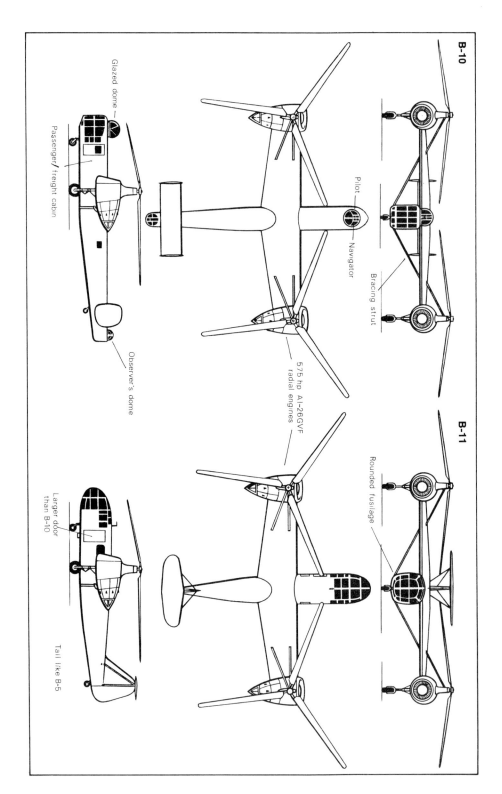

B-10

Glazed dome

Passenger/freight cabin

Pilot

Navigator

Bracing strut

575 hp AI-26GVF radial engines

Observer's dome

B-11

Rounded fusilage

Larger door than B-10

Tail like B-5

24

B-11

The B-11 was the Bratukhin OKB's entry. Two prototypes were completed in April 1948, the first flying two months later and the second in September. Externally similar to the B-5, although with the B-10's bracing struts, the B-11's two 550 hp AI-26GR(F) engines and rotors were mounted at the wingtips. The pilot sat in front with the other two crewmembers or passengers side-by-side behind. One stretcher patient could be carried. Comprehensive tests included single engine qualification during which the first prototype completed 47 minutes with one engine shut down. The B-11 was very stable and easy to control but suffered from severe vibrations at higher speeds. This was traced to the lack of lift being generated by the wings which resulted in overloading the rotors which came uncomfortably close to thrashing themselves to pieces. Other vibrations were caused by the rotor hubs. At the end of August the flight test programme was suspended while research into reducing the vibration was made. A thorough analysis was carried out and then trials were resumed, although with some misgivings. But a few days later, in December 1948, the second prototype crashed due to a manufacturing defect in one of the blades of the starboard rotor and the test pilot Ponomarev and his crewman were killed. The crash embarrassed the OKB-3 and Bratukhin was called upon more than once to defend his work. The first prototype was dismantled and rebuilt. Substantial modifications were incorporated: fitting fully supercharged AI-26GVFs giving an extra 25 hp; strengthening the fin, rudder, engine mountings, blade attachment forks and rotor heads; providing an escape hatch for the crew; and installing flaps fixed at 30° below the stub wings. Trials resumed at the beginning of 1949 but it was clear that all was not well and limitations had to be imposed: a speed of 150 kph (93 mph) and a height of 2,500 m (8,200 ft). In May 1950 the programme was abandoned since, by this time, it was obvious that the B-11 could not match the Mil Mi-1. A deaf ear was turned to impassioned pleas to be allowed to make further modifications to improve performance and have the limitations lifted. The B-11 was the last helicopter completed by the OKB-3. It was displayed at Tushino in August 1948 just before being grounded for the first time.

This was not the end of Bratukhin's OKB which lingered on until 1951 before being disbanded. Various projects were undertaken but without any real hope of success or official encouragement. The four-seat, multi-purpose B-12 never got off the drawing board but test rigs were at least built for a single rotor helicopter. In 1950 Bratukhin proposed a twin rotor, ten-seat convertiplane with a gross weight of around 5,900 kg (13,000 lb), a configuration which resembled Kamov's Ka-22 *Hoop* which appeared in 1961. This proposal was ignored.

Jet propulsion

Even while Bratukhin was working on his conventionally-powered helicopters he was also experimenting with jet propulsion and rotors tip-driven by small ramjets. The tests went reasonably well but Bratukhin was not allowed to exploit his initial successes. Also involved in similar work was a group led by B. J. Zherebtsov in which were included J. S. Braginski and J. L. Starinin. Beginning in 1947, this group built and tested several 7 m (23 ft) diameter rotors which they could extend to 8 m (26 ft) or even 9 m (29 ft 6 in). The culmination of these tests was the construction of a single-seat helicopter, the *Zherebtsov*. It had a simple tubular frame fuselage with a fixed tail unit on an outrigger. It was first flown in 1950 by test pilot Smirnov and later by G. A. Tinyakov and performed well. It was, however, never intended to be more than a research vehicle. Tip ramjet propulsion had few supporters – high fuel consumption, excessive noise and reduced rotor lift were major disadvantages – and the group was inevitably disbanded without making further progress.

First Yakovlev helicopter

The Yakovlev design bureau was able to enter the competition with a fair degree of confidence as it had already gained some helicopter experience through building a two-seat, single-engined, co-axial type which first flew in 1947 (2). The first tentative designs were begun as early as the end of 1944 by Skrzhinsky who by this time had joined Yakovlev's bureau. The machine was rather unimaginatively dubbed EG, *Eksperimentalnyi Gelikopter* (3). The forward section of the fuselage was of welded steel-tube with a metal surface while the rear section was fabric-covered. There was a short tailplane with twin fins and rudders. The crew of two sat side-by-side. A tricycle undercarriage with a single nosewheel and two single main wheels was used. Each fully articulated rotor system had two blades, made of wood and fabric-covered. The engine was a 140 hp M-11FR-1 five cylinder aircooled radial. An interesting feature was the automatic autorotation capability: when the engine stopped the flow of oil to the hydraulic cylinder ceased and a spring was released, automatically reducing collective pitch.

Yakovlev's first helicopter, a co-axial, contra-rotating design, which first flew in 1947. The tail unit was later removed when tests revealed that the centre of gravity was too far aft. (Pilot Press Ltd)

Some five hours of tethered flight and fifteen hours of free flight were successfully achieved by the test pilot, V. V. Tezavrosky. Many modifications were needed during their course. Very early on it was realised that the centre of gravity was too far to the rear. To bring it forward the simple expedient of completely removing the tail unit was employed together with moving the oil tank. This first Yakovlev helicopter, however, was subject to longitudinal oscillations which apparently began to make the pilot nervous at any speed over about 32 kph (20 mph). Top speed reached was 60 kph (37

mph) and in achieving this considerable courage and strength were required of
Tezavrosky. It may be imagined that the cyclic stick forces were almost too much for
one man.

Yak-100

The Yak-100 was the Yakovlev OKB entry for the competition. The programme was
managed by Igor Yerlikh who decided that the time available allowed little originality.
To the unsuspecting the Yak-100 was a Sikorsky S-51, pirated from the USA without a
production licence. To the more observant the only external differences were the shape
of the tail which was straight in the S-51 but cranked upwards in the Soviet aircraft, and
the more solid main wheel struts of the S-51. Abandoning the co-axial configuration of
the earlier Yakovlev helicopter, the Yak-100 had a single three-bladed main rotor and
a three-bladed tail rotor. Empty weight was just over 1,800 kg (3,968 lb), somewhat less
than that of the S-51. A 575 hp AI-26GRFL nine cylinder aircooled radial engine was
installed.

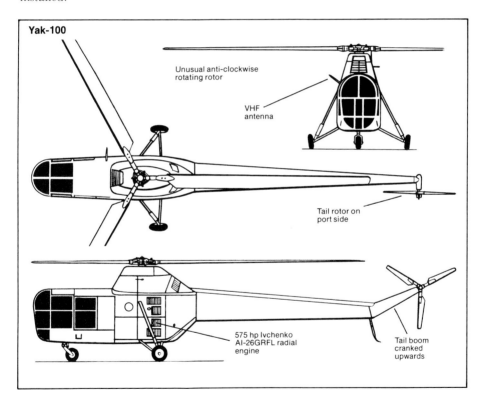

The Yak-100 was designed in two versions: a tandem two-seat trainer and a three-
seat communications helicopter. As in the S-51 the crew and passengers sat in a glazed
cockpit offering excellent visibility. The first prototype was ready for flight in
November 1948 and the second, the two-seater with dual controls, in July 1949. The
congenital Russian disease – vibration – was present from the start (although this was
not discovered until later) and, to reduce it, the centre of gravity of the fully articulated
wooden rotor blades was moved towards their leading edges. This measure also cured

the rotor blade flutter which began when rotor rpm reached 210. Nonetheless the helicopter was not ready for its acceptance tests by State pilots until mid-1950 when the OKB tests belatedly ended. Although a successful design, the Yak-100 was not considered the equal of the Mi-1 and consequently was cancelled (4). It did, however, achieve a maximum speed of 170 kph (106 mph) and a service ceiling of 5,250 m (17,224 ft).

Mi-1 Hare

Mikhail Mil's OKB, the last of the helicopter bureaux to be established, began work on 12 December, 1947 to develop his entry for the competition. At first known as the GM-1 (*Gelikopter Mil*), it later came to be called the Mi-1 with the NATO designation Hare. While working earlier on autogiros Mil began to appreciate what the helicopter had to offer. He saw it principally as a short take-off and landing (STOL) transport vehicle. A talented theoretician, he was determined to develop the full theory of rotary-wing flight before attempting to produce a practical helicopter. As he proceeded with his theoretical work over the years he was forced to make some concessions to the practical, to build helicopters. In doing so during the 1950s he applied his own aerodynamic knowledge, as we shall see, to Western designs: the Mi-4 bore a close resemblance to the Sikorsky S-55 but had twice the disc loading. During this decade it would be true to say that while Western technology and production were ahead of the Soviet Union's capabilities, the West trailed when it came to theory.

The first of three Mi-1 prototypes was rolled out in September 1948, a bare 11 months after publication of the government specification and only nine months after his OKB was formed. The Mi-1 was the first genuine Soviet helicopter to be completed with single main and tail rotors – although Yuriev's 1912 helicopter was of the same layout – flying a couple of months earlier than its rival, the Yak-100 with its dubious parentage. It featured a three-bladed, fully articulated single main rotor, the blades being based on those of the A-15 autogiro, and three-bladed tail rotor mounted on the starboard side of the tail boom. The composition and planform of the main rotor blades

Polish Mi-1 Hare on a field exercise. Note the large external fuel tank.

28

have undergone many modifications over the years. The initial construction consisted of a three-section, tapered steel tube spar with the rest of the blade being wood with a plywood and fabric cover. Fatigue life was no more than 200 hours. Nine years later the new main spar of a single variable section steel tube was fitted. In 1961 one version of this helicopter the *Moskvich*, received all-metal blades. By 1966 fatigue life had risen to 2,000 hours. Planform also changed from the early tapered trailing edge to parallel chord. Rotor rpm are 232.

The fuselage is an enclosed metal-skinned steel tube structure with an all-metal semi-monocoque tail boom. Two or three passengers are able to sit on a bench behind the pilot but they are unable to see out well. At the rear of the fuselage there is room for personal baggage. As with the Bell 47 stretcher cases may only be carried externally in panniers. An internal tank can take 173 kg (382 lb) of fuel while, in common with most other Soviet helicopters, there is provision for an external tank of 114 kg (251 lb) capacity on the port side. The early Mi-1s had no stabiliser at the tail but this was installed on all production models. The tricycle undercarriage is wheeled with a steerable nosewheel and two single main wheels. Mil used the 575 hp Ivchenko AI-26V seven cylinder radial engine with fan-assisted cooling. Empty, the Mi-1 was only 45 kg (100 lb) lighter than the Yak-100 but maximum take-off weight was 370 kg (815 lb) more than its rival.

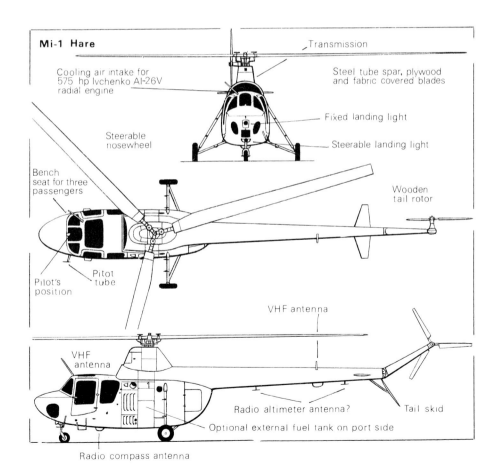

Mi-1 Hare

Transmission

Cooling air intake for 575 hp Ivchenko AI-26V radial engine

Steel tube spar, plywood and fabric covered blades

Fixed landing light

Steerable nosewheel

Steerable landing light

Bench seat for three passengers

Wooden tail rotor

Pilot's position

Pitot tube

VHF antenna

VHF antenna

Radio altimeter antenna?

Tail skid

Optional external fuel tank on port side

Radio compass antenna

Early on in the flight test programme the first prototype got out of control at 5,000 m (16,400 ft) and the test pilot, Baikalov, had to bale out, being lucky to escape with his life. He was in fact killed later in the second prototype when the tail rotor failed. M. L. Gallai and V. V. Vinitsky, who was later to capture some world records in the machine, were the senior test pilots. A maximum level speed of 190 kph (118 mph) and a hover ceiling in ground effect of over 3,350 m (11,000 ft) were achieved during factory tests. By September 1949 State Acceptance Tests had been completed and production recommended by the two State test pilots, G. A. Tinyakov and S. G. Brovtsev. They, however, suggested that maximum permissible speed should be limited to 170 kph (106 mph) for fear of retreating blade stall at higher speeds. Maximum speed has subsequently been raised to 204 kph (127 mph). The decision to begin production was taken almost immediately, before the Yak-100 had been evaluated, at which time the designation became Mi-1. Eight pre-production models took part in the Tushino Air Display in 1951 and by the end of that year the Mi-1 had entered Air Force service.

The Mi-1 was the first Soviet helicopter to enter quantity production and remained in production in the USSR and Poland until about 1965. Some 1,800 Soviet examples of the Mi-1 are thought to have been built. It represented a major advance in Soviet helicopter design philosophy and enabled the country to catch up with contemporary Western helicopters of similar size and power. Between 1957 and 1968 the Mi-1 and the Polish-built variant SM-1 set 24 world records, including six by female crews, in its class. With one exception, the Mi-12 Homer, the Mil OKB has retained the basic Mi-1 configuration ever since.

The Mi-1 is capable of undertaking a wide variety of civil and military tasks. Although usually unarmed, a Soviet film has shown a Hare armed with anti-tank missiles. Modifications and improvements have been incorporated over the years and two major variants have been built: the dual control trainer with side-by-side seating, variously designated as the Mi-1U (*Uchebnyi*, Instructional), T (*Trenirovochnyi*, Training) or UT (*Uchebno-Trenirovochnyi*, Instructional-Training); and the Mi-1NKh (*Narodnoe Khozyaistvo*, National Economy), an all-weather, multi-purpose civil model. Used for crop spraying, forestry and fishery patrol, the Mi-1NKh carries a hopper on either side of the fuselage when employed in the former role. Less successful was the Mi-1S (*Sanitarnyi*) ambulance version, wrongly dubbed the Mi-3 at one time in the West because it had a four-bladed main rotor to cope with the extra weight of the externally-attached panniers. It appeared briefly in 1954 but never went into production, presumably because it was thought then that the standard Mi-1 could manage. In 1958 pontoons were made available for the Mi-1 and this version was then called the Mi-1P, sometimes being used on whaling ships. Finally, the Mi-1 *Moskvich* was developed in limited quantities in 1961 for Aeroflot as a VIP transport. It had all-metal blades, better sound-proofing, hydraulic controls and more comprehensive instrumentation. It could carry three passengers.

In 1955 production was transferred to the Wytwornia Sprzetu Komunikacyjnego-Polskie Zaklady Lotnicze (WSK-PZL) factory in Swidnik, Poland. The principal reason for this move was to free Soviet factories for the production of the larger Mi-4 Hound and Yak-24 Horse. The Mi-1 was redesignated the SM-1 and incorporated a licence-built AI-26V engine which was given the new designation LiT-3. During the next ten years over 1,700 machines were built here, of which about 250 were exported to the Soviet Union. The Poles built various versions: the SM-1W with metal rotor blades; the SM-1WS ambulance version with two external stretcher pods; the SM-1SZ as a dual control trainer; and the SM-2, a five-seater which entered production in 1961. The most interesting Polish experiment with the Mi-1 was to install stub wings with a span of 7.8 m (25 ft 7 in), a length equivalent to 54% of the rotor diameter.

The five-seater SM-2, a Polish development of the SM-1.

Although celebrating the 40th anniversary of its first flight in 1988 the Mi-1 and SM-1 are still in service, both in military and civil use, particuarly in East Europe, the Middle East and some other Third World countries. This is in direct contrast to contemporary Western helicopters, few of which remain in service. A case in point is the victory of an Mi-1, flown by Aleks Kapralov and Lev Chekalov, in the individual class of the 1973 World Helicopter Championships and the Mi-1's success in the 1978 Championships held at Vitebsk in the Soviet Union.

Notes

1.   The Red Army was renamed the Soviet Army in early 1946.

2.   Yakovlev, of course, was already famous as the designer of successful fighter aircraft but he was obviously keen to try his hand at vertical flight. The Yakovlev bureau is still interested and has combined vertical flight with fighter aircraft in the shape of the early Freehand and now the Yak-38 Forger found aboard the Soviet 'Kiev' class carriers. It is perhaps a matter of some wonder that, absorbed in the design and development of fighters, the Yakovlev bureau could spare the time and staff in 1944 to study helicopter designs.

3.   *Gelikopter* was not a pure Russian word and before the decade was out it had been replaced as the word for helicopter by '*vertolet*'.

4.   Some 290 S-51s were produced by Sikorsky between 1946 and 1951 and another 139 under licence by Westland in the United Kingdom as the Dragonfly.

31

CHARACTERISTICS

Designation	**Bratukhin 2 MG Omega**	**Bratukhin Omega II**
Engine	2 × MV-6	2 × MG-31F
	2 × 220 hp	2 × 350 hp
Rotor diameter	2 × 7.0 m (23 ft)	2 × 7.0 m (23 ft)
Fuselage length	8.2 m (26 ft 11 in)	?
Empty weight	1,763 kg (3,886 lb)	1,880 kg (4,144 lb)
Max gross weight	2,050 kg (4,519 lb)	2,300 kg (5,070 lb)
Max speed	116 kph (72 mph)	150 kph (93 mph)
Range	250 km (155 mls)	?
Service ceiling	6,000 m (19,685 ft)	3,000 m (9,840 ft)
First flight	August 1941	September 1944

Designation	**Bratukhin G-3**	**Bratukhin G-4**
Engine	2 × P&W R-985-AN-1	2 × Ivchenko AI-26GR
	2 × 450 hp	2 × 500 hp
Rotor diameter	2 × 7.0 m (23 ft)	2 × 7.7 m (25 ft 3 in)
Fuselage length	8.2 m (26 ft 11 in)	8.1 m (26 ft 7 in)
Empty weight	2,195 kg (4,838 lb)	2,363 kg (5,210 lb)
Max gross weight	2,600 kg (5,732 lb)	3,000 kg (6,614 lb)
Max speed	170 kph (106 mph)	150 kph (93 mph)
Range	?	233 km (145 mls)
Service ceiling	2,500 m (8,200 ft)	2,717 m (8,915 ft)
First flight	Early 1945	October 1947

CHARACTERISTICS

Designation	**Bratukhin B-5**	**Bratukhin B-10**
Engine	2 × Ivchenko AI-26GR(F)	2 × Ivchenko AI-26GVF
	2 × 550 hp	2 × 575 hp
Rotor diameter	2 × 10.0 m (32 ft 10 in)	2 × 10.0 m (32 ft 10 in)
Fuselage length	?	?
Empty weight	2,932 kg (6,464 lb)	3,185 kg (7,020 lb)
Max gross weight	4,032 kg (8,889 lb)	3,900 kg (8,598 lb)
Max speed	235 kph (146 mph)	220 kph (137 mph)?
Range	595 km (370 mls)	440 km (273 mls)?
Service ceiling	6,400 m (20,995 ft)	6,400 m (20,995 ft)?
First flight	1947	1947

Designation	**Bratukhin B-11**
Engine	2 × Ivchenko AI-26GVF
	2 × 575 hp
Rotor diameter	2 × 10.0 m (32 ft 10 in)
Fuselage length	9.76 m (32 ft 0½ in)
Empty weight	3,400 kg (7,496 lb)
Max gross weight	4,150 kg (9,149 lb)
Max speed	150 kph (93 mph)
Range	328 km (204 mls)
Service ceiling	2,500 m (8,200 ft)
First flight	June 1948

CHARACTERISTICS

Designation	**Yakovlev Yak-100**
Engine	Ivchenko AI-26GRFL
	575 hp
Rotor diameter	14.5 m (47 ft 6 in)
Fuselage length	13.9 m (45 ft 7½ in)
Empty weight	1,805 kg (3,980 lb)
Max gross weight	2,180 kg (4,805 lb)
Max speed	170 kph (106 mph)
Range	325 km (202 mls)?
Service ceiling	5,250 m (17,224 ft)
First flight	November 1948

CHARACTERISTICS

Designation	**Mil Mi-1**	**Sikorsky S-51**
Engine	Ivchenko AI-26V	P&W R-985-AN-7
	575 hp	450 hp
Rotor diameter	14.35 m (47 ft 1 in)	14.93 m (49 ft 0 in)
Fuselage length	12.1 m (39 ft 8 in)	12.5 m (41 ft 1 in)
Empty weight	1,760 kg (3,880 lb)	2,018 kg (4,450 lb)
Max gross weight	2,550 kg (5,620 lb)	2,495 kg (5,500 lb)
Max speed	204 kph (127 mph)	167 kph (104 mph)
Range	330 km (205 mls)	482 km (300 mls)
Service ceiling	4,000 m (13,120 ft)	4,025 m (13,200 ft)
First flight	September 1948	February 1946

The

Kamov helicopters

Nikolai I. Kamov died in November 1973 at the age of 71 after an aeronautical career spanning six decades. During this time all his helicopter designs which reached the production stage, except the Ka-26, were operated by the Soviet Navy, even if only on a trial basis. Because of the need to minimise the dimensions of flight decks and hangars aboard ship Kamov's naval helicopters have had to be as light and compact as possible. By adopting a co-axial, contra-rotating rotor system with a comparatively small diameter no tail rotor was needed. The tail boom could thus be kept short enough not to protrude beyond the rotor disc and therefore, unlike some Western naval helicopters which have folding tails, only the main rotor blades had to be capable of folding. Other advantages offered by this rotor system, long since abandoned by Western designers (1) included enhanced lift and manoeuvrability and comparative insensitivity to wind direction in the hover and at low speed. It has disadvantages, as may be expected, considerable mechanical complexity and high drag, which limit the helicopter's forward speed, being among them.

Ka-8

As Kamov settled his OKB down after its forced evacuation from Moscow in late 1941 he realised that his A-7 and AK autogiros were at the bottom of Stalin's priority list for aircraft. Despite pleas for support these were not forthcoming and after some desultory work Kamov's design and production staffs were disbanded in 1943. Within two years, as the war ended, he resolutely gathered together some of his erstwhile colleagues and began work on what is sometimes sportively called his *Vozdushnyi Mototsikl* (Flying Motorcycle). The dimensions and weight of this machine were such that it could be operated from ships. This fact intrigued the Soviet Navy and Merchant Navy who saw in it respectively an excellent observation platform for military purposes and the location of whales and various obstructions. It was to incorporate the distinctive design feature common to all but one of his subsequent helicopters: two co-axial, contra-rotating rotors. Such a configuration was hardly an innovation – Sikorsky, d'Ascanio, Bréguet-Dorand and others had all used it – but it was still the best way to counter torque although demanding a heavy and complex transmission. Kamov's intention was to build the simplest single-seat helicopter that man could devise. To a modified 27 hp M-76 (BMW) two-cylinder motorcycle engine, an as uncomplicated transmission as he could design to two three-bladed contra-rotating rotors, a fuel tank and a tubular steel framework mounted on two flotation bags, he added one luxury: a seat for the dubious pilot. Originally designated the K-17 *Vertolet* (Helicopter), the Ka-8, as the machine came to be called later, weighed just 183 kg (403 lb) empty. In accordance with traditional motorcycle practice the flying controls consisted of handlebars: push them forward for forward flight, sideways for lateral flight and rotate them for turns. This system was a complete failure and Mikhail Gurov, the test pilot, soon let it be known that he preferred a less frivolous arrangement. Conventional controls were substituted. The throttle was placed on the starboard side with the collective lever attached to the seat. For directional control rudder pedals were installed. The machine boasted only two instruments: an airspeed indicator and an rpm tachometer. The first was quickly seen to be superfluous, merely adding unwanted weight: the engine was simply not powerful enough to lift the 'motorcycle' off the ground with its rider in attendance and sufficient fuel to do anything useful.

For the first test the Ka-8 was tethered to the ground by ropes. Gurov climbed aboard and started the engine. In the words of Vladimir Barshevsky, Kamov's chief engineer: "The engine roared and the Ka-8 vibrated but it showed no inclination to leave the ground. We then siphoned off most of the fuel, removed several accessories, including the airspeed indicator, and Gurov tried again, revving the engine for all it was worth. But still the Ka-8 would not budge. In fact, it was not until Gurov had climbed from the seat leaving the engine running that the Ka-8 left the ground, fortunately restrained by the ropes. We had a helicopter but it would only take-off without the pilot!"

Eventually in 1947 a few extra horsepower – another 17.8 to be exact – were coaxed out of the engine by changing the cylinder heads, plugs and carburettor, and beefing up the compression ratio. This enabled the helicopter to take along Gurov with it and attain a hover ceiling of 4 m (13 ft) and a maximum speed of 80 kph (50 mph). Intensive flight testing took place during the winter of 1947/48 resulting in numerous modifications. The groaning engine one day failed at 79 m (260 ft) and the machine was damaged after an autorotational descent: two of the rotor blades snapped and the structure was badly distorted. Fortunately Gurov escaped with minor injuries. The Ka-8 was rebuilt.

The heat of the summer in 1948 was such that the rotor blades could not provide sufficient lift for the machine to climb. Power was enhanced by using a mixture of alcohol and petrol, called by Barshevsky *Spirtzin* (*Spirt i benzin*). The drawback was that the plugs had to be changed after every flight. However, it was found possible to demonstrate the machine publicly at Tushino in July 1948. The performance stunned the onlookers who were amazed by the manoeuvrability of the Ka-8 and its ability to take-off and land on the back of a lorry. Although two more examples were built it had become quite clear that this helicopter was not going far, either figuratively or physically. The Kamov bureau had not really succeeded in building a true *Vozdushnyi Mototsikl* but many important lessons had been learned. The engine designer, Aleksandr Ivchenko, was now invited to develop a more powerful engine for the Ka-8. The four cylinder AI-4V of 55 hp, however, was rather too grand for the humble Ka-8 and the Ka-10 had to be designed to incorporate it.

Ka-10 Hat

The Ka-10 Hat was merely a stretched version of the Ka-8 with improvements in the engine, transmission and control system and a larger diameter rotor of laminated wood and plastic. Rotor rpm were reduced from 475 to 410. It was fully instrumented and was even sophisticated enough to come with a radio. The prototype was first flown by O. K. Yefremov on 30 August 1949 (twelve months after the Mi-1) after modifications had been made to reduce vibration experienced during static tests. The Hat was still underpowered; empty weight had risen to 234 kg (516 lb). It was rudimentary but its

The second of Kamov's designs, the Ka-10M Hat demonstrating its manoeuvrability by landing and taking off from the back of a lorry. The earlier version of the Ka-10 had a single rudder. (Novosti)

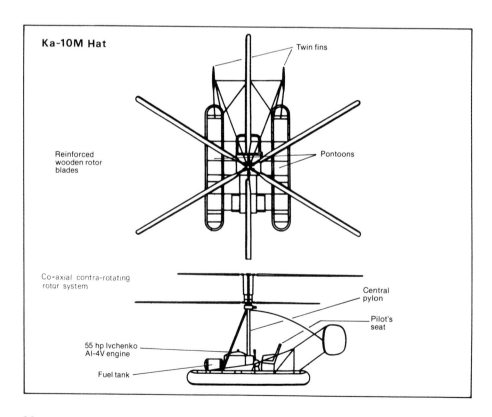

Ka-10M Hat

Twin fins

Reinforced wooden rotor blades

Pontoons

Co-axial contra-rotating rotor system

Central pylon

Pilot's seat

55 hp Ivchenko AI-4V engine

Fuel tank

performance was significantly improved over that of the Ka-8. The hover ceiling was now a more respectable 500 m (1,640 ft) and the service ceiling 1,000 m (3,280 ft). Maximum speed attained was 116 kph (72 mph). The Soviet Navy again expressed interest and indeed displayed the Ka-10 on Navy Day in 1950 from the Khimki Reservoir in Moscow. Four prototypes were built, to be followed by eight Ka-10Ms (*Modifikatsirovannyi*) in 1954. With various modifications including twin rudders in place of the single rudder, a new blade section and a new control system, the -10M had an empty weight of 270 kg (596 lb) and an increase in maximum take-off weight of 24.5 kg (54 lb) to 400 kg (881 lb). Both versions, the Ka-10 and-10M, were evaluated by the Soviet Navy but, with little obvious potential, no further development was pursued. Those -10Ms that had been built were finally issued to the whaling fleet and a few served aboard icebreakers. One example thrilled the crowd at Tushino in 1955.

Ka-15 Hen

Even before the first Ka-10M had been rolled out Kamov had started to lose interest in it and instead turn his attention to the design of something demanding less raw courage from the pilot: a larger two-seater with an enclosed cabin and a wheeled undercarriage. In this venture he was encouraged by the Navy which wanted just such a helicopter provided it retained a co-axial contra-rotating rotor system. So with a similar rotor configuration but with a diameter now of 9.98 m (32 ft 8 in) and a rotor rpm further reduced to 330, the Ka-15 Hen emerged with a tailplane, twin fins and rudders, twin castoring nosewheels and two main wheels with brakes. The rotor blades were made of laminated wood, the hollow sections being filled with plastic foam and the outer

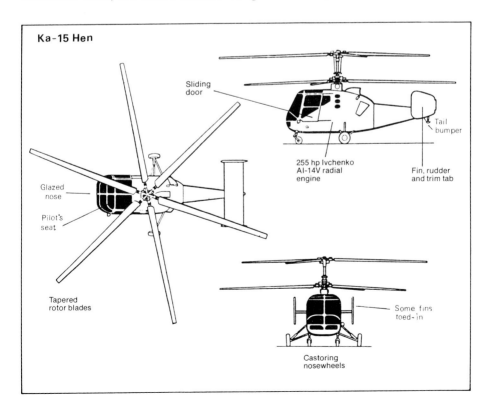

Ka-15 Hen

Sliding door

255 hp Ivchenko AI-14V radial engine

Tail bumper

Fin, rudder and trim tab

Glazed nose

Pilot's seat

Tapered rotor blades

Some fins toed-in

Castoring nosewheels

surfaces being plywood. The stumpy fuselage used a metal frame with plywood covering and stressed skin at the rear. Power was provided by a 255 hp Ivchenko AI-14V nine cylinder air-cooled radial engine positioned directly behind the cockpit. Contrary to general Western helicopter practice the pilot's seat was on the left side of the cockpit to which entry was gained by sliding doors.

The first prototype was completed in early 1952, V. V. Vinitsky being at the controls for the first flight. After almost totally trouble-free factory and State tests the Ka-15 entered service, principally with the Soviet Navy and Merchant Navy, in about 1955. During the tests the Ka-15 achieved a level speed of 150 kph (93 mph) and an altitude of nearly 3,050 m (10,000 ft), a substantial improvement in performance and confirmation that the Hen was much more than an overgrown Hat. In some respects it could be compared with the early versions of the Kaman H-43 Huskie operated by the US Marine Corps in the late 1950s.

Main tasks for the Hen were communications, training and particularly reconnaissance aboard icebreakers. The training version was designated the Ka-15U (*Uchebnyi*). The M model was produced in three versions: passenger/mail, ambulance and agricultural. As a two-seater, of course, it could carry only one passenger or one casualty but it did prove its worth all over the USSR in all three roles. The Kamov bureau claimed that it was more economical than the Mil Mi-1NKh as a chemical spray aircraft. In 1960 a supercharged 275 hp AI-14VF (*Vertolet Forsirovannyi*, Helicopter Supercharged) engine was installed, improving performance and payload. In May 1959 test pilot Vinitsky in a Ka-15 set a new world speed record over a 500 km (311 miles) closed circuit course for helicopters in the 1,000–1,750 kg (2,205–3,858 lb) class of 170.4 kph (105.9 mph). Despite the technical advances embodied in the Hen it made comparatively little impact abroad and none was exported as far as is known.

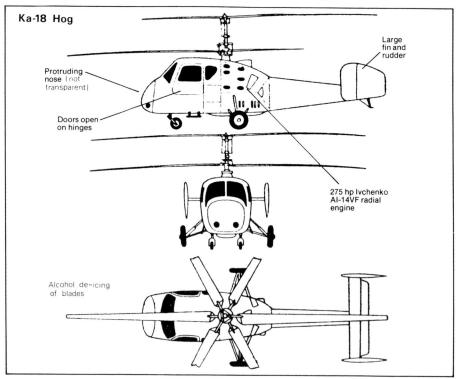

Ka-18 Hog

Large fin and rudder

Protruding nose (not transparent)

Doors open on hinges

275 hp Ivchenko AI-14VF radial engine

Alcohol de-icing of blades

Ka-18 Hog

Flight trials of the stretched version of the Hen, designated the Ka-18 Hog, began in early 1957. A predictable move, the only major change was in the fuselage which was lengthened by 81 cm (2 ft 8 in) thus permitting a pilot and three passengers to be carried in two rows of two seats. To allow the internal carriage of a stretcher the nose was also extended. A slightly enlarged fin area was mounted at the end of an elongated tail boom. The sliding doors of the Hen were replaced by standard doors. Two internal fuel tanks with a capacity of 125 kg (276 lb) could be supplemented by a 50 kg (110 lb) tank mounted externally on each side of the fuselage.

With its increased passenger load, the Hog also offered an enhanced capability through the installation of rotor and windscreen de-icing and a full instrument panel. The AI-14VF engine was fitted when it became available in 1960. Some 200 Ka-18s were used mainly by Aeroflot and the civil authorities for medical evacuation, crop spraying, aerial survey and ice, fishery and forestry patrol. The maximum freight load of 300 kg (660 lb) could be carried about 300 km (186 miles). The Ka-18 was displayed at the World Fair in Brussels in 1958 where it was awarded a Gold Medal.

Ka-22 Hoop

Seen for the first and last time at the 1961 Tushino Air Display was the mysterious Ka-22 Hoop, known in Russian as the *Vintokryl* (possibly translated as 'Screw Wing'). Its appearance amazed Western (and Russian) observers. Its great size – it was thought to be able to carry between 80 and 100 passengers or a variety of military and civil vehicles – drew excited comment from the crowd. So did the fact that Kamov, for once, had actually designed a machine (in fact, a compound helicopter) which did not rely on co-axial, contra-rotating rotors. To what extent he had advocated this configuration is not known but clearly his traditional rotor layout would not have been able to cope with an aircraft of this size. Some ten years earlier Bratukhin had been toying with a similar design, although on a much smaller scale. The Bratukhin OKB was disbanded shortly afterwards but the work done may have been passed on to Kamov's staff.

The mysterious Ka-22 Hoop, seen only once at the 1961 Tushino Air Display. Kamov's only attempt at a helicopter without co-axial rotors, the Ka-22 was a compound helicopter with each of the two engines, mounted at the wings tips, driving a propeller and a main rotor.

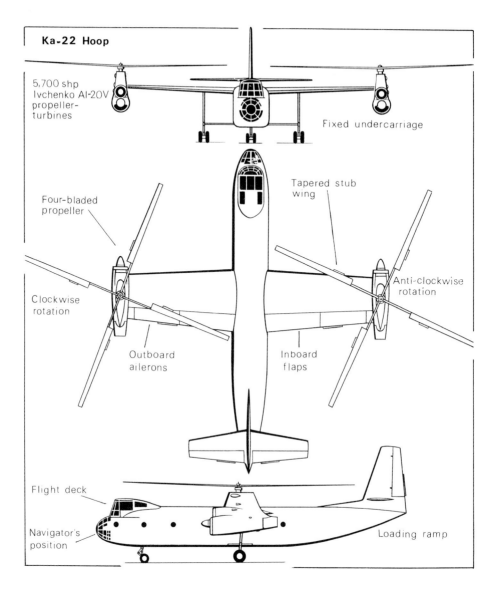

Ka-22 Hoop

5,700 shp
Ivchenko AI-20V
propeller-
turbines

Fixed undercarriage

Four-bladed
propeller

Tapered stub
wing

Clockwise
rotation

Anti-clockwise
rotation

Outboard
ailerons

Inboard
flaps

Flight deck

Navigator's
position

Loading ramp

Certainly the Hoop had a passing resemblance to Bratukhin's B-11. Possibly designed
and built as a competitor to the Mil OKB's Mi-6 Hook, no details of the Hoop were
made available. It was estimated that the gross weight was in the region of 30,000 kg
(66,138 lb) using a rolling take-off. The commentator at Tushino boasted that it was
the most powerful vertical take-off machine in the world. Given the Westland (Fairey)
Rotodyne's maximum take-off weight of some 17,235 kg (38,000 lb), no Western
observer was inclined to argue. The Ka-22 had an all-metal fuselage, including a rear-
loading ramp, of approximately the same size as the Antonov An-12 Cub, and a
conventional tail unit. The tricycle undercarriage consisted of twin spatted nose wheels
and twin spatted main wheels on the end of very long legs which were attached to the
rear spar of the high wing. The flight deck was positioned above the nose which, like
many Soviet airliners and the Mi-6, was composed mainly of glass. The Hoop

40

employed two 5,700 shp Ivchenko AI-20V propeller-turbines (2), one mounted at each end of a 27.43 m (90 ft) tapered wing. Each engine drove a four-bladed main rotor, similar in size to that of the Mi-4 Hound, and in addition a conventional four-blade propeller for forward propulsion at a much higher speed. A complicated system of drives and clutches allowed all the available power to drive the rotors for vertical take-off, extra thrust being harnessed by rotating the turbine exhausts downwards. As forward speed was gathered more and more power was transferred to the propellers until the rotors were autorotating freely like those of an autogiro. Thus the Hoop was able to combine the short and vertical take-off capability of a helicopter with the higher forward speeds of a fixed-wing aircraft.

The Ka-22 could be considered the Soviet answer to Britain's compound helicopter, the Rotodyne, which first flew in 1957 but was abandoned five years later. Although only one Hoop has ever been seen by Western observers, on 7 October, 1961 it broke the Rotodyne's world speed record in its class of 307.22 kph (191 mph) by achieving 356.3 kph (221.4 mph), a remarkable feat, given that the Hoop had a fixed undercarriage while the Rotodyne's was retractable.

A month later, on 24 November, 1961, D. Yefremov set seven more records during a single flight in which a payload of 16,485 kg (36,343 lb) was lifted to 2,588 m (8,491 ft). It is not known exactly why further development of this aircraft was not pursued. It may have been because at any stage of flight either the rotors or propellers were not earning their keep. Attempts to avoid such superfluous units whose weight reduced the useful load led in the USA to a wing with a tilting rotor, a configuration employed in the Bell XV-3 which first flew in 1955. As soon as it was realised that the Hoop did not compare favourably with the Hook it was consigned to research, although Kamov maintained that the configuration was 'still active' in 1966.

Ka-26 Hoodlum-A

Details of the Ka-26 Hoodlum-A were first announced in 1964 and the prototype made its maiden flight the next year. Although obviously a Kamov helicopter by virtue of its size and rotor configuration there was little else to betray its origins. Everything else was new, including its concept of operations and the use of plastics and glue to reduce empty weight. It was, above all, specifically designed for agricultural purposes with a single pilot and has three times the payload of its nominal predeccessor, the Ka-15. Rapid change of role is, however, possible by the ingenious use of interchangeable units which can be placed behind the cockpit close to the centre of gravity: a cargo platform with hinged sides; a passenger cabin which can accommodate six passengers or two stretchers and three walking wounded; a cargo hook for sling loads; and specialised equipment for the spraying of liquid and dry chemicals. To protect the pilot from toxic chemicals the cockpit is lightly pressurised. Besides crop spraying the Hoodlum-A has been used for search and rescue, aerial survey and mapping, ice, fishery, forestry and even highway patrol. When operating at sea flotation bags are fitted. Some have been deployed to fight forest fires. A squad of six men and their equipment are carried. A winch can be used to lower the fire-fighters or lift large buckets of water. Indeed, role equipment has been developed for at least 14 different versions of the Hoodlum-A.

The Kamov co-axial twin rotor configuration is used. The shafts are inclined forwards 6°. The main rotor blades, of which there are two sets of three, are made of glass plastic materials, are completely interchangeable and weigh only 25 kg (55 lb). The Kamov bureau claims that it was the first helicopter design organisation in the world to use such blades. An icing warning device automatically activates an anti-icing system which makes use of an alcohol/glycerine mixture which protects the blades and

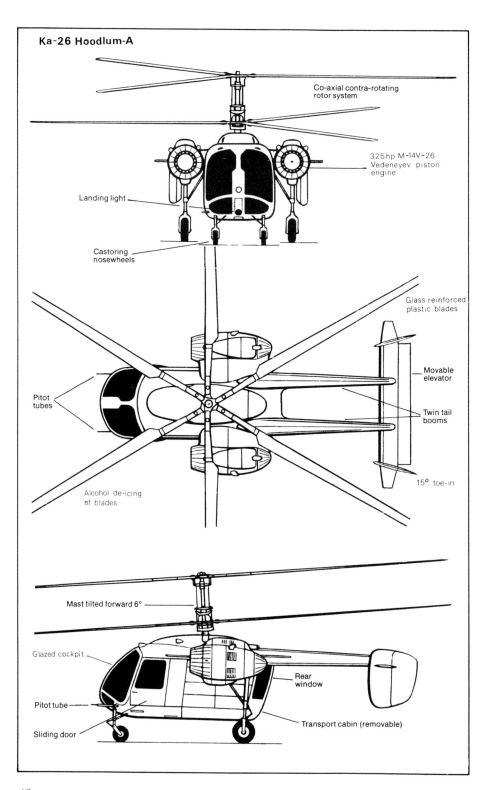

Ka-26 Hoodlum-A

Co-axial contra-rotating
rotor system

325hp M-14V-26
Vedeneyev piston
engine

Landing light

Castoring
nosewheels

Glass reinforced
plastic blades

Movable
elevator

Pitot
tubes

Twin tail
booms

15° toe-in

Alcohol de-icing
of blades

Mast tilted forward 6°

Glazed cockpit

Rear
window

Pitot tube

Transport cabin (removable)

Sliding door

Two Bulgarian Ka-26 Hoodlums; the one in the foreground has a ferry tank behind the cockpit while the other has a passenger cabin. (Author)

cockpit windscreen. The cockpit and passenger cabin are warmed by means of a combustion heater.

Somewhat unexpectedly, the Ka-26 is powered by two large, podded 325 hp Vedeneyev M-14V-26 nine-cylinder radial engines rather than turbines. These are mounted on stub wings which contain the fuel tanks. Dry weight of the engine is 245 kg (540 lb). It may be that piston engines were chosen because of the lack of a suitable turbine engine. Most likely, however, is the fact that ease of maintenance was a major factor. Hoodlums were going to have to operate in remote geographical areas, often where maintenance crews had little or no experience of turbine engines. Vehicle mechanics, on the other hand, with some minimal level of training, could service the piston engines of the Ka-26. Furthermore, spare parts would be less of a problem with a piston engine than for a new turbine. The penalty to be paid was that piston engines are heavier than comparable turbine engines. Fuel consumption with the Vedeneyev is good: 3.7 flying hours at 90 kph (56 mph). With two engines there is, of course, a greater margin of safety, particularly attractive when operating over the more inhospitable reaches of the Soviet Union. According to an Aviaexport brochure, "the Ka-26 helicopter is capable of continuing level flight with one engine operating with a gross weight . . . and it passes safely to the autorotation from any flight state, the hovering included."

Without its role equipment there is not much of the Ka-26. The light alloy stressed skin fuselage is little more than a cockpit with side-by-side seating and sliding doors. Forward and sideways visibility is excellent. Electronic and radio equipment is at the rear with the transmission and reduction gear positioned above and behind the cockpit. The tailplane, with twin fins and rudders toed in 15°, is mounted at the end of two tail booms. The fins protrude mainly below the level of the tailplane. The early models to come off the production line had a tailplane which extended more than 61 cm (24 in) beyond the fins but by 1970 these extensions had been removed. The non-retractable landing gear consists of two main wheels, which are attached to the stub wings through

An Hungarian Ka-26 crop-spraying.

The co-axial, contra-rotating rotor system of a Ka-26.

the rear end of the engine nacelles and have brakes, and two separate castoring nose wheels.

A high load-to-weight ratio and cost effectiveness were key considerations in the design of the Hoodlum. Certain parameters were established, the most important of which were that the cost of spraying one hectare (2.47 acres) should not exceed three roubles and that the optimum payload over short distances should be about 680 kg (1,500 lb). Getting out their slide rules, Barshevsky and his engineers decided that the helicopter must be able to spray 30 hectares an hour and have high reliability and availability rates. By 1979 the Hoodlum's spraying performance was 400% better than the original requirement. In this role a chemical hopper with a capacity of 900 kg (1,985 lb) is installed at the centre of gravity behind the cockpit and a spraybar fitted. As a load carrier the Hoodlum can lift 1,065 kg (2,350 lb) on its platform or on a cargo hook; 900 kg (1,985 lb) may be taken in its passenger cabin. A winch with a 150 kg (330 lb) capacity is sometimes installed.

Because of its small size – the rotor diameter is only 13.03 m (42 ft 8 in) – and its manoeuvrability, the Hoodlum is ideal for tasks which necessitate operating from small ships. It has been used frequently on whalers and icebreakers on both the open sea and rivers for reconnaissance duties. Clearing ice from rivers has been achieved by demolitions teams ferried by Hoodlums.

Flight tests were completed in 1965 and two years later, when production began, a Ka-26 appeared at the Paris Air Show demonstrating its manoeuvrability. At the next Show in 1969 a geological version was displayed. Since then the Ka-26 has been exhibited all over Europe and in Japan where it is now in service in an agricultural role. Over 600 of the various types are in civil service and some have been exported. Military versions have been delivered to Bulgaria, Hungary and Sri Lanka although the latter country no longer operates them militarily. Besides Japan and the USSR Ka-26s can be found in civil guise in East and West Europe. In 1972 International Aviation Brokers of Stockholm leased a Ka-26 to the US firm of Brown and Root Inc. who evaluated the helicopter for possible use in pipeline construction outside the USA. Registered in Sweden, the machine was flown in the USA under a Swedish airworthiness certificate. Production ended, probably in 1979, after a run of some 800 machines.

Ka-126 Hoodlum-B

In 1981 the Kamov OKB began work on the modification of a single Ka-26. The two piston engines were removed and replaced by two very small turboshafts. In due course this mock-up underwent further change when a single 720 shp TVD-100 turboshaft engine, mounted centrally above the cabin, was substituted for the two smaller turbines. One of the major weaknesses of the piston-engined Ka-26 is that, with a full payload, it can only hover at sea level. The Ka-126 retains the layout, dimensions and maximum take-off weight of the Ka-26 but with a gas turbine engine it can hover with its full load of 1,000 kg (2,205 lb) of fertilizer or chemicals at an altitude of 1,000 m (3,281 ft). The single TVD-100 offers more power than the two M-14V-26 piston engines but is much lighter, and it has therefore been possible to increase the payload, range and endurance – factors which affect operational economy and profitability. Another reason for changing to a gas turbine engine is that practically the entire Soviet civil aviation fleet is now oriented towards this type of power plant. The availability of aviation fuel for piston engines was becoming a problem.

Besides the engine change the Ka-126 benefits from an improved cockpit layout and more compact instrument panel and the pilot's field of vision is thereby enhanced. Otherwise the new helicopter makes use of the components and assemblies of its

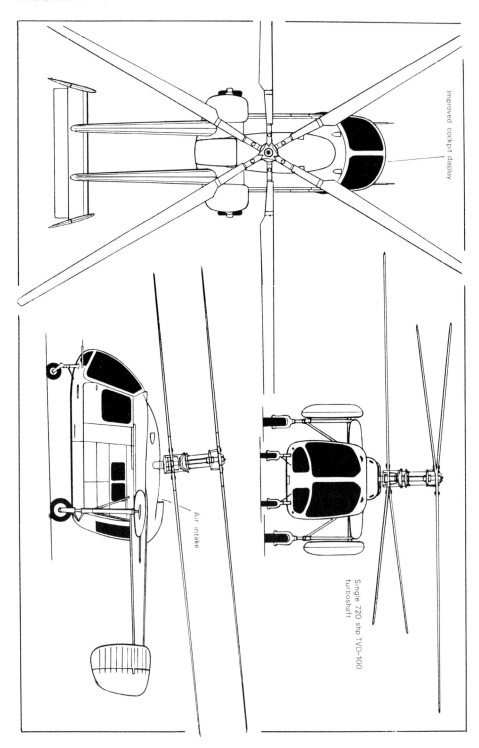

Improved cockpit display

Air intake

Single 720 shp TVD-100 turboshaft

predecessor so that, according to Sergei Mikheyev, Chief of the Kamov OKB, "Operators can look on the Ka-126 as an old friend".

By the end of 1985 a prototype Ka-126 had been built for ground testing with another under way for flight test. The following year State trials in the Soviet Union were successfully completed. However, the Ka-126 was not to be produced in the USSR. Agreement was reached with Interprinderea de Constructii de Aeronautic (ICA) at Brasov in Romania which was to undertake series production of brand new aircraft and the conversion of old Ka-26s which may eventually number several hundred. In 1987 Ka-126 production was due to begin but as far as is known it did not. Development has been protracted and may now involve modifications to the fuselage and rotor systems.

The Ka-126 is intended for use mainly in the USSR and East Europe and is expected eventually to replace all Ka-26s. It is a multi-purpose helicopter, able to carry out a wide variety of civil roles by means of specialist equipment. It is claimed to have a cruising speed of 160 kph (99 mph), a range of 600 km (373 miles) and an endurance of 4 hours 42 minutes.

Ka-32

When Kamov died on 24 November 1973 Sergei Viktorovich Mikheyev took over, at the tender age of 36, and became ultimately responsible for the Ka-32. According to Mikheyev, the problems being encountered in the development and exploitation of the northernmost regions of the Soviet Union led to the advent of the Ka-32. Specifically what was required was an all-weather, long-range helicopter for ice reconnaissance for Arctic convoys. Such a role would only require a few dozen helicopters and clearly it would not be cost-effective to build a helicopter for just this purpose. To justify proceeding other roles would have to be found. The first to be identified was the unloading of ships on the move. The Ka-32 could transfer freight underslung from ship to shore, thus obviating the need on some occasions for the ship to make a port call; it could sail straight on without even slowing down. Once a load-carrying capability over water was accepted an analysis of cargoes carried over land by helicopter was undertaken. It transpired that a significant proportion of flights involved a cargo weighing approximately 5,000 kg (11,023 lb) and usually too bulky to fit in the cargo compartment. No Soviet helicopter corresponded to this capability, the Mi-8 Hip being able to take only 3,000 kg (6,614 lb) as an underslung load, the Mi-6 Hook 8,000 kg (17,637 lb) and the Mi-26 Halo, intended to replace the Hook, 20,000 kg (44,092 lb). Thus a requirement for a helicopter which could undersling a bulky load of 5,000 kg over 80 km (50 miles) or carry internally 1,500 kg (3,307 lb) over a distance of 800 km (497 miles) could be justified; the case for the proposed Ka-32 could be further strengthened by additional roles such as rescue work and as a flying crane in the erection of power lines and other building projects. Naturally Mikheyev did not mention the military angle and the pressing need for a replacement for the Ka-25 Hormone.

On 8 February, 1981 the Soviet Army newspaper *Red Star* briefly reported that a new Kamov helicopter, the Ka-32, had entered production. It was claimed that it was to operate aboard icebreakers and whalers as a SAR helicopter and for reconnaissance purposes. Radius of action was stated as being 185 km (115 miles) and the machine was credited with a day and night capability in Arctic-type weather and the ability to lift a 5,000 kg (11,023 lb) underslung load. In late 1981 the existence of this new helicopter, understood to have made its first flight in 1976 or 1977 and to have entered production in 1980, was publicly confirmed when the first prototype went on display in Minsk with

Nadezhda Yeremina (right) talks to her colleague Tatiana Zueva after setting a new world record in the Ka-32. Note the anti-flutter weights on the lower rotor blade.

other Soviet and Polish aircraft during the Eastern bloc's Council for Mutual Economic Assistance conference on the uses of aircraft to support the national economy.

Even before this, however, in September 1981, Western eyes had seen a military version of this helicopter when two had been observed operating from the platform of the first 'Udaloy' class ASW destroyer while she was exercising in the Baltic; one helicopter was in AV-MF markings and the other in Aeroflot colours. Both, however, were configured for ASW as shown in the first pictures to appear in the Western aviation press in February 1982. This version is now known as the Ka-27 Helix and is described in detail in the next chapter together with the characteristics common to both it and the Ka-32.

More information on the civil Ka-32 was forthcoming when a prototype of the utility version, converted from a pre-series Ka-27, appeared at the 1985 Paris Air Show. According to Sergei Mikheyev, there are two basic versions of the Ka-32, both intended to be able to operate independently of ground support equipment. They are a land-based utility version with the minimum of equipment, the Ka-32T (*Transportnyi*) and the Ka-32S (*Sudovoy*, ship-based) with much more comprehensive equipment. The main function of either version of the Ka-32, however, is as a load carrier, either with up to 16 passengers or an internal load of up to 4,000 kg (8,818 lb): using the preferred method of a sling suspended from a cargo hook, it can lift 5,000 kg (11,023 lb), a payload equivalent to 39.7% of the helicopter's maximum overload weight of 12,600 kg (27,778 lb). A useful device in this connection is the automatic weight measurement of the underslung load. The Ka-32S can easily be converted for casualty evacuation or as an air ambulance with space for four stretchers in addition to six seats. Another version for the evacuation of people from high-rise buildings in the event of fire has been tested. A cradle which is capable of containing up to 20 people is slung beneath the helicopter. It is designed to be flown by a single pilot and thus only the port seat has flying controls and an instrument panel in front of it. The starboard seat is occupied, whenever the circumstances demand, by a navigator or, when radar is installed alongside the instrument panel, a radar operator. A winch capable of lifting 300 kg (661 lb) is attached above the cabin door.

The Deputy Chief Designer of the Kamov OKB, Veniamin Kasyanikov, has claimed that the Ka-32S is capable of operating over water in severe Arctic weather conditions, day or night, by means of comprehensive avionics and thermoelectric anti-icing systems for the main rotor blades, engine air intakes and windows, despite the deleterious effect on available engine power. The aircraft displayed in Paris (SSSR-31000) did not sport the latest in avionics technology but, in true Soviet style, could without doubt be counted upon for great reliability and to provide all the help the crew required. The autopilot panel controlled the electro-mechanical flight director; the autopilot system included an automatic approach and hover mode to allow hands-off Doppler radar-coupled approaches, on a selected heading, to a stationary hover at 25 m (82 ft) above, for example, an offshore oil rig or ship's deck. Also included were a large Doppler hover indicator, a horizontal situation indicator for the navigator and a radar altimeter. The Ka-32S at Paris did not carry the search radar under the nose as would normally be expected with this version, but it did have the standard Doppler radar in a box mounted under the rear fuselage.

The Ka-32S has been designed as a 'maritime truck'. Given its original raison d'être, it is not surprising that it is adept at operating from the decks of icebreakers, using its radar to measure the thickness of the ice and thereby help in selecting the path of least resistance. Some operational tests were conducted in the mountains of the North Caucasus and in the Arctic. Others were completed on the nuclear-powered icebreaker *Sibir*, the Ka-32S flying sorties of up to 300 km (186 miles) radius. It can carry enough fuel for $4\frac{1}{2}$ hours flying. It is, as planned, used as a flying crane to load and unload ships supplying remote settlements in northern waters and in a maritime search and rescue role. At least one Aeroflot Ka-32 took part in the monitoring of radiation after the catastrophe at the Chernobyl nuclear power station in April 1986. Sensors were lowered into the chimney stack of the damaged reactor by a hovering Ka-32.

SSSR-31000 is the very aircraft in which two women helicopter instructors from a club near Moscow, Nadezhda Yeremina and Tatiana Zueva, set three new world records in May 1983. On 29 January 1985 these two women set four more world records in a Ka-32. Details are in Appendix 3.

After the Ka-26 entered production in 1966 the Kamov OKB appeared unable to develop a design good enough to warrant the cutting of metal until the Ka-27/32 design was accepted for prototype building and flight test. Lean years indeed during which the future of the OKB as a separate entity might have been at stake. The appearance of the Ka-27/32 was long overdue. That the bureau was allowed to continue will probably have been due to many reasons: it will certainly have been busy even if its efforts never came to the attention of the public.

Ka-? Hokum

It was the Pentagon's fourth edition in 1985 of its *Soviet Military Power* that proclaimed the existence of a new helicopter with a co-axial, contra-rotating rotor system, named Hokum by NATO. It gave few details and did not go so far as to credit the Kamov OKB with the design.

In 1984, however, it had already become publicly known that a new co-axial, contra-rotating rotor helicopter was under flight test in the Soviet Union. Because of its rotor configuration it was nevertheless immediately assumed to be a product of the Kamov OKB although no designation was known. The few details in *Soviet Military Power* together with various artists' impressions allow a little tentative speculation – which may later prove to be wide of the mark.

Little is known about the Kamov Hokum although it is credited with having a formidable performance. This artist's impression shows a typical Kamov rotor layout but widely separated engines, a streamlined fuselage, underwing weapon stations and a starboard mounted cannon.

Ka–? Hokum

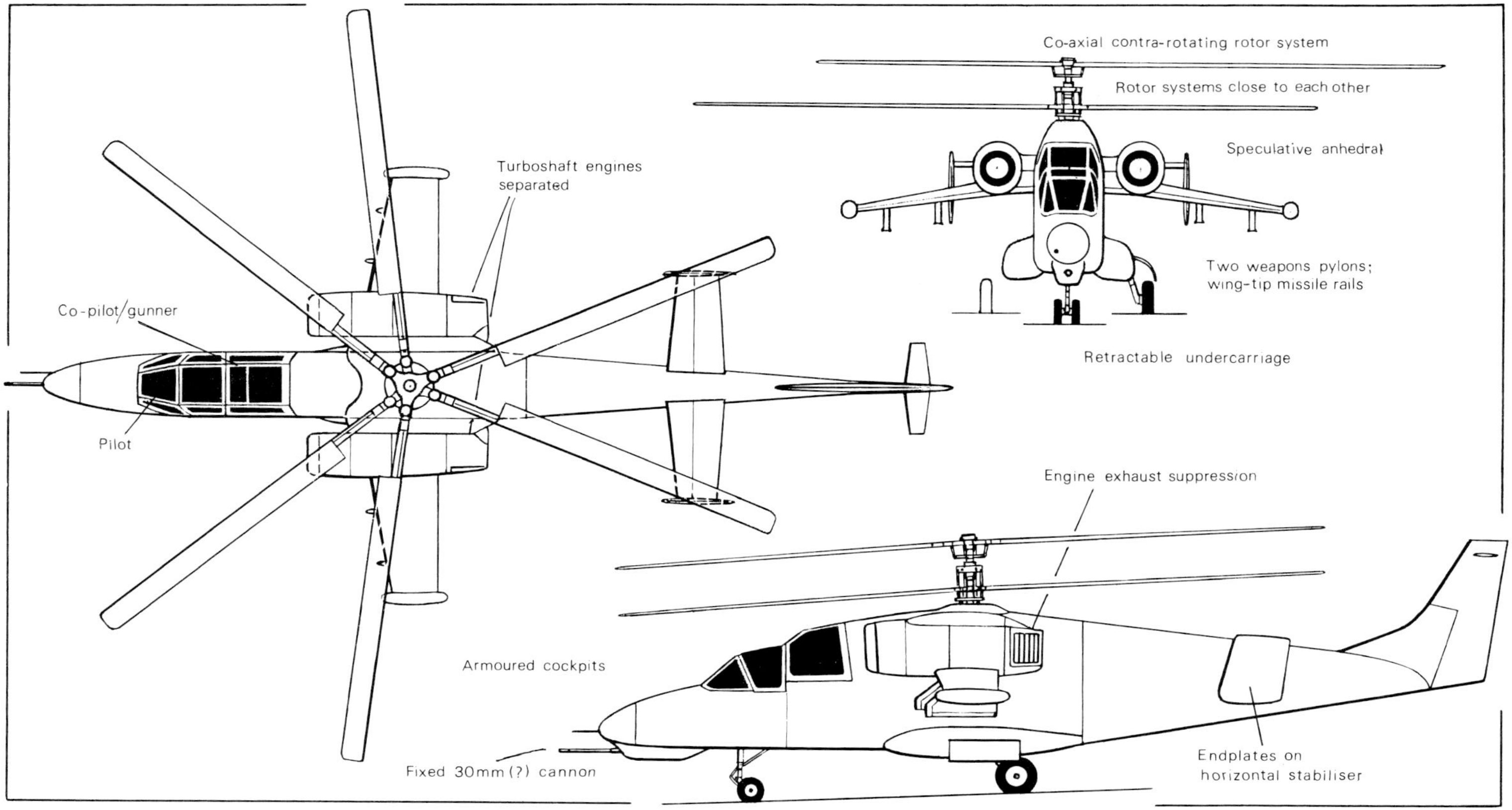

Co-axial contra-rotating rotor system

Rotor systems close to each other

Speculative anhedral

Two weapons pylons; wing-tip missile rails

Retractable undercarriage

Endplates on horizontal stabiliser

Engine exhaust suppression

Turboshaft engines separated

Armoured cockpits

Fixed 30mm (?) cannon

Co-pilot/gunner

Pilot

51

The drawings show a sleek and streamlined fuselage with a comparatively 'clean' rotor mast and hub for minimum aerodynamic drag. The stub wings, possibly with some anhedral, have a span of perhaps 7 m (23 ft) and two weapons pylons under each; there are probably missile rails, weapons pylons or other devices at the wing tips. The horizontal stabiliser has large end plates and is positioned on the upper part of the tail boom well forward of the tail fin. Some drawings show a small tailplane close to the top of the fin, others do not. The two-man cockpit has a flat plate canopy and probably armour protection. The nose and main wheels are all retractable.

It is possible that the Hokum, in its prototype form, uses two 2,225 shp TV3-117 turboshaft engines and the same dynamics as those of the Ka-27 Helix. The two engines are podded and well separated, being located on either side of the fuselage to enhance aircraft survivability. Diameter of the three-bladed rotors is thought to be about 14 m (45 ft 10 in) and they are as close together as the articulated rotor systems and stiffness of the blades will allow. Clearly the aim of the designers has been to achieve the best compromise between high dash speed and good agility and manoeuvrability. Take-off weight is estimated at about 5,450 kg (12,000 lb).

Crew workload was probably forecast to be high with no great likelihood of electronic devices or other measures being able to reduce it to the level where a single pilot could cope comfortably. Therefore the Hokum appears to have two seats in tandem. One might guess that the pilot sits in the front cockpit with the gunner using indirect view optics in the back – unlike the Mi-24 Hind and the Mi-28 Havoc.

Little is known about the helicopter's armament but a multi-barrelled cannon could be installed under the nose and various other types of weapons on the wing pylons. To make the most of its performance – the US Department of Defense gives an estimated maximum level speed of 350 kph (217 mph) although not surprisingly agility is not quantified – an air-to-air role could be expected to be a primary role and for this air-to-air missiles would be the obvious weapons fit. Something newer than the AT-6 Spiral might be predicted for anti-tank combat.

It is almost certainly the first time that the two OKBs, Mil with its Mi-28 Havoc and Kamov, have worked on designs for an adverse weather and night-capable attack helicopter at the same time – probably as a replacement for the Mi-24 Hind. That being the case an element of competition existed with the Mil bureau having its pre-eminence in the design of land-based helicopters to lose. Even if the Hokum is not accepted for service in support of the ground forces it might be taken on by the Soviet Navy for which it would fill a yawning operational capability gap as an escort helicopter for the Helix-B assault helicopter. No doubt wishing to eat into the Mil monopoly and widen its market the Kamov OKB has raised the stakes and gone for a design which embodies considerably higher technical risks than the Mi-28 Havoc. Little has been heard of the Hokum for some time and it could be inferred that all is not, or has not been, well with the project. Whether work is still proceeding towards the start of production or whether the Hokum will remain a research and development project only remains to be seen. If it does enter production and service then it might claim to be the first helicopter in the world to offer a genuine air-to-air capability.

Notes

1. Sikorsky has built two S-69s, designated XH-59A, for research purposes. Known as the Advancing Blade Concept (ABC), the sole surviving helicopter has two co-axial, contra-rotating three-bladed rigid rotors 79 cm (2 ft 7 in) apart. At high speeds the advancing blades of the contra-rotating rotors are generating practically all the lift with the consequent off-loading of the retreating blades; thus the possibility of retreating blade stall is eliminated and the helicopter can fly much faster than conventionally-designed helicopters. The XH-59A first flew in July 1973 and in March 1977 two turbojets were installed to investigate the concept at higher flight speeds.

2. One authority states that the engines were 5,500 shp Soloviev D-25V turboshafts.

CHARACTERISTICS

Designation	**Kamov Ka-8**	**Kamov Ka-10**
Engine	M-76	Ivchenko AI-4V
	44.8 hp	55 hp
Rotor diameter	2 × 5.6 m (18 ft 4½ in)	2 × 6.12 m (20 ft 1 in)
Fuselage length	?	3.9 m (12 ft 9½ in)
Height	3.62 m (11 ft 10½ in)	2.5 m (8 ft 2½ in)
Empty weight	183 kg (403 lb)	234 kg (516 lb)
Max gross weight	275 kg (606 lb)	375 kg (826 lb)
Max speed	80 kph (50 mph)	116 kph (72 mph)
Range	?	193 km (120 mls)
Service ceiling	250 m (820 ft)	1,000 m (3,280 ft)
First flight	November 1947	September 1949

Designation	**Kamov Ka-15**	**Kamov Ka-18**
Engine	Ivchenko AI-14V	Ivchenko AI-14VF
	255 hp	275 hp
Rotor diameter	2 × 9.98 m (32 ft 8 in)	2 × 9.98 m (32 ft 8 in)
Fuselage length	6.22 m (20 ft 5 in)	7.03 m (23 ft 1 in)
Height	3.35 m (11 ft 0 in)	3.35 m (11 ft 0 in)
Empty weight	968 kg (2,135 lb)	1,022 kg (2,253 lb)
Max gross weight	1,406 kg (3,100 lb)	1,501 kg (3,310 lb)
Max speed	150 kph (93 mph)	150 kph (93 mph)
Range	310 km (193 mls)	346 km (215 mls)
Service ceiling	3,000 m (9,840 ft)	3,000 m (9,840 ft)
First flight	1952	1957

Designation	**Kamov Ka-26**	**Kamov Ka-126**
Engine	2 × M-14V-26	TVD-100
	2 × 325 hp	720 shp
Rotor diameter	2 × 13.03 m (42 ft 8 in)	2 × 13.03 m (42 ft 8 in)
Fuselage length	7.75 m (25 ft 5 in)	7.75 m (25 ft 5 in)
Height	4.05 m (13 ft 3½ in)	4.05 m (13 ft 3½ in)
Empty weight	1,950 kg (4,300 lb)*	?
Max gross weight	3,250 kg (7,165 lb)	3,250 kg (7,165 lb)
Max speed	169 kph (105 mph)	180 kph (112 mph)
Range	400 km (248 mls)**	600 km (373 mls)
Service ceiling	3,000 m (9,840 ft)	?
First flight	1965	1986

  * Stripped
** 30 min fuel reserves

The Hormone and Helix and their roles at sea

The 1961 Tushino Display was also the venue for the first glimpse of what proved to be a very early version of the Ka-25 Hormone. This new aircraft was given the designation Ka-20 Harp and was referred to in the Soviet Press as a Navy rocket-carrying helicopter. Designed as a specialist anti-submarine helicopter, it was clearly much bigger than the Ka-18 from which it was derived. When seen it had a large search radar under the nose and a second fairing, possibly housing a navigational aid, under the tail boom. A pylon on either side of the cabin carried a dummy air-to-surface missile and two fixed forward-firing guns were mounted in the nose. Another major innovation was the installation of two small shaft turbines mounted side-by-side above the cabin and driving the usual Kamov rotor system. Two turbines promised to improve dramatically the Harp's performance compared to that of the Ka-18 besides giving added safety, important for aircraft operating over water. Little was seen of the Harp for the next six years when it then appeared in a new guise as the Ka-25 Hormone.

The flat undersurface of the nose radar of this Ka-25 Hormone-A distinguishes it from the B version which has a more bulbous radar.

Ka-25 Hormone-A

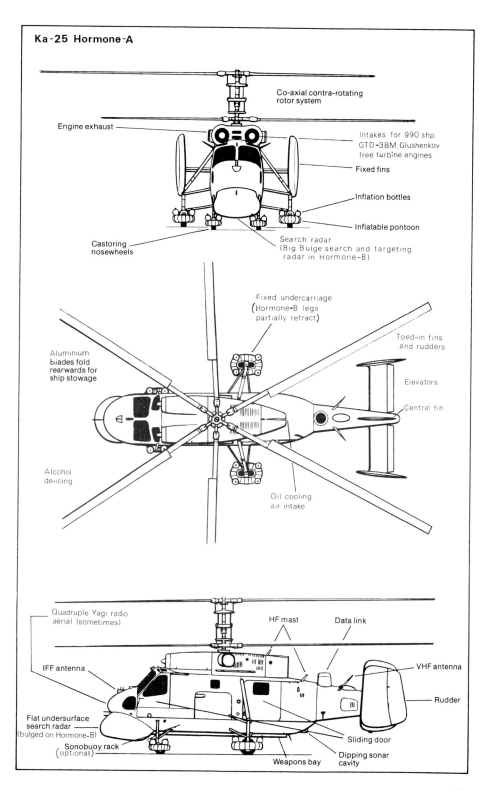

Co-axial contra-rotating rotor system

Engine exhaust

Intakes for 990 shp GTD-3BM Glushenkov free turbine engines

Fixed fins

Inflation bottles

Inflatable pontoon

Castoring nosewheels

Search radar (Big Bulge search and targeting radar in Hormone-B)

Fixed undercarriage (Hormone-B legs partially retract)

Aluminium blades fold rearwards for ship stowage

Toed-in fins and rudders

Elevators

Central fin

Alcohol de-icing

Oil cooling air intake

Quadruple Yagi radio aerial (sometimes)

HF mast

Data link

IFF antenna

VHF antenna

Rudder

Flat undersurface search radar (bulged on Hormone-B)

Sonobuoy rack (optional)

Sliding door

Weapons bay

Dipping sonar cavity

As a flying crane, the Ka-25K (*Kran*, Crane) appeared at the Paris Air Show in 1967. Despite a slightly longer nose, less rounded outer fins and a few other minor modifications, it was very similar to the military version. In place of the radome under the nose, the crane had a gondola for a rear-facing crewmember who actually flew the helicopter during the pick-up and release of loads. Maximum sling load was said to be 2,000 kg (4,409 lb). The Ka-25K was not considered worthy of further development or production.

The twin rotors of the Ka-25 have three blades of parallel chord each. Because they are fully articulated there is a considerable gap between them. To allow stowage below deck or in a small hangar on board smaller ships, the blades can be folded. So that the lower rotor may be mounted as close to the fuselage as possible, to minimise rotor mast height and to avoid interference effects, blade aerofoils begin well away from the mast.

Originally two 900 shp Glushenkov GTD-3F turbine engines were mounted above the cabin, leaving it clear for personnel or specialist payloads. In due course these engines were replaced by more powerful 990 shp GTD-3BM turboshafts. The fuselage is of the conventional all-metal, semi-monocoque structure of the pod-and-boom type. The tail unit has a central fin, a ventral fin and two large end-plate fins and rudders which are significantly toed-in. The two nosewheels and two main wheels can be fitted with an inflatable pontoon above which is a ring of small inflation bottles in case of an emergency landing in water. The complete landing gear can be pivoted upwards and to the rear in the military B model to minimise interference to signals from the nose radar. The Ka-25 is indeed a masterly design: a crew of two and twelve passengers in a fuselage just 9.75 m (32 ft) long. Actual cabin dimensions are 3.95 m (12 ft 11½ in) long by 1.5 m (4 ft 11 in) wide by 1.25 m (4 ft 1 in) high. The degree of comfort may be disagreeable

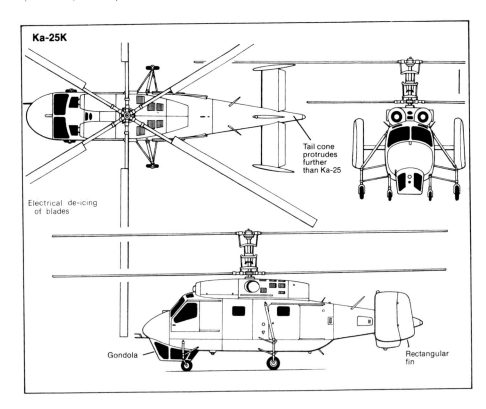

Ka-25K

Tail cone protrudes further than Ka-25

Electrical de-icing of blades

Gondola

Rectangular fin

and compared to that of the UH-60 Blackhawk's, the fuselage of which is 15.24 m (50 ft) long for a crew of three and 11 passengers.

A somewhat inelegant-looking helicopter, the Ka-25 has exhibited an ability to accept developments rivalled by few Western helicopters (Bell's UH-1 and the Sikorsky S-61 are notable exceptions). Three basic versions exist, the Hormone-A, B and C, but as many as 25 different variants have been identified at one time or another. For example, some Hormones have been seen with a streamlined blister fairing at the base of the central tail fin; some have an inverted 'flower pot' fairing above the tail boom near its centre which may house a data link or an electro-optical sensor, in which case the corresponding window below the boom is used; others have a similar fairing underneath the rear end of the fuselage. Undernose search radar radomes come in different sizes. Apart from the ASW equipment carried, electronic aids are likely to be comprehensive given the helicopter's roles and operating environment; they certainly include an autopilot and self-contained navigation system. The C model, identified in 1981, is used as a utility helicopter and in the vertical replenishment and SAR roles when it is equipped with a rotatable searchlight and hoist. It usually has a distinctive red and white paint scheme and no antenna on the upper surface of the tail boom. The B model is a special electronics variant with no ventral weapons bay but with a radome that is much more spherical on its underside than that of the A model. It houses the appropriately-named but now ageing Big Bulge radar. It also has a cylindrical radome under the rear end of the cabin. This version is employed primarily for target acquisition and the over-horizon, mid-course guidance of the 450 km (280 miles) range SS-N-3 Shaddock ship-to-ship missile and its 550 km (340 miles) range replacement, the SS-N-12; also the SS-N-19 and SS-N-22. Its data link system presumably enables its radar display to be transmitted directly to the ship firing the missiles.

The Hormone-A was for many years the principal workhorse of the Soviet Navy's helicopter fleet. The Naval Air Force (*Aviatsiya Voenno-Morskogo Flota*, abbreviated to AV-MF) is thought to operate about 180. Search radar is housed in the undernose radome and ASW equipment includes towed magnetic anomaly detection (MAD) gear, dipping sonar in a compartment at the rear of the cabin and an electro-optical sensor. Some A models have a sonobuoy dispenser fitted externally to the rear cabin

A Ka-25 Hormone-A displays its ventral weapons bay.

sides and a weapons bay under the fuselage for possibly a couple of torpedoes or nuclear and conventional depth charges. New air-to-surface missiles could be carried on pylons similar to those of the Ka-20 but no such arrangement has ever been observed. The major shortcoming of the Hormone-A, besides its relatively limited radius of action, is its lack of an automatic hover capability. This precludes the use of the dipping sonar at night or in adverse weather under which circumstances the A model can only use sonobuoys.

Not surprisingly the commissioning in 1960 of the first Polaris A-1 submarine, the USS *George Washington*, generated a good deal of thought among Admiral Sergei Gorshkov, appointed at the age of 45 as Commander-in-Chief of the Soviet Navy in January 1956 (1), and his staff. A couple of years later a significant change in Soviet naval strategy could be detected. The Soviet Navy had played virtually no part in the submarine war against the Germans but now the awesome potential of the US sea-based nuclear strike force together with the ever-improving capability of Western ASW forces steadily became more apparent. Clearly the Soviet Union would have to match these capabilities directly by building her own force of modern submarine-launched ballistic missiles (SLBMs) and submarines, and simultaneously developing ASW forces with which to counter Western submarine fleets. Admiral Gorshkov made it clear that the ASW effort was to extend beyond the hunting, detection and destruction of Western SLBM submarines to include the protection of his own submarines, the value of which he repeatedly stressed. And so the emphasis was switched from an anti-surface capability to that of anti-submarine.

The specific threat was the Polaris A-1 missile which had a range of 2,220 km (1,380 miles) and which, to reach Moscow, had to be launched from locations close to Soviet waters and thus relatively close to Soviet naval bases. Polaris submarines had therefore to be excluded from these waters or at least made aware that the risk of their detection and consequent destruction was unacceptably high. To be able to achieve such aims it was obvious that a major modernisation and expansion programme for Soviet ASW forces was urgently required, to include new submarines, a change in direction for the submarine fleet and the development of new aircraft and helicopters for the AV-MF. These forces would have to have the capability to be deployed continuously beyond those sea areas that they were accustomed to and could naturally hope to control. Existing destroyers were hurriedly converted for this role while the development and construction of new ASW surface ships and aircraft, the Ilyushin Il-38 May and the Ka-25 Hormone, was begun.

Designed originally as all-gun destroyers, the first of the eight 4,600-ton 'Krupny' class destroyers appeared in 1960 with SS-N-1 surface-to-surface missiles. Within a few years their ship-to-air capability was strengthened at the expense of their surface capability and more anti-submarine weapons were installed. With the addition of a helicopter pad in the stern this modified class was renamed 'Kanin'. The world's first gas turbine-powered warship, the 4,500-ton 'Kashin', entered service in 1963. In due course six were modified to have a helicopter pad. The four ships of the 'Kresta I' class were the first Soviet warships designed to have a helicopter as an integral part of their equipment. All four were commissioned between 1967 and 1969 and each had a landing pad and hangar at the stern for a single helicopter, in this case a Hormone-B. Despite being originally designated a 'large anti-submarine ship' (*Bolshoi Protivo-Lodochnyi Korabl* – BPK), the 'Kresta Is' used their Hormone-Bs for target acquisition and mid-course guidance for the Shaddock ship-to-ship missile. In 1977–78 these ships were redesignated missile cruisers (*raketnyi kreyser*), the ASW role being undertaken by the more capable 'Kresta II' class. Displacing about 7,500 tons, the first of these cruisers, of which only ten were built, entered service in 1969. They retained the

It is easy to see why the radar of the Ka-25 Hormone-B is called Big Bulge.

helicopter but, because the SS-N-3 had been superseded by the 56 km (35 miles) range SS-N-14 anti-submarine missile, it was a Hormone-A. The priority given to ASW did not slacken and in 1973 the first of the 9,700-ton 'Kara' class cruisers appeared, fairly bristling with a formidable array of electronics, weapons and a fantail at the stern for a Hormone-A; in all seven were built. While the 'Kresta II' and 'Kara' classes, equipped with the SS-N-14 in addition to other offensive and defensive ship-to-ship and ship-to-air armaments, were designated BPKs, they could quite reasonably be used against Western aircraft carriers. NATO, however, saw the role more distinctly, only awarding the designation of ASW ship to two specific vessels, the *Moskva* and the *Leningrad*. These two were in a class apart, displacing some 18,000 tons and designed as helicopter ASW cruisers. Their design was unique, the forward half resembling a conventional cruiser and the aft half a helicopter platform. Again, their existence can be attributed directly to the advent of the Polaris submarine. The first to appear was the *Moskva*, the first Soviet ship since the First World War designed for the operation of aircraft. In 1967 she took on board 18 Hormones and shortly after passed through the Bosporus into the Mediterranean. The *Leningrad* followed in 1969. During the last two decades these two ships have been seen all over the world, attracting a large measure of publicity. The *Leningrad's* first passage of the English Channel on 5 August 1980 was well phototgraphed despite the poor visibility.

The decision to develop the Ka-20 Harp into the production Ka-25 Hormone was taken at much the same time as it was decided to proceed with the 'Moskva' class ASW cruiser and to build a small aft flight deck for the new BPKs. As all these programmes got under way Soviet planners had good reason to be pleased with themselves. By 1967 the defence of Moscow and other key centres within range of the Polaris A-1 would be reasonably well assured. But in 1962 the Polaris A-2 with a range of 2,780 km (1,730 miles) entered service and only two years later the 4,600 km (2,860 miles) Polaris A-3 appeared. With this increase in range, the Polaris A-3 boats could stand off much further from Soviet waters while simultaneously expanding the area to something over $15\frac{1}{2}$ million square km (6 million sq. miles) from which the missiles could be launched. The balance had been upset before any of the new surface ships or the Hormone had even entered service.

The range of the Hormone with auxiliary fuel tanks and normal reserves is only about 650 km (404 miles). Allowing for time in the hover for ASW purposes radius of action is probably no more than about 200 km (125 miles). By the time they had taken to the high seas in a strategic ASW role the *Moskva* and *Leningrad* would almost literally be out of their depth. With no more than 36 Hormones between them they could hardly expect to cope with the new Polaris fleet. In deeper waters they would have to operate without protective air cover unless this could be provided from land bases within range. Furthermore, the Kremlin's strategists by now were beginning to appreciate the value of a strong Navy able to intervene in affairs throughout the globe. The introduction of the 'Moskva' class gave concrete evidence of the change in Soviet naval doctrine to a concept of 'sea denial' to enemy naval forces. This however was merely the first step towards 'sea control' to be achieved by the much bigger and more capable 'Kiev' class ships.

In January 1965 US President Johnson announced the start of the development of the 4,600 km range Poseidon C-3 (2). With this information and the dawning realisation that the two 'Moskva' class cruisers, or indeed as many as the planned 12, would be no match for either Polaris or Poseidon boats, the decision to suspend further construction of this class was taken. By 1966 the capabilities of the first Soviet vertical take-off and landing (VTOL) aircraft, the Yakovlev Freehand, were known as was the fact that the 'Moskva' class was somewhat ineffective in heavy seas; the decision not to proceed was probably not difficult to take. Instead a new, much larger ASW ship with an angled flight deck was to be built – the *Kiev*. Without catapult and arresting gear, however, she was to be limited to the operation of VTOL aircraft and helicopters. With a displacement of some 37,000 tons, she was still, somewhat surprisingly, designated an anti-submarine cruiser (3). Launched in December 1972 and commissioned in May 1975, the *Kiev* represented a significant improvement in the Soviet Navy's ability to hunt submarines in any of the world's oceans. As Captain V. G. Yefremenko wrote in *Morskoi Sbornik* in 1970: ". . . victory will belong to him who will always know the location of the other side's submarines and deploy sufficient means to destroy them." The 'Kiev' class cruisers therefore would have to have the latest search technology and armaments in addition to incorporating their own air support and air defence. The aircraft complement consists of 13 VTOL Yak-38 Forger fighter aircraft, derived from the experimental Freehand and specifically intended for shipboard operation, and about 16 Hormone or Helix-As, two or three Hormone-Bs and a Hormone-C or a Helix-D for SAR. Up to 19 Hormone-As with two Bs have occasionally been seen aboard at the same time. The primary equipment remains the helicopters, both the A versions for ASW and the Bs for the target acquisition and mid-course guidance of the SS-N-12s which give the 'Kiev' class an additional and respectable anti-ship capability.

In 1976 the *Kiev* passed through the Bosporus to join the Northern Fleet. The second 'Kiev' class carrier, the *Minsk*, was commissioned in February 1978 and in 1979 she sailed east to join the Pacific Fleet. The third, the *Novorossiysk*, was commissioned in August 1982 and the fourth, and possibly the last, the *Baku*, was commissioned in 1986.

The final measures to achieve Gorshkov's aim of a balanced, ocean-going fleet able to 'take command of the sea in a theatre of war or in part of that theatre' are now under way. An enormous capital investment has been directed towards larger and more modern shipyards and repair facilities.

That the Hormone and Helix appear to be assuming greater responsibility for strategic ASW patrol than fixed-wing aircraft is intriguing. Such a step depends on the number of helicopter platforms available at sea; that is, ships with embarked ASW helicopters. Furthermore, it might seem better for a helicopter rather than a surface ship to pursue submarine contacts at the greater ranges, given the problems associated

A line-up of Ka-25s on the carrier *Minsk*. The container on the fuselage may contain smoke or marker flares (TASS)

with the acquisition, classification and engagement of submarines at maximum anti-submarine missile range and beyond.

New classes of major surface combattants and submarines are being built at a pace unequalled in the West. Two of them possess a significant ASW capability besides increasing the number of helicopter platforms. The first of the formidable 27,000-ton 'Kirov' class nuclear-powered guided missile cruisers became operational in 1980. This class can claim to be the largest warship, besides aircraft-carrying ships, built anywhere in the world since the Second World War. Very heavily armed with ship-to-air and anti-ship cruise missiles and dual purpose guns, she also carries anti-submarine missiles, a helicopter pad and hangar space for at least three Hormone or Helix helicopters. The platform is the largest of any conventional Soviet ship. The second of this class, the *Frunze*, was commissioned in November 1983. Primarily designed for ASW is the 'Udaloy' class, an 8,000-ton BPK first commissioned in November 1980. This class has a large helicopter platform and separate hangars for two Helix-As. A very favourable impression of this class was gained by the author during a visit aboard the third unit, the *Marshal Vasilevsky*, of which her crew was very proud. She is heavily armed with two quadruple container/launchers for the SS-N-14 missiles and her sea-keeping characteristics are apparently very good. Following on from the 'Kresta II' was another destroyer class, the 7,000-ton 'Sovremenny,' of which nine ships have so far been laid down. This class has a unique telescopic hangar, located beneath the aft mast rather than in the stern, for a single helicopter. Her ASW capability is strictly limited, complementary as she is to the 'Udaloy' class, and the Hormone-B is tasked for the usual target acquisition and mid-course guidance of her eight 130 km (80 miles) range SS-N-22 ship-to-ship missiles. Commissioned in 1982 was the first ship of the 'Slava' class. Displacing 12,500 tons at full load, her principal role is surface warfare and for this she has a Hormone-B and 16 missile launchers for her SS-N-12s. The 3,900-ton 'Krivak,' which first appeared in 1970, originally had no provision for a helicopter but an excellent ASW capability nevertheless. In 1984, however, the first 'Krivak III' emerged from the Black Sea sporting a helicopter pad and a hangar for a single helicopter. She and a sister ship are designated border patrol ships and are thought to be operated by the KGB Maritime Border Guard.

As the 'Moskva' class ASW cruisers were a stepping stone to the 'Kiev' class so is this latter class but another step towards a yet more capable aircraft carrier, possibly in the 'Harrier carrier' mould – short take-off and vertical landing. Such a carrier with fixed-wing aircraft could form the nucleus of any ASW task force. The first of this class was launched in December 1985, the same month that the second was laid down. Displacement is unknown but, according to *Jane's Fighting Ships* 1987/88, is estimated to be between 65,000 and 75,000 tons and the carrier may be nuclear-powered.

The ships already described are not the only ones to have helicopter platforms. The two 13,000-ton 'Ivan Rogov' class amphibious landing ships have one pad fore and another one aft, each with a small air traffic control post, and a hangar at the rear. Four Hormone or Helix can be carried simultaneously; these deck spaces could be used by other helicopters to support an amphibious landing: Mi-8/17 or perhaps the new Kamov attack helicopter, the Hokum. In 1977 the 37,000-ton *Berezina* fleet replenishment ship was completed. She has hangar space for two Hormones. The 22,000-ton submarine rescue and salvage ship *Elbrus* carries a Hormone as do a number of other ship classes. Among these are, not unexpectedly, six classes of icebreakers, all of which can carry two helicopters for reconnaissance and observation, some support ships, research and missile range ships. To the growing number of AV-MF ship-based helicopters and available helicopter platforms may be added ships and helicopters from the merchant fleet which can be expected to provide support for naval operations whenever required.

As the Soviet ASW capability grew so the US Navy began a new nuclear ballistic missile submarine programme designed to preserve and indeed enhance the survivability and reliability of one of the United State's three strategic nuclear weapons systems. As Poseidon missiles were withdrawn from service they were replaced by the 7,400 km (4,600 miles) range Trident I (C-4) ballistic missile; the Trident II (D-5) is scheduled to begin deployment at the end of the decade. Thus, to play its part in the defence of the homeland, the Soviet Navy is faced with the need to extend its defences still further out into the world's oceans.

Soviet confidence in the effectiveness of ASW helicopters, working in conjunction with ASW surface ships, appears to be growing. Land-based ASW helicopters are used for the protection of Soviet ships and submarines operating in coastal waters and for the defence of naval bases, ports and their approaches, and the prevention of minelaying, reconnaissance and the landing of personnel on coasts. They employ the same techniques as ship-based helicopters whose task is to prevent enemy submarines from attacking targets on land and submarines and ships at sea. Thus there is a dual role for Soviet ASW helicopters of active search and destroy in open seas where enemy submarines are thought to be and the point defence of their own assets. The basic tactical ASW helicopter unit comprises two helicopters, one for search and detection and the other armed for engagement and destruction. The 'Kiev' and 'Moskva' classes are thought to be able to control two or three basic units simultaneously.

The major limitation of the Hormone has been its limited ability to operate in an ASW role at night or in adverse weather. This, combined with its limited range and endurance, contributed to the termination of its production run in about 1975 after about 460 had been built. It was clear by then that a new ASW helicopter would be needed to replace those Hormones lost, to meet expanding requirements for more ship-based helicopters and to provide an enhanced capability, particularly in terms of range and endurance and specialist equipment performance.

Ka-27 Helix-A

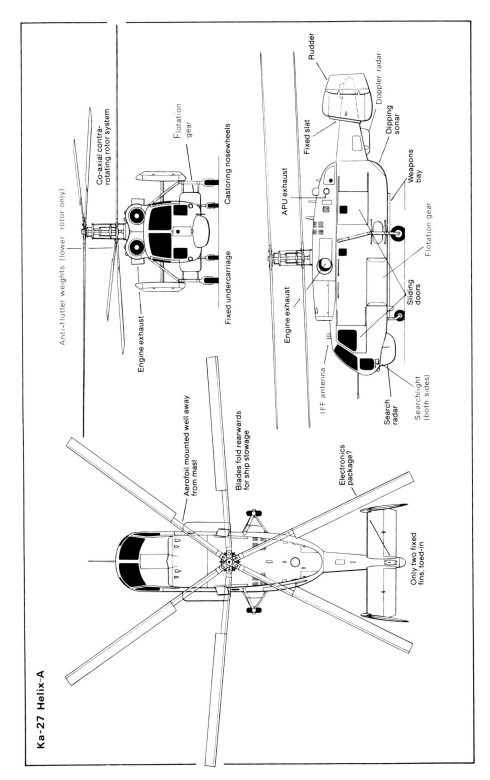

Co-axial contra-rotating rotor system

Anti-flutter weights (lower rotor only)

Flotation gear

Castoring nosewheels

Engine exhaust

Fixed undercarriage

Rudder

Doppler radar

Fixed slat

Dipping sonar

APU exhaust

Weapons bay

Engine exhaust

Flotation gear

Sliding doors

IFF antenna

Search radar

Searchlight (both sides)

Aerofoil mounted well away from mast

Blades fold rearwards for ship stowage

Electronics package?

Only two fixed fins, toed-in

Ka-27 Helix

Apart from role equipment the Ka-27 and Ka-32 are identical and, in fact, it was not until 1982 that the US Department of Defense first differentiated between the civil and military versions to the extent of designating the latter the Ka-27.

Superficially the Hormone and Helix look similar. Overall dimensions appear the same and any ship that can take one can take the other. But there the similarity ends. Because the Hormone's rotor blades extend well beyond the tail there was room for the fuselage of the Helix to be lengthened by 1.57 m (5 ft 1 in) without the overall length of the helicopter being increased. The key dimension is that which extends from the nose to the tip of the outermost rotor blade when the blades are folded to the rear. Thus neither larger ship's elevators nor hangars below deck are required. With the increasing of fuselage length it was possible to expand the cabin by 0.35 cu. m (12.36 cu. ft), despite the width being reduced by 0.2 m (8 in). The nose is less protuberant in the Helix and under it is a differently shaped radome to that of the Hormone. Titanium and composite materials have been used extensively throughout the conventional semi-monocoque pod and boom type fuselage. Particular care has been given to ensuring resistance to salt water corrosion. The lower part of the fuselage is sealed to permit the Helix to float. The emergency flotation bags are housed in suitcase-like ribbed containers below the external fuel tanks and are activated on contact with salt water.

A Ka-27 trails its dipping sonar.

The engine and transmission cowlings are also of a different shape to the Hormone and house an APU, above the exhaust of which can be seen the usual 'flowerpot'.

The Helix has a fixed incidence tailplane with elevators, twin endplate fins toed in about 25° for directional stability at low speeds, and rudders. It has no central fin like the Hormone and in its place photographs appear to show an electronic package of some kind and more flotation equipment. On their leading edges the fins have slats fitted to reduce the chance of stalling when large yaw forces are applied. The twin castoring nosewheels are smaller than the two main wheels which can be pivoted and partially retracted to minimise interference to emissions from the nose radar.

The Helix's twin fully articulated three-bladed contra-rotating rotor systems have a radius just 0.16 m (6 in) greater than that of the Hormone. The composite blades have carbonfibre and glassfibre main spars and are de-iced electrothermally whenever the engines are running. As part of the efforts to reduce the vibration inherent in any helicopter the three blades of the lower rotor each have an adjustable vibration damper, weights mounted at the root of the aerofoil part of the blade. The blades can be folded manually to the rear to a width less than the track of the main wheels. Overall length of the helicopter with blades folded is only 12.25 m (40 ft 2 in).

The Helix's maximum take-off weight is 3,515 kg (7,750 lb) greater than the Hormone's at 11,000 kg (24,250 lb); with an underslung load of up to 5,000 kg (11,023 lb) its overload weight can increase to 12,600 kg (27,778 lb). To power this heavier helicopter the twin 990 shp GTD-3BMs of the Hormone are not adequate and they have been replaced by two 2,225 shp Izotov TV3-117V turboshaft engines. The power from one of these is sufficient to maintain flight at maximum take-off weight. Easy access to these engines was a priority in the design to simplify maintenance aboard ship or in the field. The standard fuel load is carried in eight tanks under the cabin floor but two auxiliary tanks, flatter and more streamlined than those seen on earlier Soviet helicopters, can be attached to the centre of the fuselage, one on each side. Total fuel capacity is 3,450 litres (2,674 kg; 5,895 lb).

One of the shortcomings of the Hormone is its limited range and endurance and it was to be expected that the Helix would offer a significant improvement. Maximum range is doubled to 800 km (497 miles) and maximum endurance is $4\frac{1}{2}$ hours, thus giving the Helix a greater radius of action and longer time on station for submarine hunting. To reach its operating area more quickly the Helix's speed has also been increased with a maximum cruising speed of 230 kph (143 mph), 20 kph (13 mph) higher than the maximum speed of the Hormone.

Besides a better flight performance than its predecessor the Helix certainly has improved ASW equipment and avionics, giving it a night and adverse weather dipping sonar capability – a significant increase in tactical effectiveness for the Soviet Navy.

NATO has designated four versions of the Helix. The A model has an ASW role and a crew of three. Besides its undernose radar, it has a ventral weapons bay for torpedoes and other stores, two ESM radomes above the rear fuselage and tail, two radar warning antennae on top of the tailplane, the ability to take MAD gear under the tailplane and sonobuoys. The B model is a land-based assault transport helicopter and it therefore has no radar under its slightly flattened nose. It can probably carry about ten to 12 combat-equipped troops. Outriggers to carry up to four pylons for free-flight rocket pods can be installed. The Helix-B is the first helicopter specifically modified and allocated for the carriage of Soviet naval infantry – a capability gap which has haunted the Soviet Navy for many years. When necessary these helicopters can of course be deployed aboard ship. However, currently, the Soviet Navy has no ship class principally designed for amphibious assault like the British 'Fearless' or American 'Tarawa' or 'Iwo Jima' classes which can carry a battalion or more of marines together with their equipment

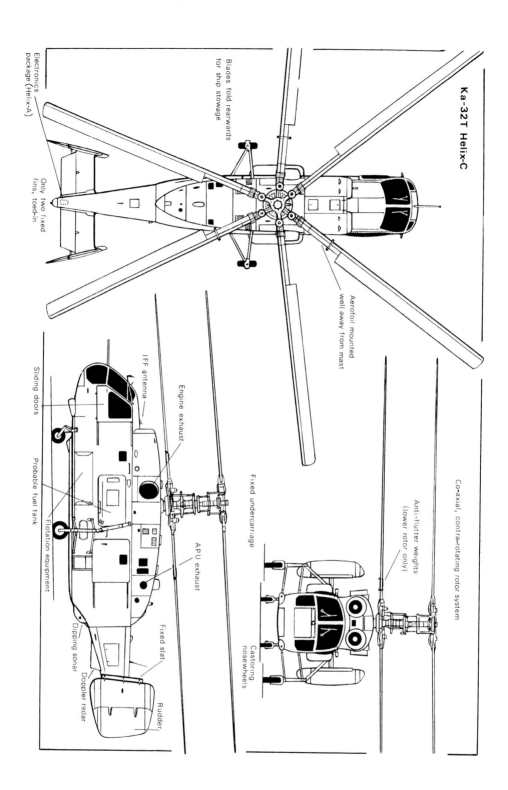

Ka-32T Helix-C

Electronics
package (Helix-A)

Blades fold rearwards
for ship stowage

Only two fixed
fins, toed-in

Aerofoil mounted
well away from mast

Sliding doors

IFF antenna

Engine exhaust

Probable fuel tank

Flotation equipment

Dipping sonar

Doppler radar

APU exhaust

Fixed slat

Rudder

Fixed undercarriage

Castoring
nosewheels

Anti-flutter weights
(lower rotor only)

Co-axial, contra-rotating rotor system

and helicopters to ferry them ashore. The C model is a utility version, virtually a Ka-32, and can be used for vertical replenishment and the carriage of passengers and freight. The Helix-D has a winch, a larger antenna on top of the rear fuselage and a different Doppler radar box below; it is used for SAR. No model has yet been identified for missile target acquisition and mid-course guidance.

The Helix completely outshines its predecessor and it is no wonder that the AV-MF is keen to deploy it as quickly as possible in place of, and in addition to, the Hormones still in service. At least 16 were seen aboard the *Novorossiysk* during her first deployment in 1983 and the *Kiev* re-equipped with the Helix in 1985. Ships with a helicopter capability are given Helix as they enter service. Foreign interest has not been lacking and the Indian Navy ordered eight Helix-As for deliveries to start in 1985; by May 1988 Yugoslavia had taken delivery of at least one, it being publicly displayed at the Zagreb Air Show. The export version is designated the Ka-28.

Notes

1. After almost 30 years as Commander-in-Chief, and at the age of 75, Admiral of the Fleet of the Soviet Union Sergei Gorshkov was somewhat suddenly and unexpectedly replaced by Admiral of the Fleet Vladimir Chernavin in December 1985.
2. While there is no difference in range between the Polaris A-3 and Poseidon C-3 the latter has a greater throw-weight (that is, weight of missile that can be delivered over a given range) and ten, as opposed to three, multiple independently-targetable re-entry vehicles.
3. This class is now designated *takticheskoye avianosnyi kreyser*-tactical aircraft-carrying cruiser.

CHARACTERISTICS

Designation	Kamov Ka-25	Kamov Ka-27/32
Engine	2 × Glushenkov GTD-3BM	2 × Izotov TV3-117V
	2 × 990 shp	2 × 2,225 shp
Rotor diameter	2 × 15.74 m (51 ft 8 in)	2 × 15.9 m (52 ft 2 in)
Fuselage length	9.75 m (32 ft 0 in)	11.3 m (37 ft 1 in)
Height	5.37 m (17 ft 7½ in)	5.4 m (17 ft 8½ in)
Empty weight	4,765 kg (10,505 lb)	6,450 kg (14,220 lb)**
Max gross weight	7,500 kg (16,535 lb)	11,000 kg (24,250 lb)***
Max speed	210 kph (130 mph)	250 kph (155 mph)
Range	400 km (248 mls)	800 km (497 mls)
Service ceiling	3,350 m (11,000 ft)	6,000 m (19,685 ft)
First flight	1960?*	1976?

CHARACTERISTICS

Designation	Kaman HH-43B Huskie	Westland Sea King Mk 5
Engine	Lycoming T53-L-1B	2 × Rolls Royce Gnome H. 1400-1
	860 shp	2 × 1,660 shp
Rotor diameter	2 × 14.32 m (47 ft 0 in)	18.9 m (62 ft)
Fuselage length	7.67 m (25 ft 2 in)	17.01 m (55 ft 9¾ in)
Height	3.83 m (12 ft 7 in)	4.85 m (15 ft 11 in)
Empty weight	2,095 kg (4,620 lb)	6,202 kg (13,673 lb)
Max gross weight	3,220 kg (7,100 lb)	9,526 kg (21,000 lb)
Max speed	193 kph (120 mph)	222 kph (138 mph)
Range	445 km (277 mls)	1,230 km (764 mls)
Service ceiling	7,620 m (25,000 ft)	3,050 m (10,000 ft)
First flight	December 1958	August 1980

   * Of prototype – Ka-20
  ** Estimated
*** Maximum loaded weight with underslung load is 12,600 kg (27,778 lb)

Horse and Hound

On 25 June 1950 North Korean forces invaded South Korea and quickly occupied much of the country. On 15 September, to retrieve a desperate situation, United Nations troops landed at Inchon, well behind North Korean lines, in a brilliantly executed amphibious attack. Follow-up forces and supplies in large quantities were flown in by American helicopters, a manoeuvre that was not lost on the watching Russians.

By October 1951 the Cold War had become positively frigid and the Korean War potentially explosive. With the possibility of war in mind, Stalin invited to the Kremlin the leading aircraft designers of the day: in addition to the helicopter practitioners (Bratukhin, Kamov, Mil and Yakovlev) were present Ilyushin and Tupolev. All were well aware of Stalin's personal interest in aviation matters. Now he did not keep the bewildered group in suspense for long, sharply accusing them of neglecting the enormous potential of the helicopter. He wanted to know what they intended to do about building large helicopters both for tactical military use and for service with Aeroflot. Ilyushin and Tupolev explained tactfully that they had no experience of building helicopters and furthermore Stalin had already ensured that their design bureaux were not short of work. Kamov was busy with his Ka-15 Hen; Bratukhin, having lost the earlier competition, was now considered more in the light of a consultant than a practical designer. Mil, with scaled-up drawings of his successful Mi-1 ready, was able to respond positively. All eyes turned to Yakovlev who explained that he too was already fully occupied but that, with a certain amount of help, he could launch a new helicopter project; his experience with his two small experimental helicopters would be of great benefit. He asked for permission to consult his staff. He was given 24 hours. Yakovlev and his staff, in particular Nikolai Skrzhinsky, Igor Yerlikh, Peter Samsonov and Leon Shekhter, pondered and discussed the problem that night, finally deciding that they were prepared to undertake further helicopter work. To prepare working drawings for a large, twin rotor machine they calculated would take a year. From what transpired the following day these deliberations were purely of academic interest. Whatever the outcome Stalin had already made up his mind.

The next evening Stalin confronted Mil and Yakovlev alone (1). He gave each of them a government directive which stated that Mil's bureau was to build a single-engine, single-rotor, 12-passenger helicopter while the Yakovlev bureau was to develop a twin-engine, twin-rotor, 24-passenger helicopter. The two designers were aghast to see that both helicopters were to be designed, built and flown within 12 months. They tried to reason that such a timetable was impossible. But Stalin explained patiently that Soviet helicopter development was in a very bad shape and falling too far behind that of the West. The time had been fixed at one year and was not to be the subject of a debate.

Mil, as befits his previous experience, was ordered to develop a complete rotor system; he was to build 12 sets and give eight to a grateful Yakovlev who was to use them on his design. Three flight test vehicles and one ground test vehicle of each design were to be built.

The next day Yakovlev summoned Skrzhinsky, Yerlikh and a small team to get to work. With such minimal experience of helicopters, the bureau faced a daunting task. Until now it had been principally concerned with speed – ever increasing the speed of its fighters. On 24 April, 1946 it had made a significant step forward in this regard with the first flight of its first jet fighter, a Yak-3 modified to take a captured German engine, the Junkers Jumo 004B, and thenceforth designated the Yak-15. But now the problem was entirely different: to get and remain airborne with no forward speed at all.

The situation was acute: time was short, both bureaux were insufficiently staffed with experienced engineers and difficult new ground was to be broken. More skilled labour was taken on, the working day lengthened to 10–12 hours and wages increased. In the background stalked the NKVD (2) chief, Lavrenty Beria, who acted as overall supervisor and who paid occasional visits to the bureaux to check on progress. In this forbidding and tense atmosphere the two helicopters were developed and the Soviet helicopter industry established.

Yak-24 Horse

In his analysis of which configuration to choose Yakovlev quickly discovered an interesting aerodynamic fact: despite using two engines of the same horsepower with side-by-side or fore-and-aft rotor configurations it was just not possible to double the useful load that could be lifted by a single rotor helicopter with the same engine. This can only be achieved by an increase in the power-to-weight ratio and if the increase is insufficient then vertical rate of climb, ceiling and other aspects of performance will suffer. Yakovlev also discovered that unless a more powerful and heavy reduction gear is used for the rear rotor in a tandem layout, the life of its components will be substantially less than those of the forward rotor system. It was simply not possible to use the same reduction gear in the Yak-24 as the Mi-4, as Yakovlev's and Mil's machines were respectively designated. In the hover there was little to choose between the side-by-side and tandem rotor configurations although losses from rotor wash over the wing in a side-by-side were thought to be greater than from wash over the fuselage in a tandem layout. In the latter case, therefore, less power was required for a vertical take-off.

A tandem rotor configuration was eventually chosen because it was considered more stable than the side-by-side layout, while also allowing a greater load and bulkier items to be carried. It was a calculated technical risk, bravely taken. No helicopter of the proposed weight or dimensions had ever been built.

Dubbed the *Letayushchii Vagon* (Flying Boxcar), the Yak-24 Horse had a cargo compartment nearly 10 m (32 ft 10 in) long and two metres (6½ ft) wide and high. The final production model could accommodate 40 passengers or up to 4,000 kg (8,818 lb) of payload which could include, for example, a couple of anti-tank guns and their crews. The floor of the upswept rear end of the fuselage could be lowered to form a loading ramp as was well demonstrated at Tushino in 1955 when jeeps, light trucks and field guns were disgorged. As an air ambulance 18 stretcher cases and a medical attendant could be carried.

At each end of the fabric-covered, steel-tube fuselage was mounted a 1,700 hp Shvetsov ASh-82V 18-cylinder radial engine, either of which was able to drive both rotors. The forward engine, located behind the cockpit, was inclined at about 45°; the

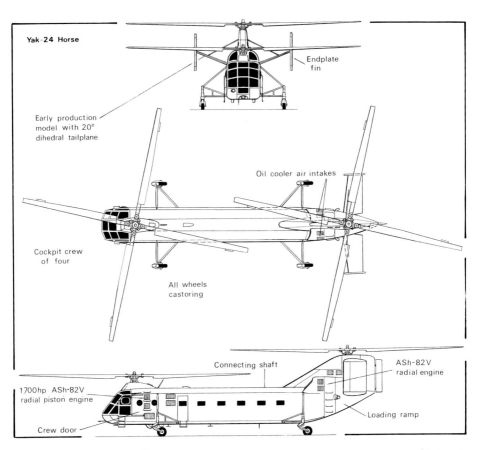

Yak-24 Horse

Endplate fin

Early production model with 20° dihedral tailplane

Oil cooler air intakes

Cockpit crew of four

All wheels castoring

Connecting shaft

ASh-82V radial engine

1,700hp ASh-82V radial piston engine

Crew door

Loading ramp

A production Yak-24U with no dihedral of the tailplane but with large endplate fins.

aft engine was installed horizontally at the base of the fin. Normal rated power was 1,430 hp. This ASh-82V engine was a version of the well-proven Shvetsov engine already used in huge numbers by Second World War fighters and bombers. Substantial modifications were nevertheless needed. The demand that one engine should be able to keep such a large aircraft flying, particularly at gross weight, was a very tough challenge to the Yakovlev bureau; even more so when using piston engines. Inside the top of the fuselage ran the transmission and synchronising gear. The rotors had four fabric-covered wooden blades each and were in the event not quite the same as those used with the Mi-4.

Yakovlev and his men worked feverishly, their progress being closely monitored by the Ministry of Aviation Industry which in turn reported regularly to Stalin. The four test vehicles were constructed simultaneously: one for laboratory static strength and dynamic tests, a second for tethered vibration testing to calculate engine and rotor life, and the final two for OKB and State flight tests. Yakovlev made use of other plants to check various components and assemblies. The gearboxes were tested at the Shvetsov bureau; the rotor blades at TsAGI where they were subjected to 12 million vibrations; the engines, fuel and cooling systems at the Aircraft Engine Research Institute.

Engine cooling was the first major problem to be encountered. Without being able to rely on forward speed like fixed-wing aircraft engine cooling had to be built-in. But more important and more persistent were the vibrations. These seriously worried Yakovlev who graphically described the problems in his book (3). Worry turned to consternation when, after completing 178 hours of a 300-hour ground endurance test, one of the prototypes was destroyed. The rear engine frame attachment points collapsed due to the vibration and the rear rotor, in Yakovlev's words, "lunged forwards and the rotor blades began to chop the machine to pieces. Petrol had gushed forth from the severed pipe lines onto the heated engine, starting a fire." Yakovlev and his team redoubled their efforts to cure the disease which as soon as it was halted in one spot broke out in another. These attempts received a warm welcome from the two test pilots, Brovtsev and Miliutichev, who had already made the first flight on 3 July, 1952 – fortunately within the stipulated 12 months and thus averting Stalin's wrath and public disgrace. Sergei Brovtsev was an experienced helicopter test pilot by this time, having been a TsAGI test pilot for some years; he was to go on to bigger things – the Mi-6 Hook. Ye.F. Miliutichev was comparatively new to testing. They jumped, hopped and hovered in the other test vehicle, according to Yakovlev, and "after their first timid flights praised the helicopter mildly." Brovtsev and Miliutichev had reported a "tiny bit of vibration" that had not been eliminated. Very sensitive vibration-measuring instruments were installed and it soon became clear that the pilots had wished to spare the designers' feelings. The "tiny bit of vibration" in fact was so bad that it "made the whole frame of the helicopter shake dangerously. For five solid months we tried to get rid of that vibration. Five months of intensive research, calculation, dozens of experimental flights – all in vain."

Yakovlev requested a TsAGI conference to be attended by all those who might possibly be able to throw some light on the matter. Yakovlev has written that "it was a very peculiar conference." On the one hand, there were those intent on solving the problem; on the other, "scientists who bent their scientific learning and technical knowledge to find and present the most convincing proof that the vibration was inevitable" – that it was inherent in the design of the helicopter. Some said, make the machine longer, others shorter, yet others that the fuselage should be completely redesigned. Yakovlev, in desperation, decided to chop half a metre (19.7 in) off each main rotor blade. The vibration was substantially reduced. In fact the basic cause of the problem had been flutter, a shortcoming shared by the Mi-4 also at that time.

On 5 March, 1953 Stalin died and to some degree the pressure was lifted from both Mil and Yakovlev.

The State trials of the Yak-24 began in the spring of 1953. During one of the static tests, with only a mechanic on board, one of the mooring guys snapped, quickly followed by the remaining three. The helicopter leaped into the air. The astonished but quick-thinking mechanic shut down the engines. From a height of about 7.5 m (25 ft) the Yak-24 made a graceless landing. The mechanic survived, the machine did not. The mooring guys were strengthened.

It was not until April 1955 that the lengthy State trials were completed and the helicopter went into production for the Air Force despite the fact that it still retained some vibration in certain flight conditions. It was the largest helicopter in the world at that time to go into full-scale production. Four pre-production models made their first public appearance at the Tushino Display in 1955. On 17 December, 1955 Tinyakov set a new world payload-to-altitude record: 2,000 kg (4,409 lb) were lifted to 5,082 m (16,673 ft) and another aircraft flown by Miliutichev lifted 4,000 kg (8,818 lb) to 2,820 m (9,251 ft), thereby setting a new world record on the way up: 4,000 kg to 2,000 m (6,562 ft). The former record was somewhat surprisingly broken just over four months later by an Mi-4. These two records were the only two captured by the Yak-24. Another pilot, Garnayev, established a non-stop run between Moscow and Leningrad, a distance of just under 645 km (400 miles).

In 1958 a new version, the Yak-24U (*Usilennyi*, strengthened) became the standard military model, having first flown in December 1957. It differed from earlier production models by reverting to the original rotor diameter, by having all 45° dihedral from the tailplane removed (4) and large endplate fins fitted, and by widening the cabin by nearly 40 cm (16 in), thus allowing a greater volume of payload.

The pre-production model could accommodate 20 fully equipped airportable infantrymen but this U model could take 37–40. A number of other modifications were made including the installation of automatic dampers, new fuel tanks, shock absorbers on the rear wheels and all-metal rotor blades and fuselage skin. When fitted with an external hook and 200 kg (440 lb) hoist a few machines were used by Aeroflot. The effect of these modifications was to increase gross weight by almost 1,590 kg (3,505 lb).

In 1960 the Yak-24A (*Aerolinyi*, airline) appeared as a civil 30-seater equipped for night and adverse weather operations. Surprisingly, it is believed that neither it nor the de-luxe eight-seat VIP version, the Yak-24K (*Kupe*, coupé), were ever operated permanently by Aeroflot. A model of a 39-passenger version, the Yak-24P (*Passazhirskii*), powered by two 2,700 shp Ivchenko gas turbines, was displayed at the Soviet Exhibition in London in 1961 but there is no available evidence that it was ever built.

Due to its technical shortcomings, production of the Yak-24 was discreetly abandoned after a run of no more than about one hundred examples. It was mainly in service with the Soviet Air Force although a few were used in some building projects as cranes. Plainly, it had not been an unqualified success. It is a measure of the influence of the Armed Forces that so much in the way of technical resources should have been sunk into a project that never looked like succeeding. While still retaining an interest in vertical flight (the VTOL Yak-38 Forger), the Yakovlev design bureau has not built another helicopter since the Yak-24.

While Yakovlev was striving to break-in his Horse, Mil was attending to the rearing of his Hound in Kiev. It is not known how much co-operation there was between the two design bureaux. That there should have been some is to be expected given that both helicopters used common engines and similar rotor systems; both subsequently suffered from an unnerving period of blade flutter. What is interesting is that neither Mil nor Yakovlev ever admitted the degree of co-operation or lack of it.

Mi-4 Hound

With a striking resemblance to the contemporary Sikorsky S-55 (H-19 Chickasaw), the Mi-4 compared favourably with the later S-58 (H-34 Choctaw) in size and performance. The Mi-4's performance capabilities and dimensions were in fact underestimated in the West when it was first revealed. Rotor diameter, fuselage length, height and maximum take-off weight were all greater than assessed.

The Hound, of course, used the same four-bladed rotor system (although the blades themselves were slightly different) as the Horse – a similar system to that of the Mi-1 but with one extra blade. The 5° forward inclination of the shaft is quite noticeable. The original diameter of the main rotor system was 17.22 m (56 ft 6 in) with the tapered wooden blades having a tubular steel spar and plywood covering. Fatigue life was 100 hours. This was increased to 300 hours in 1954. In about 1956 rotor diameter was lengthened to the present 21.0 m (68 ft 10½ in) and a year later, a variable thickness, variable section tubular steel spar was introduced; blade life was raised to 600 hours. In 1960 constant-chord, all-metal rotor blades, which had been under development since 1953, replaced all earlier blades and six years later blade life was established at 1,500 hours. Rotor rpm are slow at 178 at 2,400 engine rpm. A three-bladed tail rotor is used.

A single 1,700 hp ASh-82V engine is installed at an angle in the nose above which sit the two pilots. The drive shaft passes diagonally up between them to the gearbox. A rating of 1,350 hp is maintained up to 4,500 m (14,763 ft) by means of a two-speed supercharger. The fuselage is an all-metal semi-monocoque structure of the pod-and-boom type. In the military version a gondola for an observer/navigator is sometimes fitted below the fuselage which also has clamshell rear-loading doors to facilitate the loading of such vehicles as the GAZ-69 jeep, anti-tank guns and motor cycle combinations. The cabin can hold up to 14 fully armed troops or take 1,740 kg (3,836 lb) of cargo. Some 1,300 kg (2,866 lb) can be carried as an underslung load. An additional fuel tank is sometimes fitted in place of the gondola. The standard fuel tank, containing 775 kg (1,709 lb) of fuel, is located in the top of the fuselage behind the rotor mast. As usual the undercarriage is wheeled with two main wheels and two smaller castoring nosewheels; flotation bags can be installed. The Mi-4 also broke new ground by being the first Soviet helicopter to have the controls servo-assisted by hydraulic power.

To save time no prototypes were built. The first pre-production model was rolled out in April 1952 – just seven months after Stalin had apprised Mil of his wishes. At the same time series production was begun and before the 12-month period was complete the first three production models had started their flight tests. Despite the fact that many shortcomings and flaws still existed and would need years to be resolved, Mil's achievement was truly fantastic. The first flight was delayed, however, when it was discovered that, before reaching operating speed (at about 110 rpm), the blades threatened to strike the airframe. By fixing weights to certain points along the blades opposite inertial moments were created and the flutter was cured. The first flight with V. V. Vinitsky at the controls took place the next month. Successful factory and State trials followed almost immediately and were quickly completed by the end of the year. Despite the fact that rotor blade life was no more than 100 hours full-scale production was boldly ordered.

In January 1953 one of the pre-production models crashed. Neither testing nor production was halted during the investigations which ultimately established the fact that flutter had caused the blades to strike the cockpit. So the cure had not been completely effective and further modifications were undertaken. By August 1953 the Mi-4 was already in service with the Soviet Air Force. Eighteen appeared at the 1953

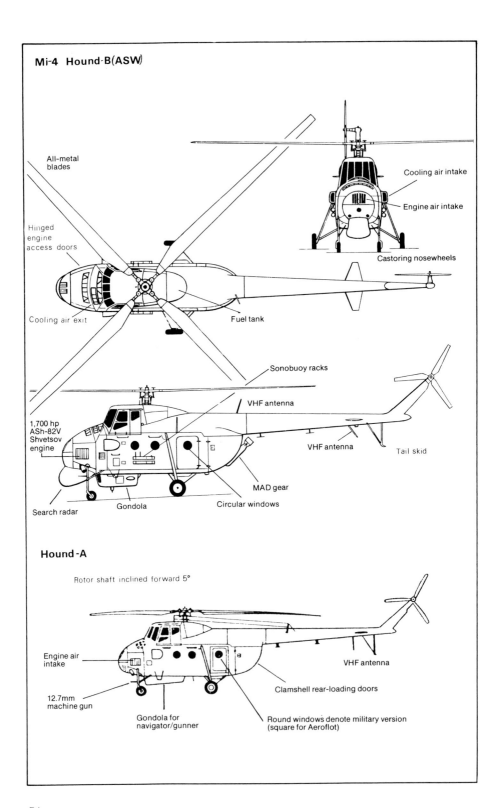

Mi-4 Hound-B(ASW)

All-metal blades

Cooling air intake

Engine air intake

Hinged engine access doors

Castoring nosewheels

Cooling air exit

Fuel tank

Sonobuoy racks

VHF antenna

1,700 hp ASh-82V Shvetsov engine

VHF antenna

Tail skid

MAD gear

Search radar

Gondola

Circular windows

Hound-A

Rotor shaft inclined forward 5°

Engine air intake

VHF antenna

12.7mm machine gun

Clamshell rear-loading doors

Gondola for navigator/gunner

Round windows denote military version (square for Aeroflot)

A Hound-B with search radar and sonobuoys in AV-MF service. The MAD gear can be seen in the retracted position immediately aft of the cabin. (Pilot Press Ltd)

Tushino Air Display and 36 three years later when they demonstrated the ability of massed helicopters to lift a large body of troops and equipment to assist in assault operations.

The basic military version is simply designated the Mi-4 Hound and is characterised by having circular cabin windows. It has been operated by the AV-MF in a shore-

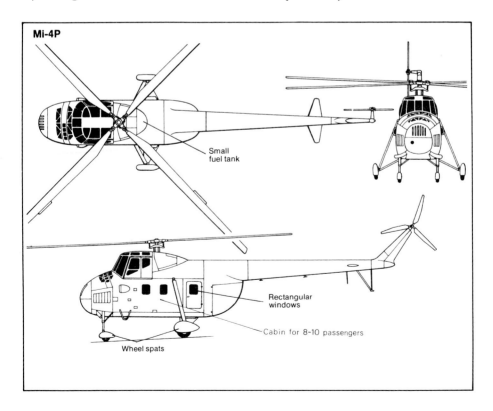

Mi-4P

Small fuel tank

Rectangular windows

Cabin for 8-10 passengers

Wheel spats

based ASW role with a search radar under the nose and MAD gear at the rear of the fuselage. Sonobuoys, marker flares, torpedoes and other search gear can be carried. In this role the Mi-4, designated the Hound-B, has been superseded almost completely by a combination of Ka-25 Hormones and Mi-14 Hazes. In 1968 a close air support version with a DShK 12.7 mm machine gun mounted in the gondola and air-to-surface rockets and missiles on outriggers was reported. All weapons were controlled by the navigator from his position in the gondola. However, these armaments decreased the helicopter's range and its vibration affected weapon accuracy. By this time it was also possible to fire weapons through portholes within the windows. But the main role of the Hound is the carriage of troops. During a major *desant* operation on Exercise *Dnepr* in 1967, the main force was landed from over 100 Hounds accompanied by several larger Mi-6 Hooks. The turbine-powered Mi-8 Hip has now largely taken over this troop-carrying role. In 1977 pictures of the Hound in a new role were published: that of a communications jammer, sprouting a rash of antennae on either side of the cabin and designated Hound-C. By the beginning of the 1980s this model had been replaced by the ECM versions of the Mi-8 Hip. An indeterminate number of Hounds, although well past their prime, has taken part in offensive operations in Afghanistan; a few have been shot down. On occasion, a pair, firing unguided rockets and their machine guns, have lead in a section of four Mi-24 Hinds. While the latter continue the attack the Hounds circle overhead, ejecting flares to decoy the heat-seaking surface-to-air missiles that the Mujahideen have.

The Mi-4P (*Passazhirskii*) is an 8–10 passenger variant with square windows and all modern conveniences, Soviet style. It first appeared in 1954. In November 1958 Aeroflot inaugurated its first helicopter service – a 20-minute flight between the holiday resorts of Simferopol and Yalta in the Crimea. Two years later Mi-4Ps were used to

Mil Mi-4s of the East German Navy undergoing servicing. The engine is located at a very convenient height.

connect all Moscow's airports and the city centre. With a baggage load of 200 kg (440 lb) and ten passengers, the Mi-4P has a range of 500 km (310 miles). A de-luxe version, the Mi-4L (*Liuks*, de-luxe) carried only six passengers. The Mi-4P is also used as a basic cargo helicopter throughout the Soviet Union including the Polar regions where it has achieved spectacular results. In 1957, according to an Aviaexport brochure, an Mi-4 flew from Moscow to the Polar station 'North Pole 6', covering a distance of 7,000 km (4,350 miles). After a year in the area it returned to Moscow along the same route which entailed a 740 km (460 miles) leg over the open sea. In that same year at the Brussels World Fair the Mi-4 was awarded a diploma and gold medal.

As an ambulance it can carry eight stretchers and a medical attendant. The cabin can even be converted into an airborne operating theatre with table, surgical equipment and the necessary lighting.

An agricultural version, the Mi-4S (*Selskokhozyaistvennyi*, rural economy), also appeared for the first time in 1954. A container in the cabin can take 1,000 kg (2,205 lb) of powder or some 1,245 kg (2,745 lb) of liquid chemical spray. Spray bars are located on either side of the fuselage behind the main wheels. The S version is, however, more often used for forestry patrol and fire fighting.

Had Stalin been alive in April 1956 he would have been pleased to hear that, in that month, the Mi-4 set three new world records:

25 April: 2,000 kg (4,409 lb) were lifted to 6,018 m (19,744 ft);
26 April: 1,000 kg (2,205 lb) were lifted to 6,048 m (19,843 ft);
29 April: a speed of 187.25 kph (116.35 mph) was achieved over a 500 km (311 miles) closed circuit course.

The Mi-4 used was specially prepared for these record attempts. On 26 March, 1950 a 1,011.5 kg (2,230 lb) payload was taken to 7,465 m (24,491 ft), thereby setting a new altitude record for a 1,000 kg load. In all the Mi-4 captured seven world records.

So that the machine could operate effectively in mountainous regions trials with a two-speed supercharger were undertaken in the early 1960s. At about 4,570 m (15,000 ft) the second stage cut in and the Mi-4, with a full fuel load, was able to reach a height in excess of 7,925 m (26,000 ft). Furthermore it was operated over a period from an airfield more than 4,875 m (16,000 ft) above sea level. For a single piston-engined helicopter with a maximum weight of 7,800 kg (17,196 lb) this was quite an achievement. This version, with an ASh-82FN engine, was designated the Mi-4V (*Visotnii*, altitude).

A Mi-4 fires unguided rockets.

Large numbers were sold to India where they demonstrated their excellent performance in the Himalayas. The Mi-4 was built in greater numbers (about 3,500) than any other Soviet helicopter save the Mi-8 Hip and Polish-built Mi-2. Production is thought to have stopped in about 1968 by which time flight performance and characteristics had been significantly improved over the early models. The machine is still employed in both civil and military service world-wide.

Troops climbing into an Mi-4 through the clamshell rear-loading doors.

Very few remain in operational service with the Soviet Armed Forces and the Warsaw Pact, however. The Mi-4 has been exported to some 30 foreign countries, with both India and Czechoslovakia receiving a hundred or more each. The Communist Chinese began licence production in 1959, building several hundred at Harbin as the

Z-5 in both civil and military versions. Some have a 1,875 shp PT6T-6 twin turboshaft from Pratt and Whitney of Canada. Production continued into the late 1970s at least. An interesting example of an Mi-4 is at the US Army Aviation Centre's museum at Fort Rucker, Alabama. It was flown to Florida by a defecting Cuban pilot.

One can do no better than quote Mil himself, writing in 1957, in extolling the virtues of the Mi-4: "Possessing equipment for blind and night flights, an anti-icing system and hydraulic servo-controls, the Mi-4 helicopters have no equals and have left foreign construction several years behind. They again brought our country to leading positions in this field of engineering." While the Mi-1 brought Mil recognition as a helicopter designer the success of the Mi-4 confirmed his position as the pre-eminent Soviet helicopter designer.

Notes

1.   It is interesting to note that Yakovlev writes that this meeting was convened "at the end of the summer of 1952." This time is not supported by evidence elsewhere. Indeed, all available facts point clearly to 1951 and even an Aviaexport brochure for the Mi-4 states that this helicopter first flew in 1952. Izakson writes: "At the end of 1951 a decision was made in our country regarding the creation of helicopters of greater load capacity than the existing. The assignment was given simultaneously to the design bureaus of M. L. Mil and A. S. Yakovlev." Perhaps the explanation is simple – a mere printing error in Yakovlev's book.

2.   Now the KGB.

3.   *Tsel Zhizni*. The Aim of a Lifetime.

4.   Some examples of the basic Yak-24 flew with 20° of dihedral and with the fixed endplate fins canted 3° 30′ to give a small degree of thrust to port.

CHARACTERISTICS

Designation	**Yakovlev Yak-24U**	**Mil Mi-4**
Engine	2 × Shvetsov ASh-82V	Shvetsov ASh-82V
	2 × 1,700 hp	1,700 hp
Rotor diameter	2 × 21.0 m (68 ft 10½ in)	21.0 m (68 ft 10½ in)
Fuselage length	21.3 m (69 ft 11 in)	16.8 m (55 ft 1 in)
Height	6.5 m (21 ft 4 in)	5.18 m (17 ft 0 in)
Empty weight	11,000 kg (24,250 lb)	5,392 kg (11,887 lb)
Max gross weight	17,000 kg (37,479 lb)	7,800 kg (17,196 lb)
Max payload	4,700 kg (10,362 lb)	1,740 kg (3,836 lb)
Max speed	174 kph (108 mph)	210 kph (130 mph)**
Range	254 km (158 mls)	595 km (370 mls)
Service ceiling	2,700 m (8,860 ft)	6,000 m (19,685 ft)
First flight	July 1952*	May 1952
	*Prototype Yak-24	**At 1,500 m (4,920 ft)

Designation	**Piasecki/Vertol CH-21C***	**Sikorsky S-55**
Engine	Wright R-1820-103	P&W R-1340-57
	1,425 hp	600 hp
Rotor diameter	2 × 13.4 m (44 ft 0 in)	14.93 m (49 ft 0 in)
Fuselage length	16.0 m (52 ft 6 in)	12.85 m (42 ft 2 in)
Height	4.7 m (15 ft 5 in)	4.06 m (13 ft 4 in)
Empty weight	3,991 kg (8,800 lb)	2,381 kg (5,250 lb)
Max gross weight	6,123 kg (13,500 lb)	3,583 kg (7,900 lb)
Max speed	204 kph (127 mph)	180 kph (112 mph)
Range	644 km (400 mls)	580 km (360 mls)
Service ceiling	2,360 m (7,750 ft)	3,930 m (12,900 ft)
First flight	April 1952**	April 1952

  * Otherwise known as the Vertol Model 43 Workhorse, H-21B or Shawnee
** Of XH-21

Designation	**Sikorsky S-58**
Engine	Wright R-1820-84
	1,525 hp
Rotor diameter	17.06 m (56 ft 0 in)
Fuselage length	14.24 m (46 ft 9 in)
Height	4.82 m (15 ft 10 in)
Empty weight	3,338 kg (7,360 lb)
Max gross weight	6,169 kg (13,600 lb)
Max speed	198 kph (123 mph)
Range	450 km (280 mls)
Service ceiling	3,200 m (10,500 ft)
First flight	March 1954

Mil's Monsters:
Hook and Harke

By the time the problems of the Mi-1 Hare and Mi-4 Hound had been more or less satisfactorily solved in the early 1950s and production was proceeding smoothly various elements of the Mil OKB had already begun to look ahead to the development of a very much larger helicopter. This was at Mil's own initiative, not at the behest of the General Staff which at this time did not know enough about helicopters to originate technical proposals or define priorities. Mil's initiative was timely. As the doctrine of the Armed Forces began to embrace nuclear war so it became clear that troop movements would have to be conducted much more quickly, both at ground level and in the air. Furthermore the payload/range capability of neither the Hare nor the Hound met the new requirement to be able to lift the heavier Army weapons. Only fixed-wing aircraft could do this and they were often unable to land close to where the equipment was needed. At the same time it was realised that a much larger helicopter could also make a significant contribution towards achieving the objectives of future Five Year Plans.

The Hound's inability to carry even two short tons over a distance of 600 km (373 miles) was a marked shortcoming, given the size and backwardness of the country. Vast undeveloped expanses existed where surface transport was limited to the horse and the camel and where airfields simply did not exist. In particular, the search for, and development of, mineral deposits in the remotest corners of Siberia and the deserts of Central Asia could only really be pursued with the help of large helicopters. Only they could lift the heavy drilling and other equipment to inaccessible sites, thus saving the need to build roads. Consequently the time to complete projects would be cut substantially. In 1954 Mil was ordered to proceed with the development of a helicopter able to lift bulky loads such as vehicles and drilling rigs. To meet such a demand a useful payload of 12,000 kg (26,455 lb) which could be carried over at least 250 km (155 miles) would be needed. Even Mil must have had some doubts in the early stages of the project as to whether the rotor system with an unprecedented 35 m (114 ft 10 in) diameter and a main rotor gearbox to match could be developed successfully. The OKB began to expand to meet the new challenge and a new helicopter production plant at Rostov-on-Don was built.

Mi-6 Hook

Mil approached the problem of building so huge a helicopter in a typically Russian way. He merely took his proven configuration and built everything much bigger, ending up with a machine twice as large as any other helicopter then flying. For 11 years the Mi-6 Hook was the largest helicopter in the world with an empty weight of 27,240 kg (60,055 lb) and a maximum gross weight of 42,500 kg (93,700 lb). At one time it held 12 world records in the E-1 class. It may be compared with the largest non-Soviet helicopter today, over 30 years after the Hook first flew: the Sikorsky CH-53E has a maximum gross weight of 33,340 kg (73,500 lb). Advanced technology and a different design philosophy have, of course, assisted in keeping this weight down. Overall length of the Hook with rotors turning is 41.75 m ($\frac{1}{2}$ inch less than 137 feet), that of the CH-53E 30.2 m (99 ft 1 in).

The Hook could claim a number of firsts:
    the first Soviet turbine-powered helicopter to go into production;
    the first twin jet helicopter;
    the first helicopter to fly at a speed in excess of 300 kph (186 mph);
    the first helicopter to have a gearbox weighing over 3,175 kg (7,000 lb)!

Without the much greater power-to-weight ratio offered by the turbine engine, Mil would not have been able to build so large a helicopter. It is, however, easier to appreciate the advantages of the turbine engine over the piston engine by comparing the Mi-1/Mi-2 and Mi-4/Mi-8 rather than by trying to compare the incomparable Mi-4/Mi-6. The Soloviev engine design bureau was building free turbines by this time and so Mil turned to this bureau for the engines and gearbox. He wanted two engines situated above the fuselage forward of the rotor mast so that the transmission would be as short as possible and weight thereby saved. Soloviev displayed little originality, following a brute force technique and producing an engine somewhat bigger and heavier than if it had been constructed in the West. Such a philosophy, however, was expected to produce an engine of long life and relatively few problems. It was noted for its comparative quietness. The prototype aircraft had installed two 4,635 shp D-25V (military designation: TV-2BM) free turbines. Production models have the 5,500 shp D-25V development. This engine is flat-rated to maintain power to 3,000 m (9,845 ft)

Only nine years separated the Mi-1 and the huge Mi-6.

or 40°C at sea level. It consists of a nine-stage axial compressor, can-annular combustion chamber, single-stage compressor turbine and a two-stage power turbine. Dry weight is 1,200 kg (2,645 lb) and, with engine-mounted accessories, 1,325 kg (2,921 lb). Acceleration time is adjusted to 10–12 seconds under load, no doubt to match the slow power turbine to the huge rotor system. The consequence is that no manoeuvres requiring a rapid increase in power are feasible. Above the engines is located an air intake for the oil system cooling fan. A 100 hp APU is also installed. The 11,000 hp R-7 gearbox, which comes as part of an engine/gearbox package, cannot be classed as a 'thing of beauty' unless one's aesthetic tastes favour sheer magnitude. It weights 3,200 kg (7,055 lb) – more than the two engines together, is 2.8 m (9 ft 2 in) high, 1.55 m (5 ft 1 in) wide, and 1.85 m (6 ft 1 in) long. It has four stages which reduce a normal turbine engine speed of about 8,000 rpm by 69.2:1 to give a rotor rpm of about 120.

Like the Hound the Hook has a pod-and-boom, all-metal, semi-monocoque fuselage and hydraulically-operated clamshell rear-loading doors. The clearance in the rear is 2.65 m (8 ft 8$\frac{1}{4}$ in) wide by 2.7 m (8 ft 10$\frac{1}{4}$ in) high. The cabin compartment is 12 m (39 ft 4$\frac{1}{2}$ in) long, 2.65 m wide and varies in height from 2.5 m (8 ft 2$\frac{1}{2}$ in) at the rear to 2.01 m (6 ft 7 in) forward; cabin volume is 80 m³ (2,825 ft³). Up to 90 passengers or 65–70 combat-equipped troops can be seated or 41 stretcher cases and two medical attendants. Tip-up seats line the cabin walls but some more can be fitted down the centre aisle. In times of emergency, without seats, fully 120 passengers could be lifted. Maximum payload internally is 12,000 kg (26,455 lb); maximum load on the sling is 8,000 kg (17,637 lb). There is a hatch in the cargo floor so that a crew chief may observe any underslung load and facilitate its hook-up and release. An electric winch with a capacity of 800 kg (1,764 lb) is installed and the floor is stressed to 2,000 kg/m² (410 lb/ft²). Much of the remaining balance of weight is taken up with 11 internal fuel tanks holding 6,315 kg (13,922 lb) of fuel and a further two optional (but usually fitted) external tanks each holding another 1,745 kg (3,847 lb), a total of 9,805 kg (21,616 lb) of fuel. This figure exceeds the gross weight of the Sikorsky UH-60A Blackhawk! A further two ferry tanks with 3,490 kg (7,695 lb) of fuel can be carried in the cabin. It is understood that Pan American World Airways examined the Mi-6 for its helicopter operations but rejected it finally due to high fuel consumption. This is said to be in the order of 2,750 kg (6,063 lb) per flying hour.

The cockpit is double-decked with the navigator, following contemporary practice, being housed in the glazed nose where he has an excellent view. Behind and above him on the flight deck are located the two pilots, a flight engineer and radio operator. In a few Hooks a 12.7 mm machine gun has been mounted under the nose. It is manually aimed by the navigator.

The main rotor sports a huge steel hub and five fully articulated blades and has a diameter of 35 m (114 ft 10 in). With a massive welded swashplate the design of the main rotor must have presented many difficult engineering problems. Construction allows field replacement of all of its parts but damage to the pressurised steel spar necessitates complete replacement of the entire blade. This is nearly 17 m (56 ft) long and weighs approximately 703 kg (1,550 lb). At 1967 prices, according to Petroleum Helicopters Inc who bought an Mi-10 which uses the same rotor system as the Mi-6, each blade cost some $30,000. The rotor shaft is inclined forwards 5°. When stationary the droop of the rotor blades is very noticeable. The diameter of the four-bladed tail rotor is 6.3 m (20 ft 8 in), greater than that of the main rotor of the Ka-10. It is mounted on the starboard side of a large vertical fin. Electro-thermal de-icing is provided for the main rotor blades, air intakes and the pilots' and navigator's canopies; a liquid anti-icing system is used for the tail rotor. To unload the straining rotor by some 20% in cruising flight, stub wings of 15.3 m (50 ft 2$\frac{1}{2}$ in) span are mounted below and behind the axis of the main rotor. They are set at an angle of incidence of 15.75°, and are usually removed when the Hook is being used as a flying crane.

The three hydraulic systems each have their own pump mounted on the R-7 gearbox and these also drive the engine cowlings which hinge upwards and downwards to create servicing platforms.

Unlike the Mi-4 the Hook has a tricycle undercarriage, non-retractable, with castoring twin nosewheels and two single low pressure main wheels which incorporate the brakes. Three main wheel struts and a system of dampers help to reduce the risk of ground resonance.

7 November, 1957 was an auspicious day marking the 40th Anniversary of the Bolshevik Revolution. Sixty-eight leaders from the 75 parties in the Communist movement around the world were invited ten days later to witness the unveiling of prototypes of the world's largest airliner, the Tu-114 Cleat, and the world's largest helicopter, the Mi-6 Hook, at Vnukovo Airport, Moscow. Principally for technical and military reasons the existence of both projects had been kept a closely guarded secret. The impact was all the greater now. Of the two aircraft, the helicopter was the bigger surprise. In September 1948 the Mi-1, with a maximum gross weight of 2,550 kg (5,620 lb) had been rolled out, flying shortly afterwards; now, just nine years later, a machine with a gross weight nearly 17 times greater had taken to the air successfully. The surprise was complete when it was learned that a prototype had already set two new, and, in the literal sense of the word, incredible world records on 30 October, 1957: lifting the heaviest load (12,004 kg, 26,464 lb) to 2,000 m (6,562 ft) and reaching the greatest altitude (2,432 m, 7,980 ft) with a load of 10,000 kg (22,046 lb). The existence of the Mi-6 was only revealed in the West when the FAI was informed of these astonishing records after the unveiling ceremony.

Five prototypes were built, the first being completed in mid-1957. Flight testing under R. Kaprelyan began with the first flight in September. These five were followed by an initial production batch of 30. Subsequently about 1,000 Hooks are thought to have been manufactured for military and civil use between 1959 and 1981. Perhaps about half this number is still in service with the Soviet Air Forces and the AV-MF; maybe 100 or more are still flying with Aeroflot. With the comparatively slow introduction into service of the Mi-26 Halo the Hook is likely to be around for some years yet. Total service life was originally planned as being 12,000 flying hours but this was raised provisionally to 20,000 hours in steps of 1,000, subject to the satisfactory condition of selected components. Nevertheless, problems associated with metal fatigue must be appearing and measures to minimise them no doubt result in a restricted flight envelope. Among other countries Hooks have been sold to Egypt, which originally received about 50, some of which were destroyed in both the 1967 and 1973 wars, Iraq, where they have played a role in the war with Iran, and North Vietnam. Here they were used for moving heavy artillery and SA-2 Guideline surface-to-air missiles (SAMs) to inaccessible sites. At least two were shot down by US fighters in 1967. As far as is known the only countries in the Warsaw Pact to have received any Hooks for military purposes are Bulgaria and Poland.

As might be expected the Hook contemptuously demolished all previous helicopter load records, holding them until the Mi-12 Homer lumbered onto the scene. On 13 September, 1962, for example, a payload of 20,117 kg (44,350 lb) was lifted by Kaprelyan to 2,738 m (8,983 ft) (no doubt using a running take-off). Wishing to show that the Hook was not only a ponderous weight-lifter, Boris Galitsky with a crew of five sped over a 100 km (62.14 miles) closed circuit course at a breathtaking speed of 340.15 kph (211.36 mph) on 26 August, 1964. Indeed, on 21 September, 1961 the Hook had been the first helicopter to exceed 300 kph (186 mph) and on the strength of this

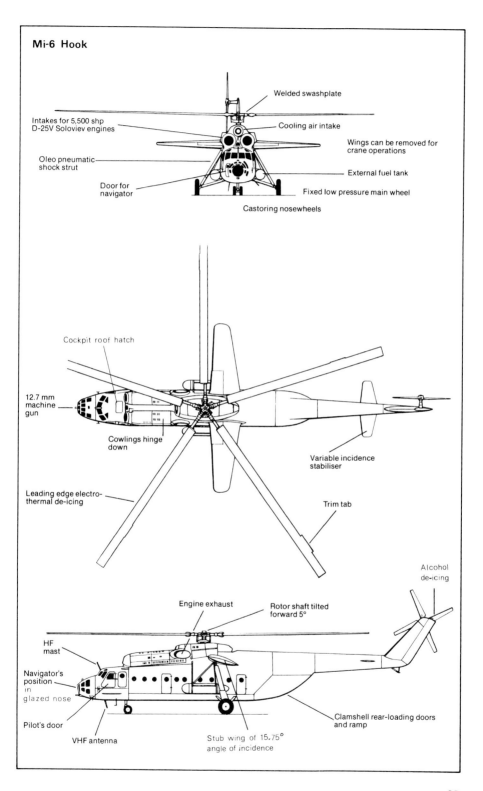

Mi-6 Hook

Welded swashplate

Intakes for 5,500 shp
D-25V Soloviev engines

Cooling air intake

Wings can be removed for
crane operations

Oleo pneumatic
shock strut

External fuel tank

Door for
navigator

Fixed low pressure main wheel

Castoring nosewheels

Cockpit roof hatch

12.7 mm
machine
gun

Cowlings hinge
down

Variable incidence
stabiliser

Leading edge electro-
thermal de-icing

Trim tab

Alcohol
de-icing

Engine exhaust

Rotor shaft tilted
forward 5°

HF
mast

Navigator's
position
in
glazed nose

Pilot's door

VHF antenna

Stub wing of 15.75°
angle of incidence

Clamshell rear-loading doors
and ramp

achievement had won the Igor Sikorsky International Trophy. These speeds are all the more remarkable given the large fixed undercarriage.

In its military guise (the Soviet Air Force is believed to have taken delivery of over 500) the Hook has taken part in many exercises in Eastern Europe and on the Chinese border, carrying both troops and such equipments as tactical missiles, FROG rockets, guns and various kinds of light combat vehicles. It has been seen operating closely with large transport aircraft. (1) It is often used on the flanks of an advance lifting AA and anti-tank guns and missile systems, their crews and ammunition. It can also act as a flying fuel tank, carrying 12,000 kg (26,455 lb) of fuel in palletised tanks in the fuselage. Using its APU it can refuel four tracked or wheeled vehicles simultaneously. Hooks have played a significant part in operations in Afghanistan, Kampuchea, Vietnam and during the Ogaden War in 1977/78. In supporting an Ethiopian advance they once carried Cuban troops, supplies and PT-76 tanks across a range of mountains to launch a totally unexpected attack on the unsuspecting Somalis. One Arab military attaché is quoted as saying: "It was almost over before it started. It was the kind of manoeuvre that up to now has been done only on maps in staff college." A few Hooks have been configured in an airborne command post role, this version being known as the Hook-B.

At the massive display of Soviet air power at Tushino in July 1961 an Mi-6 appeared underslinging a replica of Yuri Gagarin's Vostok space capsule while six other Hooks landed in two groups of three and disgorged two ground-to-ground missiles, their transporters and support equipment. The commentator yelled exuberantly: "We can see a land-to-land rocket" as the clamshell doors opened. In 1965 an Mi-6 was exhibited abroad for the first time: a prototype with wings was demonstrated at the Paris Air Show. Two years later two versions appeared there. One was a civil passenger version, the Mi-6P, equipped with seats, four-abreast, for 80 people. It had large

Aeroflot Mi-6s have played a major role in the exploitation of resources in remote regions of the Soviet Union. They have also been used as firefighters.

Mi-6 helicopters are sometimes used as flying fuel tanks. Here one can be seen refuelling a T-62 main battle tank.

rectangular windows in place of the usual circular ones. Nothing has been heard of this version since then although it was planned to be able to complete the London–Paris run, city-centre to city-centre, in one hour and twenty minutes. The fact that this route was specially chosen indicates that the Russians were originally keen to offer this version for export. The second was fitted out for fire-fighting. After the show it was flown down to the south of France by Yuri Garnayev but crashed there while fighting forest fires; Garneyev and his crew were killed. A year earlier, in 1966, an Mi-6 without stub wings had toured Western Europe demonstrating its qualities as a fire-fighter. It was able to discharge 12,000 litres (2,640 Imp gals) of water through eight nozzles in 20 seconds and to fill its water tank without the need to land in two minutes. It also showed off its paces as a load-lifter by hauling high voltage transmission towers around the Alps. Thirty-one were installed in three days whereas, according to local experts, installation of a single tower by conventional means usually took about three weeks. The Hook also hauled a 100-passenger cable car to a mountain top, a project, carried out in 90 minutes, which would normally have taken months. This helicopter has of course been put to spectacular use in Siberia by helping in the construction of bridges and the erection of pylons, TV masts and drilling rigs. All over Eastern Europe, in particular, the Hook has played a key role in the movement and assembly of power lines, pipelines, roofing, chimneys, steel towers and even monuments. In 1976, for example, the 4.57 m (15 ft) high statue of King Jagiello on his horse was lifted from Gliwice and installed in the centre of Krakow with the help of a Hook operated by the Polish company, Instal. The helicopter division of this company specialises in airborne transportation and assembly using helicopters as flying cranes. Mi-6 Hooks have participated in cosmonaut recovery in the USSR by underslinging the *Soyuz* descent module from its touchdown point back to base.

As may be expected Hooks were put to good use after the Chernobyl accident when some were used to drop protective material onto the damaged reactor.

Mi-10 and 10K Harke

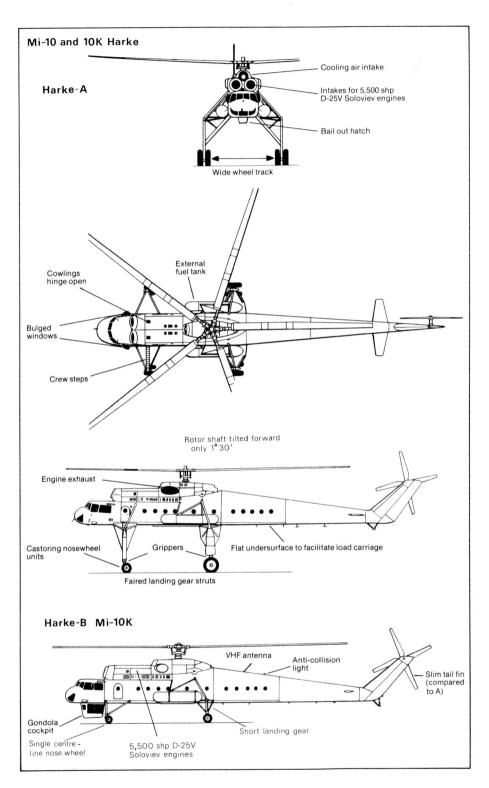

Harke-A

Cooling air intake

Intakes for 5,500 shp D-25V Soloviev engines

Bail out hatch

Wide wheel track

Cowlings hinge open

External fuel tank

Bulged windows

Crew steps

Rotor shaft tilted forward only 1° 30'

Engine exhaust

Castoring nosewheel units

Grippers

Flat undersurface to facilitate load carriage

Faired landing gear struts

Harke-B Mi-10K

VHF antenna

Anti-collision light

Slim tail fin (compared to A)

Gondola cockpit

Single centre-line nose wheel

Short landing gear

5,500 shp D-25V Soloviev engines

Mi-10 Harke-A

The process of improving a sound basic design by adding refinements and even by limited re-design is well-established; capabilities can be enhanced at minimum risk and cost. It was a reasonable prediction then that by using its rotor system as the basis a special crane version of the Hook would be developed. The resulting Mi-10 (2) Harke first flew at the end of 1960, the decision to proceed with its development having been taken in January 1959 and was publicly demonstrated at the Tushino Display in 1961.

The Hook and Harke are of the same general dimensions. The engines, transmission, hydraulics and rotor systems are common. The main differences are in the landing gear and fuselage where the top of the rear half of the Harke's slopes down towards the flat undersurface which runs unbroken from nose to tail. This permits external loads to be carried flush with the fuselage and between the tall 3.75 m (12 ft 3½ in) quadricycle undercarriage. With a nosewheel track of 6.01 m (19 ft 8¾ in) and a main wheel track of 6.92 m (22 ft 8½ in) this allows the Harke to straddle its load (defuelled ICBMs, for example) like a beast of prey. The machine has no stub wings since speed is largely irrelevant in crane operations. Designed to have only one small fuel tank (capacity: 585 kg, 1,290 lb) internally, the Mi-10 has a large external tank on each side of the fuselage with a total capacity of 6,340 kg (13,977 lb). Two ferry tanks may be carried in the

An Mi-10 Harke demonstrates its heavy lift capability.

cabin: they have a total capacity of 1,920 kg (4,233 lb). Fuel is pumped from the external tanks up to the service tank and thence to the engines. Situated aft of the main gearbox and at the same level as the engines, the service tank may gravity feed in an emergency. Besides normal refuelling the Harke is able to refuel itself at a rate of 323 kg (712 lb) a minute, a very desirable quality in underdeveloped areas where only drums of fuel may be available.

An unusual design feature is the 1°30′ inclination of the fuselage, engines and main gearbox to starboard. This is to compensate for fuselage rotation as a result of tail rotor thrust. Simultaneous lift-off of the landing gear is ensured thus preventing slipping and banking during take-off and landing. This inclination to starboard is accomplished by shortening the starboard landing gear by 298 mm (11.7 in). So that the crew is properly oriented with the horizon the cockpit is rotated laterally to port and is pitched up 4°15′ for level flight.

The undercarriage, quite different from that of the Mi-6, consists of four sets of twin wheels. Only the main, or rear, wheels have brakes and these are air-actuated. A small compressor on the No. 1 engine provides the compressed air. Control is by means of a lever on the cyclic stick; as it is pulled the brakes are gradually applied. Independent left or right braking is not possible. Taxying turns are achieved simply by using the rudder pedals; the nose wheel units are castoring. Running take-offs and landings may be undertaken at speeds up to 100 kph (62 mph) – no doubt an exciting manoeuvre given the height of the undercarriage legs. The port nose landing gear incorporates steps for the crew to enter the door placed just aft of the cockpit. This opens into a small compartment. A door to the left offers access to the cockpit while another opposite leads into the cabin. In an emergency on the ground escape from the cockpit is achieved by the effective, if rudimentary, method of sliding down two rubber-covered cables which extend from the cabin roof to the forward undercarriage legs. A telescopic bail-out hatch can extend below the cabin to prevent a parachutist striking the landing gear. All landing gear struts have fairings.

To achieve the long flat undersurface of the fuselage it has been reduced in height,

Entry into the Mi-10's cockpit is by means of steps set into the forward port landing gear strut; external cables facilitate an emergency exit.

while that of the tail boom has been increased. Such modifications have resulted in an internal cabin length of just over 14 m (46 feet), a width of 2.5 m (8 ft 2½ in) and a much reduced height of 1.68 m (5 ft 6 in). Thus about 60 m³ (2,120 ft³) of usable space is offered. Bench seats for 14 passengers each side are provided, although without the benefit of sound-proofing or air-conditioning, considerable persuasion may be needed to get such unfortunates to travel twice in the machine. Cargo can, of course, be carried internally – but it is more normal to carry loads on a wheeled freight platform under the fuselage or simply by means of hydraulic grips rather than underslinging. This arrangement allows the Harke to undertake a running take-off, thus permitting a heavier payload than with a vertical take-off. Further, the ability to 'secure' a large low-density load by means of the grips eliminates oscillations associated with sling loads and higher airspeeds are possible. The unique grip system consists of two front and two rear hydraulically-adjustable struts. At the top end they are connected to the undercarriage legs while the other end consists of a 'gripper'. The grippers at the rear incorporate additional hydraulic cylinders which act as mechanical guides and help to hold the cargo securely. Control of the grippers is effected from the cockpit or a remote panel. Depression of a button on the pilot's collective lever allows emergency jettison of the load. Photographs of such loads as a large passenger coach and a prefabricated building have been published. Maximum weight of the platform and load together is 15,000 kg (33,069 lb); maximum load on the platform is 13,600 kg (29,983 lb). By dispensing with the platform loads up to 19.98 m (65 ft 7 in) long, 10 m (32 ft 9½ in) wide and 3.1 m (10 ft 2 in) high can be lifted.

To assist in loading operations the pilots' windows are bulged and a closed circuit TV system (which replaced a retractable 'dustbin') with cameras trained on the load from the tail and down through the hatch is installed. The TV screen is located in the centre of the pilots' instrument panel. Lack of depth perception, however, does not allow the TV to be used as the sole 'hook-up' aid and marshallers are also required. Using the sling capability, and therefore confined to a vertical take-off, the maximum load that can be lifted is reduced to 8,000 kg (17,637 lb).

The Harke has been used extensively in the construction industry all over the USSR. It was invaluable in helping to erect the 29 masts of the Ukhta-Vuktyl-Punga-Nadym radio relay system in 1981. Most of the masts were some 50–60 m (164–197 ft) tall but eight of them were 100 m (328 ft) long and weighed up to 45,000 kg (99,206 lb). Clearly one Harke alone could not lift such a load. Each mast was thus assembled on the spot and fixed to its foundations with hinges attached to two of its feet. One Harke was then attached to the top of the mast by a 10 m (33 ft) cable while another was attached to the middle of the mast. The two helicopters, working together, then slowly raised the tower, the one attached to the middle taking the initial strain; the helicopter part of the operation took 2½ minutes. The two crews involved, headed by G. Maltsev and civil test pilot N. Vakulin, also erected the 242 m (794 ft) TV tower in Kharkov in a joint operation.

A prototype Mi-10 was on display at the 1965 Paris Air Show. On 28 May, 1965 a specially modified Harke with a single short nosewheel and short, lightweight main gear lifted a payload of 25,105 kg (55,347 lb) to 2,840 m (9,317 ft). A long running take-off of over 2,000 metres (6,560 feet) was used with the nosewheel held on the ground for as long as possible. G. Alferov was the captain. A year later an Mi-10 undertook a successful tour of Europe (installing more pylons in the Alps among other things), ending up at Gatwick Airport in England in March 1967, the first time a Soviet helicopter had ever flown in that country. Besides being keen to find overseas markets, the Soviet delegation wanted to gain experience of British airworthiness standards. The demonstration was organised by Aviaexport. Cost of the Harke was given as approximately £600,000 (at 1967 prices).

In keeping with the rest of the machine the ventilated and soundproofed cockpit is, to say the least, spacious. Two pilots are needed; the flight engineer sits behind the captain and the radio operator, if present, behind the co-pilot. There is also a jumpseat in the centre for a navigator. During the flight demonstration at Gatwick, however, up to nine eager people crammed themselves into the cockpit. Two British pilots flew in the co-pilot's seat with Boris Zemskov, Chief Test Pilot at the Ministry of Aviation Industry, as captain. The two Britons noticed the somewhat ponderous fuselage 'stir' from the undercarriage legs during engagement of the rotor. They remarked that thereafter the 'machine had a noticeable (rotor) vibration'; and that 'it requires considerable force to overcome the spring bias of the cyclic control', perhaps to prevent large cyclic movements which are not compatible with such a large diameter rotor system. Nevertheless it was agreed that this vibration was more or less confined to the transition into forward flight. Rotation of the twist grip throttle is in the opposite direction to Western practice. The helicopter handled well and was very solid in the hover, unaffected by minor gusts of wind. Those it generated itself on take-off, however, blew some of the assembled photographers to the ground. Like the Hook which is also involved in a great deal of hovering, the Harke is equipped with an excellent autopilot.

In December 1967 Petroleum Helicopters Inc revealed that they had bought an Mi-10 and an Mi-8 nine months earlier and assembled them in great secrecy at their Louisiana facility using specially translated manuals supplied by Aviaexport. The machines came in crates and took eight months to put together. Total cost was said to be $2 million. It is understood that the Mi-10 was originally bought by KLM Nordsee who resold it to PHI for use in exploratory operations with oil prospectors in Bolivia. Since the FAA did not recognise Soviet airworthiness standards, the helicopter could not be used in the USA. PHI were impressed by the simplicity of the design rather than by its sophistication. At the expense of a little added weight greater reliability and ease of maintenance were achieved. And ease of maintenance was placed high on the list of priorities by the Mil OKB. Ample space and easy access to components has been provided; to the engines and main gearbox by hydraulically-operated engine cowling side panels which can be used as work platforms. Associated ground equipment is thus much reduced. Interestingly, in over 170 hours of operation the hydraulic system leaked only a 'cupful of oil'. This was attributed to lower operating pressures and components manufactured to very close tolerances. The spares support, however, was so bad that flying operations could not be maintained and the Mi-10 was eventually scrapped in South America.

It is thought that about 70 Harkes were built between 1965 and 1981. Besides the USA, Iraq and Pakistan may be the only countries outside the Soviet Union to have received the Mi-10 although this situation could of course change even now. The Mi-10 is believed to have recommenced production in 1977 after an interval of six years.

Mi-10K Harke-B

On 26 March, 1966 the Mi-10K (*Korotkonogii*, short-legged) was first publicly demonstrated in Moscow. Its most apparent modifications are its shortened landing gear, a slimmer tail fin and an extra pilot's cabin under the nose. It is from this cabin that the pilot responsible for load hook-up and release flies the helicopter while the pilot in the conventional cockpit acts as a safety pilot and as primary pilot when the helicopter is in transit. The Mi-10K can be operated by a crew of only two pilots. The gondola cockpit has full flying controls and a rearward-facing seat to facilitate the pick-up and release of loads. Maximum sling load has been increased to 11,000 kg (24,250 lb); with Soloviev D-25VF turboshaft engines, (3) rated at 6,500 shp, this load can be

An Mi-10K, showing the short undercarriage, built-in airstairs and gondola cockpit for a rear-facing pilot. (Pilot Press Ltd)

raised to 14,000 kg (30,865 lb). The tail skid fitted to the model displayed at Paris in 1967 appeared to have earned its keep, according to interested observers. Little has been heard of the K model, also known as the Harke-B, in the last ten years or so, although in December 1979 it was reported that Aeroflot machines were helping in the erection of pylons in Bulgaria and East Germany, lifting loads too heavy for the resident Mi-8s.

Notes

1. It may well be that the Hook, able to lift about half the payload of the An-12 Cub, was sized to complement that aircraft in military and civil service.

2. The prototype was known as the V-10.

3. The installation of these engines has never been confirmed.

CHARACTERISTICS

Designation	**Mil Mi-6**	**Mil Mi-10**
Engine	2 × Soloviev D-25V	2 × Soloviev D-25V
	2 × 5,500 shp	2 × 5,500 shp
Rotor diameter	35.0 m (114 ft 10 in)	35.0 m (114 ft 10 in)
Fuselage length	33.18 m (108 ft 10½ in)	32.86 m (107 ft 9½ in)
Height	6.71 m (22 ft)	6.65 m (21 ft 10 in)
Empty weight	27,240 kg (60,055 lb)	27,300 kg (60,186 lb)
Max gross weight*	42,500 kg (93,700 lb)	43,700 kg (96,340 lb)
Max sling load	8,000 kg (17,637 lb)	8,000 kg (17,637 lb)
Max speed	300 kph (186 mph)	260 kph (161 mph)
Range	620 km (385 mls)**	250 km (155 mls)***
Service ceiling	4,500 m (14,763 ft)	3,000 m (9,840 ft)
First flight	September 1957	1960

   * For vertical take-off
  ** With 8,000 kg internal payload
*** With platform payload of 12,000 kg (26,455 lb)

Designation	**Mil Mi-10K**
Engine	2 × Soloviev D-25V
	2 × 5,500 shp
Rotor diameter	35.0 m (114 ft 10 in)
Fuselage length	32.86 m (107 ft 9½ in)
Height	4.65 m (15 ft 3 in)
Empty weight	24,680 kg (54,410 lb)
Max gross weight*	38,000 kg (83,776 lb)
Max sling load	11,000/14,000 kg (24,250/30,865 lb)?
Max speed	260 kph (161 mph)
Range	250 km (155 mls)?
Service ceiling	3,000 m (9,840 ft)
First flight	1965

* For vertical take-off

Designation	**Sikorsky S-64 (CH-54B)**	**Sikorsky S-80 (CH-53E)**
Engine	2 × P&W JFTD 12A-1	3 × GE T64-GE-416
	2 × 4,050 shp	3 × 4,380 shp
Rotor diameter	21.94 m (72 ft 0 in)	24.08 m (79 ft 0 in)
Fuselage length	21.41 m (70 ft 3 in)	22.35 m (73 ft 4 in)
Height	5.66 m (18 ft 7 in)	5.66 m (18 ft 7 in)
Empty weight	8,725 kg (19,235 lb)	15,071 kg (33,226 lb)
Max gross weight	19,050 kg (42,000 lb)	33,340 kg (73,500 lb)
Max sling load	9,070 kg (20,000 lb)	14,515 kg (32,000 lb)
Max speed	203 kph (126 mph)*	315 kph (196 mph)**
Range	370 km (230 mls)	500 km (310 mls)
Service ceiling	2,740 m (9,000 ft)	5,640 m (18,500 ft)
First flight	May 1962	March 1974

  * At 17,237 kg (38,000 lb) take-off weight
** At 25,401 kg (56,000 lb) take-off weight

The Second Generation:
Hip and Hoplite

By 1958 the single piston-engined Mi-1 and Mi-4 had proved themselves and the Mil OKB began to turn its attention to second generation machines using free-turbine engines. The turboshaft engine offers many attractive advantages over the piston engine. First, it has a vastly improved power-to-weight ratio and thus for a given mission a smaller, lighter helicopter is possible. Secondly, a much wider, and cheaper, range of turbine fuels can be used rather than expensive high octane gasoline. Thirdly, a turboshaft engine is very much smaller than an equivalent output piston engine. It can therefore be positioned close to the hub of the main rotor, thus simplifying the transmission and reducing drag by being faired into the fuselage profile. And fourthly, no cooling is required, a distinct boon for a machine which often has to hover at sustained high power. In deciding to use turboshaft engines Mil was thus able to improve performance characteristics dramatically. Comparative weights could be reduced: the eight-seat Mi-2 Hoplite was developed directly from the three-seat Mi-1; even with two engines the Mi-2's empty weight is only 612 kg (1,349 lb) more than that of its predecessor. The weight difference between the 14-seat Mi-4 and its replacement, the 28-seat Mi-8 Hip, is even more startling: a mere 1,232 kg (2,716 lb) for a machine carrying double the number of people. As far as size is concerned Mil did not have to build much larger helicopters: the Mi-8 is only 1.37 m (4 ft 6 in) longer than the Mi-4 despite the impression that the former is much longer. So, as new turboshaft engines became available the Mi-2 and the Mi-8 (originally designated the V-2 and V-8 respectively) were developed more or less simultaneously. First flight of both prototypes was in 1961.

Mi-8 Hip

To speed development of the Mi-8 the Mil OKB decided to use the Mi-4's hub, rotor blades and tail boom. Everything else was new and the layout quite different. Following the practice adopted for the Mi-6 the single free-turbine engine was placed directly above the fuselage forward of the main transmission and the cockpit, instead of being above the cabin as in the Hound, was moved to the nose.

The Mi-8 was designed as a 28-passenger helicopter to be used over an optimum stage length of 300 km (186 miles). There were two major changes before the final basic configuration was agreed. The first prototype, the Hip-A, had a single 2,700 shp Soloviev turbine and it was this aircraft that was publicly demonstrated at the Tushino Display on 3 July, 1961 having made its first flight earlier in the year. But more power was needed and for reasons of safety two less powerful engines were considered more appropriate than a single more powerful one. Thus the second prototype, designated the Hip-B, employed two 1,400 shp Izotov TV2-117 turboshaft engines and also all-metal constant chord, rather than tapered fabric-covered, blades. This second version first flew on 17 September, 1962 and eight days later was demonstrated to interested members of the Soviet government. Neither of these two prototypes reached production status.

During 1963 the four-bladed rotor gave way to a scaled-down version of the five-bladed Mi-6 rotor system, evidence of this further development becoming available in April 1964 when one world distance and one speed record were claimed. This version was designated Hip-C and was considered by the Russians as worthy of production which began in 1964. Substantial commonality with the Mi-4 simplified the process. The Mi-8 was displayed at the Paris Air Show the next year. Since that date few major modifications have been thought necessary apart from those connected with specialised role equipment. One exception, however, was the uprating of the engines to 1,700 shp TV2-117A standard; 1,500 shp was achieved in 1966. The fuselage is an all-metal, semi-monocoque structure of the pod-and-boom type.

The civil passenger variant, the Mi-8P, which entered production in 1966, has standard seating for 28 in tip-up seats, four-abreast. The cabin is approximately 6.36 m (20 ft 10¼ in) long, 2.34 m (7 ft 8¼ in) wide and 1.8 m (5 ft 10½ in) high. It offers a lavatory, a cupboard for coats and a baggage compartment. By removing the cupboard four more seats can be installed. Freight-loading clamshell doors with an airstair inset are at the rear of the cabin. A de-luxe version, known as the Mi-8 *Salon* and demonstrated at the Paris Air Show in 1971, offers 9–11 seats of greater comfort, tables and a galley in addition to normal fittings. A radio telephone is also installed and there is provision for a flight attendant. This version has a range of 380 km (236 miles) with a 30 minute fuel reserve. Both the standard and de-luxe passenger versions have large rectangular windows. Aeroflot uses the third civil version, the Mi-8T, as a passenger and load carrier. This utility machine has been operated in the Antarctic for patrol, survey and casualty evacuation.

An East German Mi-8 Hip-F with six Sagger anti-tank missiles and six pods for 192 57 mm rockets. It also has a nose-mounted 12.7 mm machine gun.

In addition to the utility Mi-8T the Mi-8P can easily and quickly be converted for cargo carrying. Approximetly 23 m³ (812 ft³) are available for loads weighing up to 4,000 kg (8,818 lb). Loads up to 3,000 kg (6,614 lb) can be lifted underslung. A winch capable of moving 200 kg (440 lb) can be installed in the Mi-8T to facilitate loading. When used as an ambulance there is room in all versions for 12 stretchers and an accompanying attendant. Further, hook-up ramps are available for the loading of vehicles through the clamshell doors. These doors may be removed, for example, for parachuting.

Both the Hip and Hoplite have very similar landing gear: in both cases a non-retractable tricycle type. The twin-wheel nose unit is steerable, though lockable in flight. The single main wheels have pneumatic brakes. All wheels and even the tail skid have oleo-pneumatic shock absorbers.

One has to sit in the cockpit really to appreciate the excellent lookout. This is achieved by having two small and widely-separated panels with only flight and rotor/engine rpm instruments in front of each pilot and locating practically all other instruments, switches, circuit breakers etc in the roof; the auto-pilot control panel is positioned on the floor between the two panels and does not impede visibility. A jump seat is available centrally behind the two pilots. Because the Hip is needed to operate in all climatic conditions and in the remotest corners of the world it is equipped with a comprehensive array of flight and navigational systems. The more important of these include a four-axis autopilot to give stabilisation in roll, pitch, yaw and altitude in normal flight and in the hover; a radio altimeter; a radio compass and astro compass for flying in Polar regions; normal communications and IFF. A conspicuous antenna box for a Doppler radar can often be seen under the tail boom. It is for the measurement of

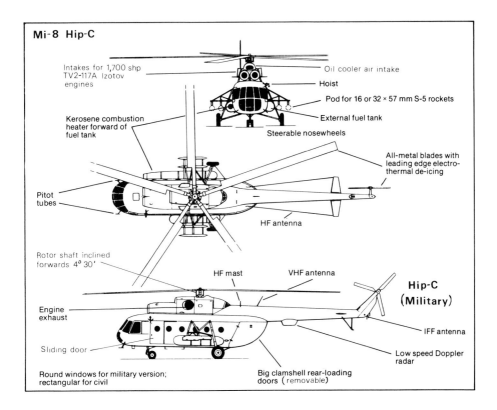

Mi-8 Hip-C

Intakes for 1,700 shp TV2-117A Izotov engines

Oil cooler air intake

Hoist

Pod for 16 or 32 × 57 mm S-5 rockets

External fuel tank

Steerable nosewheels

Kerosene combustion heater forward of fuel tank

All-metal blades with leading edge electro-thermal de-icing

Pitot tubes

HF antenna

Rotor shaft inclined forwards 4° 30'

HF mast

VHF antenna

Hip-C (Military)

Engine exhaust

IFF antenna

Sliding door

Low speed Doppler radar

Round windows for military version; rectangular for civil

Big clamshell rear-loading doors (removable)

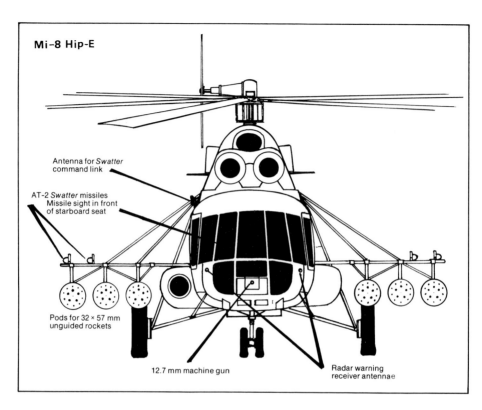

Mi-8 Hip-E

Antenna for *Swatter* command link

AT-2 *Swatter* missiles
Missile sight in front of starboard seat

Pods for 32 × 57 mm unguided rockets

12.7 mm machine gun

Radar warning receiver antennae

The six crossed dipoles on both sides of the fuselage indicate that this is an Mi-8 Hip-K used to jam communications.

drift and low speed manoeuvring when the pitot static system becomes ineffective below about 60 kph (37 mph). An oxygen system is available for the crew which may be necessary for flight above 3,050 m (10,000 ft) and for casualties when the Hip is being used in an evacuation role.

A heavy but reliable engine, the TV2-117A has a dry weight of 330 kg (727 lb) while the VR-8A main rotor gearbox weighs 745 kg (1,642 lb). The two engines and gearbox are considered a single package which has a control system which maintains the main rotor speed, synchronises the power output from both engines and, in the event of failure of one, increases power on the other. The governor can be cut out and manual throttle used. A box-shaped filter can be installed ahead of the intakes to protect the engines from sand ingestion in desert terrain; Egyptian Hips, for example, are equipped with such filters. The Hip has only one internal fuel tank with a capacity of 345 kg (761 lb) installed behind the main rotor gearbox. It is quite predictably supplemented by two external strap-on tanks; one on the port side of the fuselage with a capacity of 577 kg (1,272 lb), the starboard one holding 527 kg (1,162 lb). At the forward end of the starboard tank is a kerosene burner, fan and heat exchanger which warm ambient air and duct it into the cabin. Total fuel capacity is therefore 1,449 kg (3,194 lb). Up to two more ferry tanks may be carried in the cabin offering another 1,418 kg (3,126 lb) which bring the total fuel capacity to 3,700 litres (814 Imp gall). Fuel consumption in the cruise is said to be about 655 kg (1,444 lb) an hour.

The main rotor hub has flapping, drag and feathering hinges and hydraulic drag dampers. The all-metal main rotor blades have a constant chord and are interchangeable. The spar is of aluminium alloy. The all-metal tail rotor has three blades, although it is believed that at one time a four-bladed tail rotor was tested with a view to improving directional control at low airspeeds. An electro-thermal de-icing system protects all rotor blades and cockpit windows. An ice accretion sensor detects the imminent formation of ice along the rotor blades and triggers an electric current along them to prevent any build-up.

The Mil OKB devoted much effort to keeping maintenance requirements to the minimum and designing the helicopter so as to make major components easily accessible. Thus the engines, main gearbox and main rotor hub can be serviced without the need for ground equipment. The engine cowling side panels when open form maintenance platforms. They can be reached through a hatch in the cockpit. This arrangement is particularly valuable when servicing in the field is necessary.

In February 1967 Petroleum Helicopters Inc in the USA took delivery of an Mi-8, in crates, at the same time as an Mi-10. They did not use it for long, passing it on to a firm in Peru to be used for carrying tourists between archaeological sites. In the same year British European Airways despatched a team to the Soviet Union to evaluate the Mi-8 for passenger operations in the United Kingdom. The team was led by Capt Cameron who had already had the opportunity to fly the machine during the 1965 Paris Air Show. He reported that he appreciated the space in the cockpit and the relative lack of vibration, and said that the helicopter compared favourably with the Sikorsky S-61. He was somewhat disconcerted by the absence of seat belts which apparently the Mil OKB considered then to be superfluous. However, the Mi-8 did not offer a sufficient improvement over the S-61 as far as operating costs or performance were concerned and BEA did not purchase any.

In July 1967 at the spectacular Domodedovo Air Display the Hip appeared in military colours. Since then it has become the standard Soviet utility/assault helicopter, able to carry 24 armed troops, and very much to the fore in the development of Soviet airmobile concepts. It is austere, as are all military helicopters, having no furnishing and small circular windows. These have support brackets and may be opened so that infantrymen can fire their rifles in flight.

Following US and European practice in the 1960s various armaments can be 'buttoned-on'. A number of options are available as can be seen from published photographs. The basic military Mi-8, also referred to as the Hip-C, can have an outrigger structure with two pylons, able to take a load of perhaps 500 kg (1,100 lb), attached to each side of the fuselage just in front of the main landing gear. Each pylon can take a 16 or 32-shot 57 mm rocket pod or a 250 kg (550 lb) bomb. This armaments load has been progressively increased; following Soviet Press reports in early 1977, a new variant, the Hip-E, was seen with six rather than four pylons. Together these can carry up to six bombs, or six 16/32-shot rocket pods and four anti-tank guided missiles, usually the Swatter which has a maximum range of 4,000 m and a consequent flight time of some 20–25 seconds. To assist the firing of these missiles a 9Sh121 gyro-stabilised sight is installed in front of the co-pilot/gunner who sits in the starboard seat. The antenna for the missile command link is positioned just above the cockpit window. With such a sight the gunner is not aware, while tracking the target, of any change in the helicopter's heading. The pilot is free to turn away from the missile's line of flight provided that he does not allow the aircraft to exceed the post-launch constraints or outmanoeuvre the sight's ability to keep track of the target. This mix of weapons makes the Hip-E very versatile and, with the inclusion of a flexibly-mounted 12.7 mm machine gun in the nose, a very heavily armed helicopter. The use of bombs of course necessitates overflying the target but the Russians consider them a good weapon against dug-in infantry and strong-points. When fully fuelled and armed the Hip-E can still lift 12–14 troops, but when operating at maximum gross weight there is little power available for manoeuvre at low speed and in the hover.

The Hip-F entered service at much the same time as the E model and is its export version. The East German *Adolf von Lützow* combat helicopter regiment was the first to get this variant which is armed with six Sagger wire-guided anti-tank missiles rather than the four Swatters of the Hip-E. The East Germans bought this system before the Russians had decided to export the Swatter missile. It is not known which other countries now operate the Hip-F, if any.

In 1974 the Hip-D, a converted C model, appeared for command and control duties and radio relay. It can be recognised by rectangular-shaped canisters located in place of the weapons pylons and additional HF, VHF and UHF antennae above and below the tail boom. A more modern communications variant and airborne command post is the Hip-G which materialised in 1981, boasting extra whip and dipole antennae, one conspicuous below the tail boom and aft of the Doppler box. This G model was probably purpose-designed and not a converted C model. The Hip-J and K appeared in East Europe at the start of the 1980s. The J is thought to be a radar jammer with two box-like structures on each side of the fuselage and a number of other blisters. The Hip-K is instantly recognisable by the six cross dipole antennae mounted on each side of the rear fuselage. Other devices are mounted on the underside of the fuselage and in place of some of the fuselage windows. The Doppler antenna box below the tail boom has been removed. It would seem that this K model may be a communications jammer and a replacement for the Hound-C. The point about using helicopters for such EW tasks is that they are mobile and by using altitude they can increase their effective jamming range and get a line of sight to their intended target. By standing well back from the forward edge of the battlefield (FEBA) they can go quite high with some degree of safety and this positioning, combined with their mobility, contributes to greater survivability. The Hip-H is the NATO designation for the Mi-17 and is described separately.

The Hip has played an important part in many Warsaw Pact exercises but it has also tasted battle, notably in Afghanistan and the Yom Kippur War of 1973. According to a report in *Aviation Week and Space Technology* a force of some 100 armed Hips carrying 18-

man commando teams was launched across the Suez Canal on the first evening of that war. The aim of the raid was twofold: to attack Israeli oilfields and to hinder the movement forward of Israeli reinforcements. Both were greeted with some success although Israeli anti-aircraft fire downed several helicopters with total loss of life. The commandos, armed with Sagger and RPG-7 anti-tank weapons, were supported by Hips armed with rockets and bombs. The helicopters themselves made direct attacks on armoured columns particularly when, due to the terrain, the tanks were unable to deploy. Other Hips were modified to take two fixed heavy machine guns and up to six light machine guns to provide intense suppressive fire around landing zones. Hips were also reported to have carried out napalm attacks on Israeli strong-points along the Canal. The bombs were apparently merely rolled out through the clamshell doors by means of a conveyor system. Egyptian commanders later expressed themselves well pleased with the helicopter-commando assault teams which helped to delay and minimise Israeli counter-attacks.

Since that war the Hip, mainly the C model, has seen action in many parts of the world: Afghanistan, Angola, Chad, Iran/Iraq, Mozambique, Nicaragua (where one Hip crashed while carrying 75 children and 17 adults on a mercy mission) and the Ogaden War between Ethiopia and Somalia, among others. It has generally acquitted itself well.

Nevertheless, the Hip has its shortcomings and it is obsolescent. Its external fuel tanks, fixed undercarriage and weapons pylons produce considerable drag and thus degrade speed and fuel economy. The E and F models, though heavily armed, have no armour plating. Unprotected and slow, they cannot sensibly go within range of aimed enemy fire. Steps have been taken to improve the survivability of the Hip-E and examples have been seen with antennae for a radar warning receiver and devices to reduce the infra-red signature of the aircraft.

It is clear that the Hip admirably meets the requirements for a short-range, all-weather, medium-lift helicopter for both civil and military purposes. Deployed all over the remoter areas of the Soviet Union singly, in pairs or greater numbers and indeed in equally obscure regions around the world, it has proved itself to be extremely rugged and reliable. Aeroflot has a vast number, running into thousands, in its inventory. As possibly the primary vehicle in the Soviet Air Rescue Service, Hips have carried out many rescues, for example, of downed aircrew and people cut off by flooding; Hips play an important role in the recovery of cosmonauts. An electrically-operated hoist capable of lifting 150 kg (331 lb) is fitted above the port door for rescue missions. Hips have been used to fight forest and industrial fires and to support the oil and gas industries, geological work and the construction of pipelines in addition to the normal carriage of people and cargoes. Aeroflot Hips helped to fly in troops during the invasion of Afghanistan; this huge fleet of medium helicopters may be used to support the Soviet Armed Forces at any time. The Hip has been an immensely successful helicopter and great credit is due to the Mil OKB.

However, there are critics of the Hip. Writing in a November 1986 issue of *Vozdushnyi Transport* a senior pilot-inspector of the Kirghiz Civil Aviation Directorate claimed that Mi-8s built between 1981 and 1983 weighed 360 kg (794 lb) more than those built between 1968 and 1973; furthermore, after each overhaul they 'gained' another 40–60 kg (88–132 lb)! Rotor thrust was lost and, due to changes in turbine blade manufacture, engine power reduced. As a result, in the mountains in spring and summer, the newest Mi-8s were no more productive than the Mi-4. Although it is not known how many Mi-8s and -17s in either civil or military guise have been built it is no wonder that *Jane's* in its 1987/88 edition reported that the figure exceeds 10,000, much greater than even the highly successful Mi-1 and Mi-4. According to the US

Department of Defense some 2,000 Hips of different types are operated by the Soviet Armed Forces and perhaps another 1,500 have been exported to 40 countries or more. The Mi-8 as such is no longer in production, the plants at Kazan and Ulan Ude now being devoted to the Mi-17 Hip-H.

Besides the roles already noted it should be mentioned that the Hip is often used by KGB Border Guards, with dogs, to patrol the frontiers of the Soviet Union. It can be used for minelaying. A conveyor system and chute protruding out of the rear doors can be fitted for dispensing mines quickly at very low level and at a speed of about 15 kph (9 mph). PFM-1 'butterfly' anti-personnel mines have been strewn in profusion by Hips in Afghanistan. The machine has also been to sea. In 1974 two Hips operated from the deck of the ASW helicopter cruiser *Leningrad* as they helped to sweep mines from the southern end of the Suez Canal. It is not unlikely that Hips have carried out sea trials from the decks of the larger 'Kiev' class anti-submarine cruisers. There is no evidence to date, however, to indicate that any version of the Hip has been permanently deployed aboard ship. Indeed, this is most unlikely given the existence of the Ka-27 Helix.

Mi-14 Haze

As the 1970s approached it was becoming clear that the ASW version of the Mi-4 Hound was near to obsolescence. Few were available and their performance was

A derivative of the Mi-8, the Mi-14 Haze serves in the Soviet Navy. It is shore-based and undertakes such roles as ASW, mine countermeasures and SAR. Here is a Haze-A showing its ventral bay doors open and its MAD gear deployed. The forward of the three orifices near the MAD is for the dunking sonar, the other two are possibly sonobuoy chutes.

Mi-14 Haze-A

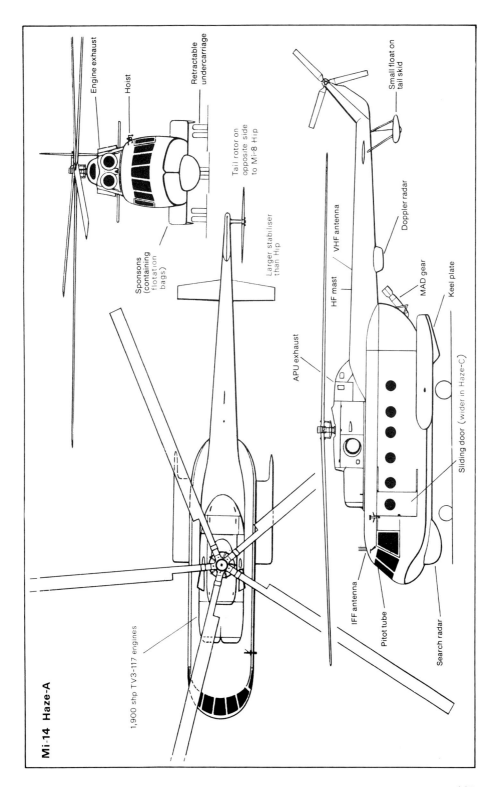

Engine exhaust

Hoist

Retractable undercarriage

Tail rotor on opposite side to Mi-8 Hip

Sponsons (containing flotation bags)

Larger stabiliser than Hip

Small float on tail skid

Doppler radar

VHF antenna

HF mast

MAD gear

Keel plate

APU exhaust

Sliding door (wider in Haze-C)

1,900 shp TV3-117 engines

IFF antenna

Pitot tube

Search radar

inadequate. There were not enough Hormones to replace them for coastal ASW and simultaneously to equip the growing number of ships designed to have embarked helicopters. If the requirement for a Hound replacement was not to be met by an entirely new helicopter – which would take time to design, develop and produce – then substantial modifications to an existing one would be cheaper and quicker. In assessing Western progress in this field, particularly the Sikorsky SH-3 and the Westland Sea King, it became obvious that a derivative of the very successful Hip would be the answer in the search for a comparatively large hunter/killer submarine helicopter.

While its antecedents are clearly recognisable, development of the Haze turned out to be a protracted affair, given the need for a largely new fuselage and retractable landing gear.

Begun in about 1968 it did not prove easy to convert the Hip into an ASW helicopter and the first flight did not take place until 1973. Production probably began in 1974. General dimensions and dynamic components are thought to be the same or very similar to those of the Hip. The prototypes, designated V-14, and the first production Haze had two TV2-117 turboshafts and the same tail rotor as the Hip. However, because of the usual demands made on a naval helicopter for lengthy periods in the hover and for good directional control when in the hover and at low speeds, these engines were subsequently replaced by 1,900 shp TV3-117 turboshafts with shorter nacelles and the tail rotor was moved to the other side of the fin. An improved gearbox was fitted. New features include a boat hull and sponsons at the rear on each side to give an amphibious capability. These sponsons have a vertical fin on the bottom to aid stability when in the water and a fairing on the outside which hinges upwards to release inflatable flotation bags. Besides also housing the main twin wheel landing gear the sponsons may contain fuel, the Haze having no external fuel tanks. All four units of the landing gear retract; the tail skid has a small float. Equipment for ASW seems to include a search radar in the undernose radome, a retractable sonar unit housed just aft

Two Yugoslav Mi-14 Haze helicopters on static display to celebrate Air Force and Air Defence Day in May 1987. (Author)

and to starboard of the weapons bay, two chutes possibly for sonobuoys and a towed MAD 'bird' stowed against the rear of the fuselage. Torpedoes and depth charges can be carried in the ventral weapons bay.

So far the Haze has only been seen operating with the AV-MF from shore bases. It is unlikely ever to operate permanently from the 'Kiev' class carriers since it is far too big to get down the elevators. Modifications to give the Haze folding blades and tail boom are most improbable and to remain on deck throughout a long voyage in a peace or war environment is unthinkable. Even the new class of aircraft carrier is not expected to have elevators large enough to accommodate the length of the Haze which exceeds 25 m (82 ft) with rotors unfolded.

As a replacement for the Hound-B the Haze-A is several times more capable. With a comprehensive load of sensors and weapons it can act autonomously as a hunter/killer when necessary, although usually it flies as part of an integrated shore-based defence system. It can operate at a greater range than the Hound, get there faster and stay there longer. Because of its retractable undercarriage and lack of weapons pylons, at maximum take-off weight, the Haze has a maximum cruise speed some 20 kph (12 mph) faster than that of the Hip.

Copying the American example the Haze-B is employed in the mine countermeasures role following extensive tests at the Feodosia naval test establishment in the Crimea. This version is distinguished by a fuselage strake and pod forward on the starboard side, no MAD gear and a small box under the tail boom forward of the Doppler box. It can tow a mine-activating sled along the surface.

The Haze entered service in mid-1975. Production was reported initially to be very slow although it appears to have increased now to perhaps two a month. It cannot be considered one of the Mil OKB's greater successes and according to the US Department of Defense only about 100 are thought to be in service with the AV-MF split between the four fleets. As far as is known Bulgaria was the first export customer for the Haze but now at least eight countries have the type including Cuba, Libya, Syria and Yugoslavia. A version of the Haze for SAR to be a replacement for the Hip which has been used over coastal waters in this role for many years was not unexpected. In 1987 this version was designated Haze-C. It has a wider cabin door on the port side and a hoist above it.

Mi-17 Hip-H

Unveiled for the first time in the West at the 1981 Paris Air Show was the Mi-17, apparently a variant of the Mi-8 with a few external changes. But while it resembles the Mi-8 it differs in many important respects, enough to attract a new designation for the Russians but not for NATO identification purposes. The reason for developing the Mi-17 seems to have been a desire to introduce a more capable and efficient helicopter in the same weight class and general configuration as the Mi-8 – there was no need to alter radically a successful design. According to Polish sources the prototype was built in 1976 as the Mi-18. Various modifications were undertaken followed by the decision to re-designate the machine Mi-17.

The most obvious difference in the two types is that on the Mi-17 the tail rotor is on the port side of the fin and rotates in the opposite direction, thus effectively becoming a 'puller' as opposed to the Mi-8's 'pusher'. But the most significant change is the installation of two 1,900 shp Izotov TV3-117MT turboshafts, outwardly recognisable by their shorter nacelles, which offer nearly 30% more power and reduced fuel consumption. In the event of failure of one the other can develop 2,200 shp. The increased output from these engines has allowed a 60 kph (37 mph) rise in cruising

An Afghan Mi-17 Hip-H of the 'Hero of the Revolution' regiment. Note the ribbed box-like exhaust suppressor.

speed at maximum gross weight, and a more than doubling of the hover ceiling out of ground effect and rate of climb at a normal take-off weight of 11,100 kg (24,470 lb). Range has also been increased slightly. An APU is installed above the cabin with small exhausts on either side to the rear of the rotor mast. Other important improvements include a rotor hub made of titanium alloys and a new main rotor gearbox, both of which are lighter than those of the Mi-8, and more modern navigational devices and flight instruments. The Doppler box under the tail boom resembles that on the Haze, slightly different to that on the Mi-8. The Mi-17 has been made easier to maintain and the time between the overhaul of various components lengthened, thus reducing costs.

The helicopter displayed in Paris (SSSR 17718) sported engine intake guards to give protection against sand and dust ingestion, and foreign object damage, and these seem to be standard equipment. An electrically-driven winch was mounted just above the port door. Although marked in Aeroflot colours the Mi-17 had the small circular cabin windows associated with the military version of the Mi-8. This may simply be because the production line is no longer geared to the larger rectangular windows. On the bottom surface of each main undercarriage leg was mounted a light angled in towards the centre to shine on any underslung load.

While internal and underslung payloads remain the same some of the Mi-17's dimensions are different by a few inches (according to an Aviaexport brochure). Its maximum gross weight is 13,000 kg (28,660 lb), 1,000 kg (2,205 lb) more than that of the Mi-8.

The Mi-17, as another version of the Hip, has seen military service in Afghanistan since 1982. Like the Hip-E the Hip-H has three pylons on outriggers on each side of the fuselage for the carriage of rockets, bombs and machine guns. The nose gun appears to be different to that of the Hip-E. An innovation has been a single-barrelled 7.62 mm or, more likely, a 12.7 mm gun flexibly-mounted in the starboard rear clamshell door. In addition photographs have revealed a decoy flare dispenser attached to the underside of the tail boom aft of the Doppler box, an IR jammer aft of the APU and IR suppressors on the engine exhausts – all to provide protection against heat-seeking missiles. Some Hip-H have been seen with armour plating below the pilots' side windows.

Export of the Mi-17 may be expected to gather pace and many Mi-8 operators will be tempted to procure the Mi-17. So far, however, only the Armed Forces of Angola, Cuba, India, Nicaragua, North Korea and Syria are thought to possess the Hip-H. The Mi-8/17 Hip has proved to be such a success that a completely new helicopter in this weight class may be some way off – unless tilt rotor development is well enough advanced to merit production.

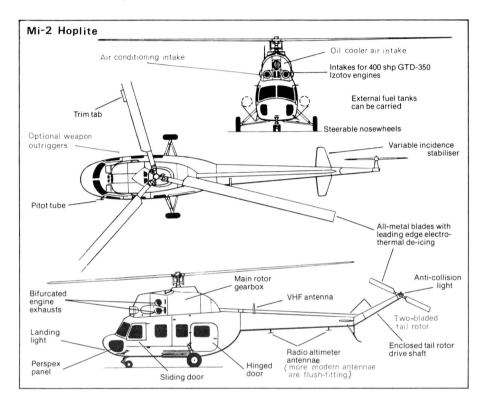

Mi-2 Hoplite

The payload of the Mi-1 Hare suffered from the fact that the single piston engine and transmission contributed some 25% of the helicopter's empty weight. By using two turbine engines above the cabin more space would be made available for passengers or cargo and the payload could be increased without any significant change to the overall dimensions of the helicopter. Two 400 shp Izotov GTD-350 free turbines were chosen and these produced 40% more power than the Hare's AI-26V engine at half the weight. The result was a payload $2\frac{1}{2}$ times greater than that of the basic Hare.

The new machine was called the Mi-2 Hoplite (1). It was the Mil OKB's original intention to build an Mi-1 replacement retaining its basic configuration and using as many of the Mi-1's parts as possible. In the event, only the engines and airframe were new. As experience was gained various other new components were introduced and some Mi-6 technology adopted.

Details of the Hoplite were publicly announced in the autumn of 1961 and the prototype flew for the first time in September that year. Together with the Mi-8 it was

An Mi-2 Hoplite armed with four Sagger anti-tank missiles.

demonstrated to the Soviet government and Communist Party leaders on 25 September, 1962. Further development and State trials followed. Although only two prototypes were flying an agreement was signed with the Polish government in January 1964 whereby the Mil OKB relinquished its responsibility for the project and WSK-PZL in Swidnik, Poland took it over (2). The first Polish Mi-2 flew on 4 November, 1965 and production began the next year. An Mi-2 was exhibited at the Poznan Fair in 1966 and at Paris the following year. Production at one time approached 300 machines a year. The first flight of the 3000th Polish-built Mi-2 took place in Swidnik in September 1979.

By the end of 1986 over 5,000 Mi-2 had been built in at least 24 different military and civil versions. About 85% have been exported. In the 1970s PZL Swidnik started to incorporate improvements to Mil's original design. The 11-seat Mi-2M, first flown in 1974, had two 450 shp GTD-350P engines which much enhanced flight performance and, according to the factory, was better than the basic Mi-2 even with one engine inoperative. Other refinements included plastic main and tail rotor blades. Only one prototype was built and flight tested; production was not approved. The Mi-2B is distinguished from the basic Mi-2 by having improved avionics and a different electrical system which does not permit rotor blade de-icing. Apart from having slightly lower empty weights for its passenger and cargo versions, it is the same as the Mi-2 in every other respect.

The Mi-2 was designed as a light utility helicopter able to carry up to eight passengers with six seated back-to-back. One passenger can sit next to the single pilot and the eighth seat is in the rear. All are removable. The cabin itself measures 2.27 m (7 ft 5½ in) long by 1.2 m (3 ft 11¼) wide by 1.4 m (4 ft 7 in) high. The Mi-2 is an extremely versatile helicopter, able to accept a wide variety of specialist role equipment and thus to undertake a comprehensive range of tasks. As an air ambulance four stretchers and a medical attendant may be carried. Up to 700 kg (1,543 lb) can be taken in the cabin; 800 kg (1,763 lb) can be lifted as an underslung load. Other versions include convertible passenger/cargo, passenger, cargo only with a hoist or sling and SAR. In Yugoslavia, for example, yellow-painted Mi-2s support the motoring organisation Auto-Moto Savez Jugoslavije during the summer months by patrolling some of the main tourist routes.

The Mi-2 has been a particular success as an agricultural helicopter, this version receiving its certificate of airworthiness on 1 March, 1975. It is used in this role throughout most of Eastern Europe, the Soviet Union and other countries, particularly in the Middle East. Known in Poland as the Bazant (Pheasant), this version has a hopper installed on each side of the fuselage, each with a capacity of 500 ltr (110 Imp gals) or 374 kg (825 lb) of dry chemical. A spraybar or dry chemical distributor is fitted as appropriate. The spraybar gives a swath width of some 46 m (150 ft). Over 50 Mi-2s are now used for agricultural purposes in Poland. They are operated by an enterprise specially formed in 1975: *Zespol Eksploatacyjnych Uslug Smiglowcowych* (Helicopter Operations Company), happily abbreviated to ZEUS!

The military version of the Mi-2, the Hoplite, can perform a variety of missions from troop transport and casualty evacuation to covert infiltration of enemy lines, armed reconnaissance and light attack, equipped with Swatter anti-tank missiles, guns and rockets. The associated missile sight is installed inside the cockpit on the starboard side. Recent photographs show a box behind the cabin and below the tail boom and a 23 mm cannon mounted on the port side of the fuselage. The purpose of the box is unknown.

Two armed Hoplites took part in the flypast to mark the 30th Anniversary of the Liberation in July 1974 in Warsaw. One was armed with four missiles, believed to have been Saggers, and the other with machine guns. The Hoplite also serves in the Bulgarian Navy and the Polish Naval Air Division in the SAR role with a 120 kg (264 lb) capacity electrical hoist and a 30 m (100 ft) steel cable. Finally it has found a niche as a training aircraft and is so used in the Air Forces of many countries including Soviet.

The all-metal, semi-monocoque fuselage is of the pod-and-boom type. The cabin may be entered by a forward door on each side and by a large door on the port side behind the landing gear strut. Above the cabin are mounted the VR-2 main rotor gearbox and twin 400 shp Izotov GTD-350, or optionally two 450 shp GTD-350P, turboshafts built under licence in Poland at the PZL Rzeszow factory. Dry weight of the GTD-350 is 135 kg (297 lb). Though mounted side-by-side the engines are separated by the intakes for the air conditioning system and oil cooling. Under the cabin floor is a single 464 kg (1,022 lb) fuel tank. As is to be expected a fuel tank with a capacity of 186 kg (410 lb) can be fitted on each side of the fuselage. Endurance using only the main tank and with 5% reserves is two hours and 24 minutes. Using all three tanks and with the same reserves endurance is raised by two hours.

As already noted the prototype employed the same rotor system as the Mi-1. This was soon changed and the fully articulated three-bladed main rotor now has all-metal blades of rectangular planform with hydraulic dampers. The main rotor system cannot be folded but the blades are interchangeable. A PZL Swidnik brochure describes the extruded duralumin blade spars as being filled with compressed gas, the possible leakage of which through cracks or insufficient tightness is indicated by a warning device built into the spar. Both the main and two-bladed tail rotor (3) have automatic electro-thermal de-icing; the windscreen a manually-operated electric heater. The horizontal stabiliser is of variable incidence and is controlled by the collective lever in the cockpit. Standard communications and navigation equipment are installed.

Flight performance of the Mi-2 is modest but it enjoys remarkably low vibration levels in all stages of flight.

PZL Swidnik is now beginning to branch out from Soviet tutelage. The demand for the standard civil or military versions of the Mi-2 has now dwindled to a trickle and three new projects are seen as giving a new lease of life to the Polish helicopter industry, something that will assuredly receive the encouragement of the Soviet Union.

The Kania (Kittyhawk), with two 420 shp Allison 250-C20B engines in place of the original GTD-350s, flew for the first time on 3 June, 1979. Two Mi-2 were converted for flight test and certification. Work on a more refined version, the Kania Model 1, took place between 1982 and 1986. With American engines a military version of the Kania is unlikely and thus no prospect of a Polish replacement for the Mi-2 is in sight. The second project is the W-3 Sokol (Falcon). This is the first all-Polish helicopter design; the prototype made its first flight on 16 November 1979. The Sokol is larger than the Mi-2/Kania, carrying a crew of two and 12 passengers or an internal load of 2,100 kg (4,630 lb). This helicopter could turn out to be a Mi-4 replacement as production, which started in 1985, gathers pace. The third project, begun in 1985, closely resembles the Soviet Mi-34. Known as the PZL Swidnik SW-4, it is a four-seat multi-purpose helicopter but with a turbine engine rather than the piston engine of the Mi-34. Whether the SW-4 and the Mi-34 merge into a single project with production undertaken in Poland remains to be seen. It must be a possibility.

The disturbances in Poland which began in August 1980 included strikes at the PZL Swidnik factory, causing delay in the development of the Kania and Sokol and in the production of the Mi-2.

Notes

1.   The dictionary definition of Hoplite is ': "A heavily armed foot soldier of ancient Greece."

2.   The Aviation and Engine Industry of Poland, PZL, is one of the most important of the country's industries. Its foreign trade agency is known as Pezetel. One of the most advanced and largest industrial plants in the Lublin region is the *Wytwornia Sprzetu Komunikacyjnego – Polskie Zaklady Lotnicze Swidnik* (Transport Equipment Works – PZL Swidnik) factory which also bears the name of a Polish aircraft designer, Zygmunt Pulawski. It is situated 100 miles south-east of Warsaw and was built in 1949. It has since become the Communist centre for the manufacture of light helicopters. About 10,000 people are employed at Swidnik building not only helicopters but also gliders, motor cycles and fixed-wing components etc. Affiliated to the factory is a research and development centre.

3.   Until the appearance of the Mi-34 the Mi-2 was the only Soviet helicopter to have a two-bladed tail rotor.

CHARACTERISTICS

Designation	**Mil Mi-8**	**Mil Mi-17**
Engine	2 × Izotov TV2-117A	2 × Izotov TV3-117MT
	2 × 1,700 shp	2 × 1,900 shp
Rotor diameter	21.29 m (69 ft 10½ in)	21.29 m (69 ft 10½ in)
Fuselage length	18.17 m (59 ft 7½ in)	18.42 m (60 ft 5½ in)
Height	4.75 m (15 ft 7¼ in)	4.75 m (15 ft 7¼ in)
Empty weight	7,260 kg (16,007 lb)*	7,100 kg (15,653 lb)
Max gross weight	12,000 kg (26,455 lb)**	13,000 kg (28,660 lb)

Max speed	230 kph (143 mph)	250 kph (155 mph)
Range	445 km (276 mls)***	465 km (289 mls)
Service ceiling	4,500 m (14,760 ft)	3,600 m (11,810 ft)
First flight	1961	1979 ?

Designation	**Mil Mi-14**	**Mil Mi-2**
Engine	2 × Izotov TV3-117	2 × Izotov GTD-350
	2 × 1,900 shp	2 × 400 shp
Rotor diameter	21.29 m (69 ft 10$\frac{1}{2}$ in)	14.5 m (47 ft 6$\frac{7}{8}$ in)
Fuselage length	18.31 m (60 ft 1 in)	11.4 m (37 ft 4$\frac{3}{4}$ in)
Height	5.65 m (18 ft 6 in)	3.75 m (12 ft 3$\frac{1}{2}$ in)
Empty weight	8,500 kg (18,700 lb)***	2,372 kg (5,229 lb)
Max gross weight	13,000 kg (28,660 lb)	3,700 kg (8,157 lb)
Max speed	255 kph (158 mph)	200 kph (124 mph)
Range	800 km (497 mls)***	440 km (273 mls)****
Service ceiling	4,500 m (14,764 ft)	4,000 m (13,124 ft)
First flight	1973	1961

    * Military version
  ** Vertical take-off
 *** Approximate
**** Max internal fuel, no reserves

Designation	**Bell 205 (UH-1D)**	**Sikorsky S-70A (UH-60A)**
Engine	Lycoming T53-L-11	2 × GT T700-GE-700
	1,100 shp	2 × 1,560 shp
Rotor diameter	14.63 m (48 ft 0 in)	16.36 m (53 ft 8 in)
Fuselage length	13.58 m (44 ft 7 in)	15.26 m (50 ft 0$\frac{1}{2}$ in)
Height	4.09 m (13 ft 5 in)	3.76 m (12 ft 4 in)
Empty weight	2,140 kg (4,718 lb)	4,819 kg (10,624 lb)
Max gross weight	4,310 kg (9,500 lb)	9,185 kg (20,250 lb)
Max speed	220 kph (138 mph)	296 kph (184 mph)
Range	526 km (327 mls)	600 km (373 mls)*
Service ceiling	3,840 m (12,600 ft)	5,790 m (19,000 ft)
First flight	August 1961	October 1974

* 30 min fuel reserves

Designation	**Sikorsky S-61 (SH-3D)**
Engine	2 × GE T58-GE-10
	2 × 1,400 shp
Rotor diameter	18.9 m (62 ft 0 in)
Fuselage length	16.68 m (54 ft 9 in)
Height	4.72 m (15 ft 6 in)
Empty weight	5,382 kg (11,865 lb)
Max gross weight	9,300 kg (20,500 lb)
Max speed	267 kph (166 mph)
Range	1,006 km (625 mls)**
Service ceiling	4,480 m (14,700 ft)
First flight	1964

** 10% fuel reserves

The

Mi-12 Homer

Dominating every other aircraft in the Show including the Soviet supersonic airliner, the Tu-144 Charger, the Mi-12, or V-12 as it is sometimes designated, was publicly unveiled at the Paris Air Show of 1971. Parked between it and the T-144 was an Mi-8 which was made to look positively insignificant and undersized although, as we have seen, it is bigger than the S-61. The Mi-12 Homer is the largest and heaviest helicopter ever to have flown in the world and it caused a sensation. Flown most of the way through bad weather by Vasily Koloshenko, holder of the title Hero of the Soviet Union, the route from Moscow entailed stops in Warsaw, Berlin, Copenhagen and Amsterdam before arrival at Le Bourget. Until its appearance at the Show not much was known of the machine beyond what could be derived from a few official photographs and some payload-to-altitude record claims made in 1969. It was further reported that year that Mikhail Mil had been awarded the Order of Lenin on his 60th birthday in November 1969 for his development of the helicopter, although the award was rather the culmination of his aeronautical achievements over a long and distinguished career. By this time, however, he was suffering gravely from cancer from which he was to die just two months later on 31 January, 1970. Marat Tishchenko took over Mil's post as Chief Designer of the Mil OKB and it was he who led the Mil design team in Paris.

While the Homer had an obvious military potential Mil OKB representatives said that it was designed as a civil venture to lift loads too heavy and bulky for the Mi-6 and Mi-10 in construction projects in the remoter regions of the USSR where surface transport was rudimentary or simply did not exist. But there is little doubt that in fact the principal reason for developing the Homer was to be able to deliver intercontinental ballistic missiles to their silos in secret; airlift was less likely than roads or rail to give away these locations. For the journey from the production plant to the nearest airstrip the huge Antonov An-22 Cock transport aircraft was built. The intention then was for the Homer to rendezvous with it and continue the carriage of the missile to the launch site. Thus the dimensions of the missile dictated the dimensions of the cargo holds of both the Cock and Homer which were identical but for the Homer's hold being 4.87 m (16 ft) shorter. The Cock first flew in 1965 and as the realisation that its performance on grass strips at the higher weights (maximum take-off weight is 250,000 kg, 551,155 lb and maximum payload 80,000 kg, 176,370 lb) was at best marginal so greater priority was given to the development of the Homer.

Besides the carriage of missiles, of course, the Homer would be able to lift the majority of equipments in the Soviet Ground Forces' inventory apart from the main battle tanks and some complete missile and rocket systems.

Design work on this helicopter began in 1965. Three basic configurations were

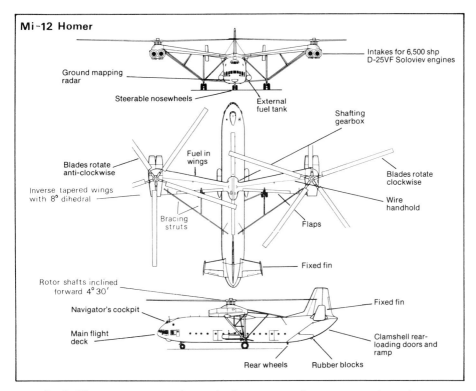

Mi-12 Homer

Intakes for 6,500 shp D-25VF Soloviev engines

Ground mapping radar

Steerable nosewheels

External fuel tank

Shafting gearbox

Blades rotate anti-clockwise

Fuel in wings

Blades rotate clockwise

Inverse tapered wings with 8° dihedral

Wire handhold

Bracing struts

Flaps

Fixed fin

Rotor shafts inclined forward 4° 30′

Fixed fin

Navigator's cockpit

Main flight deck

Clamshell rear-loading doors and ramp

Rear wheels

Rubber blocks

examined. These were a very large single rotor, tandem rotors or lateral rotors on outriggers or wings similar to the earlier Bratukhin designs. To minimise the technical risk the twin rotor designs were to use two modified Mi-6 rotor systems. According to Tishchenko, the general consensus of opinion appeared to favour the single rotor layout, but it was soon realised that it would be quite impossible to design a main rotor gearbox of reasonable size and weight.

The Mi-12 Homer, the largest helicopter ever built. (Brian Mackenzie)

113

A single rotor configuration would also mean the design and development of a completely new rotor system which would take time and money. Neither was available in sufficient quantities. Furthermore, to build a helicopter of the size envisaged with a single rotor very definitely involved a high technical risk. The tandem layout had its advantages but was eventually eliminated in favour of the lateral configuration since studies showed that payload/range would be better and that stability, reliability and fatigue life would all be enhanced. These benefits outweighed the major disadvantage of the low ratio of payload to take-off weight of the helicopter for normal operations which was about 1:4.

In describing Kamov's Ka-22 Hoop Mil had earlier written: "This machine recalled the great advantages of the side-by-side configuration in flying range and lift capacity with a running take-off which must be accounted for in a successful design." Mil recognised, however, that vertical take-off characteristics in a side-by-side configuration are not as good as with a tandem rotor due to greater loss of lift from rotor wash. In forward flight, on the other hand, or in a rolling take-off rate of climb is better.

One inherent problem in a side-by-side layout with engines and rotors mounted at the tips of the wings is the natural flexing and twisting of the wing in both vertical and horizontal planes. Unless controlled this may conflict with normal rotor-induced vibration. Ground resonance and considerable airframe vibration when close to the ground could result. The Mil OKB, in its efforts to keep these unwanted characteristics at bay, decided to keep the wings as light and small as possible while making them sufficiently strong and rigid in torsion and bending.

This side-by-side configuration is, to date, the only time that the Mil OKB has departed from its conventional single main and tail rotor layout.

Despite using as much of the Mi-6 rotor and dynamic systems as possible many problems confronted the design team. Considerable use was made of computers to help solve these design problems. The rotor diameter of the Mi-6 is 35 m (114 ft 10 in) and one question was whether the blades should extend over the fuselage or indeed overlap. In the event they did overlap by 1.5 m (4 ft 11 in). The rotor shafts were inclined forwards 4°30′ and the rotors themselves were cross-coupled by shafting within the wings and a gearbox in the top of the fuselage between the wings to ensure synchronisation and to maintain rotation if one or both engines on one side were to fail. Viewed from above the port rotor system rotated anti-clockwise; the starboard clockwise. After much discussion these directions were chosen for one simple, basic, reason: so that advancing blades should be over the fuselage. With their increased lift they would tend to rise above the fuselage thus decreasing the chances of them striking it. To cater for the length of the main rotor blades and the weight of the engines the so-called stub wings had to be long and strong (span from rotor tip to opposite tip was 67 m (219 ft 10 in) – a distance that exceeded the span of the Boeing 747 by 7.3 m (24 ft). Another problem therefore would be the amount of interference caused by this large wing in the rotor downwash. To reduce the interference to a minimum in the hover the all-metal stub wings were mounted at the top of the fuselage and increased in chord from root to tip. They were of aerofoil section with a high angle of attack and about 10° dihedral. They included two-part, fixed, trailing edge flaps. The wings were braced by a complex array of struts to the landing gear and fuselage and looked most unpleasing aerodynamically. However, given the configuration and weights involved, it was difficult to see what else could have been done. With speed relatively unimportant the drag penalty was probably acceptable. It is not known to what degree the wings off-loaded the rotors; a conservative estimate might be about 10%. The top of the wing had a wire guideline used as a handhold when walking along to the engines and rotor head. The wings contained the fuel tanks but the quantity of fuel is not known. One advantage to mounting the rotors and engines so far away on wings was the remarkably quiet and low vibration cabin. Rotor rpm were 112 with a maximum of 122 and at these speeds the Homer was significantly quieter than contemporary Western helicopters with their higher rotor rpm and disc loading.

The massive size of the Homer is not easily appreciated without physically seeing it. As photographs do no real justice to the Grand Canyon nor do they give a true impression of the immensity of this helicopter. A catalogue of dimensions only helps in a small way. The fuselage length was 37 m (121 ft 4½ in) – just 4.5 m (14 ft 9½ in) less than that of the Boeing 727-200 – with the square section cargo hold measuring 4.39 m (14 ft 5 in) high and wide and 28.14 m (92 ft 4 in) long. The machine had an overall height of 12.5 m (41 ft). The all-metal fuselage was of a semi-monocoque structure and had clamshell rear-loading doors and ramp. The doors, operated hydraulically, opened to the side allowing the ramp to swing down. On the undersurface of the ramp were two large rubber blocks to protect it from scraping along the ground. Along rails in the roof of the cargo section moved an electrically-operated crane which had four loading points, each with a capacity of 2,495 kg (5,500 lb). This system helped in loading and unloading and of course the arrangement of cargo within the hold. Between 50 and 60 folding seats could be placed on each side of it. Besides the clamshell rear doors a sliding door forward of the external fuel tank gave access to the hold. Two emergency exit doors, one on either side, were located at the rear of the hold. Strapped on to each side of the fuselage was an external fuel tank.

The nose section accommodated two air-conditioned cockpits for the normal crew of six. The lower had the large main flight deck with the pilot (port side) and co-pilot sitting side-by-side. The flight engineer sat behind the pilot and the electrical systems engineer behind the co-pilot. The upper cockpit, also offering excellent visibility, was for the navigator and behind him the radio operator. The pilots' panel was uncluttered and, if only in SSSR-21142 shown in Paris, somewhat basic. The navigator had a ground-mapping radar, housed in a small blister under the nose.

At each wing tip were mounted, as a pair, two Soloviev D-25VF turboshaft engines. These were similar to the Mi-6's engines but had been uprated to 6,500 shp by the inclusion of a zero stage on the compressor and by accepting higher operating temperatures. Maintenance work platforms could be created by hinging downwards the cowling side panels and hand cranking the bottom panels downwards about 1.8 m (6 ft). Thus no special ground equipment was necessary. An Ivchenko AI-8V APU was used for engine starting.

The tricycle landing gear was non-retractable with twin steerable nosewheels and twin main wheel units. The gear was stressed for rolling take-offs and landings. To protect the fuselage during such take-offs and landings two pairs of small tail wheels were attached to the rear fuselage.

It is understood that the tail unit was redesigned as a result of early troubles. It consisted of a conventional fin and rudder, dihedral tailplane and elevators. At the ends of the tailplane were small fixed fins, toed inwards.

The Homer was reportedly easy to fly with the help of automatic stabilisation; it could however be landed manually if need be. It would be interesting to know the autorotational characteristics of such a large helicopter in this configuration. No doubt considerable study was devoted to this aspect and in particular what effect the wings would have. It is possible that it was to improve these characteristics that the trailing edge flaps were fitted: to be able to reduce wing chord, and area, at will by moving them upwards when entering autorotation. For take-off, of course, they could be lowered to increase lift.

The first flight of the Homer took place on 10 July, 1968. Mystery surrounded this flight and various accounts were subsequently published; some, however, concerned the second prototype, not the first. This first-ever flight is thought to have been so short that it qualifies for the *Guinness Book of Records*. Sources differ but it is thought to have lasted less than 30 seconds and ended spectacularly. The starboard rotor system suffered damage and the landing gear on that side was substantially re-arranged. The second prototype is also believed to have crashed on its way back from the Paris Air Show – it is not known where. One or both engines on the same side failed and the machine landed heavily on its nose, fortunately with no serious injury to any of the crew.

Nevertheless, on 22 February, 1969 Koloshenko and a fellow test pilot, L. V. Vlasov, in the second prototype set five world records, a comparatively easy task in such a machine! Climbing at a rate of some 183 m (600 ft) per minute, a payload of 31,030 kg (68,409 lb) was lifted to 2,951 m (9,682 ft) and this broke the Hook's existing records for the maximum load to 2,000 m (6,562 ft) and for altitude attained with loads of 15,000, 20,000, 25,000 and 30,000 kg. On 6 August, 1969 Koloshenko, with a full crew of six, shattered his own record by taking the huge load of 40,204.5 kg (88,636 lb) to a height of 2,255 m (7,398 ft), thus setting three new records. The enormity of this payload may be judged from the fact that it was more than twice as heavy as the maximum take-off weight of any other helicopter in the world except for the Hook and Harke. These flights, of course, were for record purposes only. A more normal vertical take-off payload would have been perhaps 22,700–24,950 kg (50–55,000 lb); with a rolling take-off this might have been increased to 29,500 kg (65,000 lb). Even at a normal take-off weight of some 97,000 kg (213,850 lb) the Homer was considerably heavier than the Boeing 727-200 (86,410 kg, 190,500 lb) and the Lockheed C-130H Hercules (79,380 kg, 175,000 lb maximum overload) at take-off. For comparative purposes the C-130H had 4,050 eshp Allison turboprops and a payload of 20,410 kg (45,000 lb).

The Homer was expected to be present at the 1969 Paris Air Show but almost at the last moment the Russians said that it would not be possible due to the demands of the flight test programme – understandable, given the fact that one of only two prototypes had recently crashed although this fact was not mentioned. A prototype did, however, appear at the 1971 Show. One may only guess at the reason for its appearance. Not accompanied by the usual support facilities and marketing techniques normally associated with a vigorous sales campaign, it must be assumed that this was merely an exercise in boosting prestige and capturing headlines. The exercise succeeded.

The Homer has not been seen outside the Soviet Union since 1971. For some years thereafter it was not clear whether it had entered production or not. It had not and therefore, despite the records it had set, it must be adjudged a failure. The project was simply too ambitious – principally because the engines, despite offering 26,000 shp in all, were insufficiently powerful for the tasks demanded of them. Three or four machines only are thought to have been built. One was probably a ground test vehicle. It may be assumed that any available prototypes have been used for research during the last ten years.

Useful lessons will have been learned from the project: one was certainly to reinforce the belief that a single rotor system, whatever the size of the helicopter, is preferable, given the existence of a suitable transmission.

CHARACTERISTICS

Designation	**Mil Mi-12**
Engine	4 × Soloviev D-25VF
	4 × 6,500 shp
Rotor diameter	2 × 35.0 m (114 ft 10 in)
Fuselage length	37.0 m (121 ft 4½ in)
Height	12.5 m (41 ft 0 in)
Empty weight	63,500 kg (139,991 lb)
Max gross weight	105,000 kg (231,485 lb)
Max speed	260 kph (162 mph)
Range	500 km (311 mls) at 35,380 kg
	(78,000 lb) payload
Service ceiling	3,500 m (11,483 ft)
First flight	1968

The Mi-24 Hind:
the first Soviet attack
helicopter

In the early days of the German advance into the USSR in 1941 only the Ilyushin Il-2 *Shturmovik* (1) was able to make its presence felt in a ground attack role, being flown with great determination and courage. Again, at the battle of Stalingrad, this aircraft distinguished itself by its success against the German positions in and around the city. It was called 'Black Death' by the Germans and the 'Flying Tank' or 'Hunchback' by Russian troops. It was provided with considerable armour protection and was armed at different times with forward-firing cannon of 20 mm, 23 mm and 37 mm calibre and rockets which wreaked great havoc on German tanks. Both German and Soviet accounts of the fighting dwell on the exploits of the Il-2 which, like the German Ju 87 Stuka, has secured its place in the history and legends of war. The achievements and battlefield survivability of the *Shturmovik* are still recalled with pride today and the lessons learned have not been forgotten.

But when the fighting stopped new equipment priorities emerged and the *Shturmovik* gradually lost its pre-eminence. Spurred on by the fear that West Germany would not idly accept defeat but would soon begin to rearm, supported by the Western Allies, the Soviet Armed Forces were ordered to build up their air defence capability with particular emphasis on interceptor aircraft. This programme continued for many years, to some degree at the expense of close air support aircraft and helicopters, although resources were allocated to the MiG-17 Fresco for this role.

With the introduction of American helicopters, albeit mainly in the casualty evacuation role, into the Korean War a new machine of war was born. Its progress was closely monitored, yet in the Soviet Union at this time the helicopter was still regarded merely as a means of transportation. But the massive American exploitation of helicopters, particularly those that were armed, in Vietnam, where loss rates were remarkably low (2) in comparison with fixed-wing aircraft, much impressed Soviet analysts. The American experience, which was to prove very influential in the shaping of future Soviet helicopter tactical philosophy, and subsequent trials on both sides of the Iron Curtain, indicated that armed helicopters could play a significant part in the land battle – particularly if they were given some protection against small arms fire.

Western armies were the first to exploit the new potential of armed helicopters in the late 1950s. By strapping-on guns and rockets, the French in Algeria and the Americans in Vietnam gave themselves an armed capability. But even by 1965 it was realised that the Bell UH-1B was too slow and too lightly armed to fill the role of an effective gunship in Vietnam. With the introduction of the AH-1G Hueycobra to meet the requirement for a faster and more heavily armed helicopter the decisive step to a true attack helicopter was taken.

Only at about this time did Soviet Frontal Aviation begin to strap-on armaments to its troop-carrying helicopters. The Hare, Hound and Hip particularly were festooned with unguided rockets, machine guns, wire-guided anti-tank missiles and, later, bombs. On Exercise *Dnepr* in 1967 Hounds and Hips were used extensively in a close air support role against troop and tank concentrations. The frontier with China is some 7,000 km (4,350 miles) long and armed clashes took place in 1969 after some years of tension on the border. Soviet commanders were faced with the immense problem of concentrating their tanks at the critical points within a few hours. A 'flying tank', unconstrained by the terrain or minefields, heavily armed and with high speed, might be the answer: thus a new helicopter, designed from the start to take weapons and have some armour protection, rather than a utility helicopter with strap-on armaments.

These thoughts, given added force by the Viet Cong's belief that the armed helicopter constituted a threat greater than any other weapon system, spurred the decision to develop the Mi-24 Hind. It was a decision that represented a significant change in Soviet thinking both as far as the tactical employment of helicopters was concerned and also in design practice.

The design and development of a tandem two-seat dedicated attack helicopter in the mould of a Hueycobra may well have had some advocates including, it is thought, the Mil OKB. This proposal, however, was rejected in favour of a multi-role battlefield helicopter with integrated weapons. The primary role was to lift up to eight combat-equipped troops into defended areas using the helicopter's weapons to suppress enemy fire. The Hip could not cope with such a role and so what was needed was a less vulnerable helicopter with greater speed, better protection and more effective weapons.

It was probably in 1967 that serious development of the new armed assault helicopter began. The priority was high and progress was quick. Towards the end of 1971 three prototypes of the Hind were available for operational testing by which time concepts of employment and tactical procedures had become more refined due to the lessons learned by the use of other helicopters in these roles. The example of the Cobra in Vietnam during these years caught the imagination of Soviet planners and the assault transport role gradually became subordinate to a more aggressive close fire support role.

The new ideas, however, were more akin to those of the *Shturmovik* than to a helicopter with its hover and low speed capability. The high speed, diving attacks of the Cobras in Vietnam merely confirmed the desire of the Russians for such basically fixed-wing tactics. The Hind was not expected to use terrain as an aid to survival, but rather speed and armour. NATO helicopter pilots see the matter rather differently: an environment where, such is the density and lethality of modern weapons, helicopters are unlikely to survive unless at very low level. To enhance their prospects of survival, exposure to enemy fire must be kept to the minimum and this means making the best use of terrain features. To be able to do this hover and low speed performance are paramount. It could be argued that high speed in a battlefield helicopter is less important; agility, particularly forward acceleration and deceleration, lateral acceleration and vertical rate of climb from the hover, an essential characteristic. Nevertheless, there appeared in a Soviet military publication the following comment: "It (the Hind) is a typical rotary-wing aircraft at first sight. But at the same time it resembles a latest modification supersonic MiG. The resemblance is enhanced by short wings carrying special grips for on-board weapons . . . Everything about the aircraft points to its high speed characteristics, manoeuvrability and perfect aerodynamic shape."

To save time the Mil OKB adopted some of the design features, such as the same engines and transmission, of the Hip but of course were intent on improving certain characteristics necessary for a combat helicopter, in particular speed from the same power output.

Two distinct versions underwent more or less simultaneous development. The Hind-A was characterised by stub wings with pronounced anhedral whereas the B model's wings, like those of the Hook, had no anhedral or guided weapon rails at the tips. Nor did the latter model have a nose-mounted machine gun. The B model preceded the A, probably making its maiden flight in late 1969 or in early 1970; the few Bs built quickly went into a series of vigorous development and operational trials. A comparison of the performance of the different wing shapes was probably an important element of the trials of the two models. It was the A model, however, which began series production in 1972 at the Arsenyev and Rostov plants simultaneously. By the spring of 1974 the Hind-A reached the 16th Tactical Air Army, a part of the Group of Soviet Forces Germany (GSFG), stationed in East Germany. Two regiments were formed with about 45 Hinds in each together with the normal complement of Hips. The A model exceeded Soviet expectations as a battlefield helicopter and, with some modifications, its potential as a combat helicopter could readily be seen. It would inevitably suffer from certain drawbacks in this role as a result of the original requirement, large size and inadequate flight performance for example, but these were considered acceptable in the interests of saving time and money. The decision was thus taken to develop it into a dedicated, and even tougher, attack helicopter. A new model, designated the Hind-D with a completely redesigned front fuselage section began production in 1975. In 1976 it reached the Group of Soviet Forces Germany (GSFG) supplementing the two Hind-A regiments at Parchim and Stendal, west of Berlin. The export version of the Hind-D is sometimes known as the Mi-25.

NATO also has a reporting name of Hind-C, a version originally conceived for pure troop transport but now usually used for training with instructor and student pilot sitting side-by-side. Similar to the A model, the C has no nose gun nor wing-tip missile rails.

In late 1979 NATO designated a new Hind variant: the Hind-E. First seen on Moscow TV in 1977 and entering service in 1978, this model may be distinguished from the Hind-D by a different sensor package under the nose and different missile rails, allowing it to carry four of the new tube-launched AT-6 Spiral missiles. Its export version may be dubbed the Mi-35.

Yet another variant, the Hind-F, was seen during Exercise *Druzhba 82* (Friendship 82). Actually coming into service in 1980 or 1981, the F model (though not given that designation until 1986) sported a fixed twin-barrel 30 mm cannon mounted on the starboard side of the fuselage. In its issue 5 of 1987 the Soviet military magazine *Znamenosets* (Banner Carrier) published a picture of a new version of the Hind, the G model, with the wing-tip missile rails replaced by unidentified devices and other modifications.

Excellent photographs of all models published in the world's aviation Press now allow a comprehensive assessment of the Hind and its capabilities. Weights and performance figures, however, can be no more than approximate and speculation on other attributes is inevitable. It is to be hoped that some information gained as a result of the defection of two Afghan Hind-Ds to Pakistan in July 1985 and the capture of Libyan Hinds in Chad in 1987 will be released in due course.

All versions of the Hind that have appeared so far use the same airframe, transmission and main rotor system. Differences are obvious in the nose section, tail rotor, armaments fit and operational equipment. Because of their limited significance the B and C models will not be considered further.

The Hind's fuselage is of a conventional, all-metal, semi-monocoque structure of the pod-and-boom type with a heavy bulkhead frame behind the cockpit and four more main frames in the fuselage to carry the attachment points for the engines, main rotor

Mi-24 Hind-A

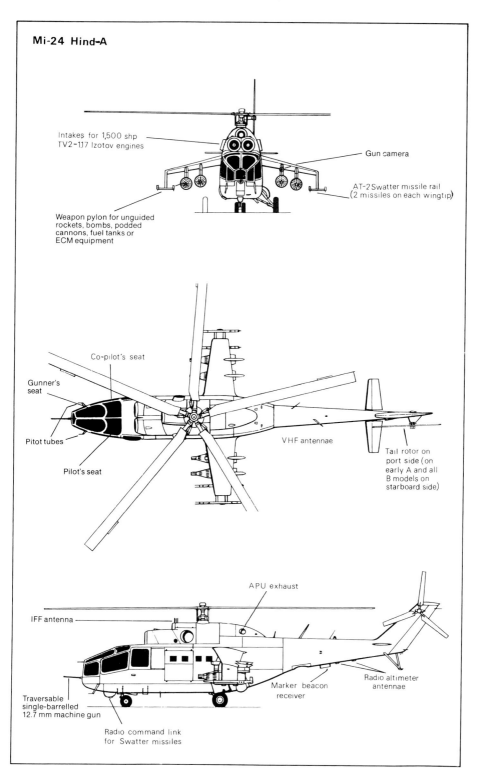

Intakes for 1,500 shp
TV2-117 Izotov engines

Gun camera

AT-2 Swatter missile rail
(2 missiles on each wingtip)

Weapon pylon for unguided
rockets, bombs, podded
cannons, fuel tanks or
ECM equipment

Co-pilot's seat

Gunner's
seat

Pitot tubes

Pilot's seat

VHF antennae

Tail rotor on
port side (on
early A and all
B models on
starboard side)

APU exhaust

IFF antenna

Radio altimeter
antennae

Marker beacon
receiver

Traversable
single-barrelled
12.7 mm machine gun

Radio command link
for Swatter missiles

121

The Mi-24 Hind-B has wings with no dihedral and only two weapon pylons; absent are the guided missile rails at the wing tips and the guidance pod under the cockpit.

gearbox, wings and undercarriage. Length of the fuselage is approximately 17 m (55 ft 9 in), somewhat longer than that of the Cobra or AH-64 Apache but some 1.2 m (3 ft 11 in) shorter than the Hip. Compared to the 91 cm (36 in) width of the Cobra, the Hind appears much broader but, even so, it is streamlined as far as Soviet helicopters go.

Because of its original assault transport role, and unlike the American attack helicopters, the fuselage contains a cabin which can accommodate eight battle-equipped troops or maybe ten passengers in a pure transport role, all very tightly packed. The interior of the cabin is believed to be only 1.22 m (4 ft) high which makes for very cramped conditions. Each of the eight cabin windows can be opened and each has a rifle clamp to assist the occupants in firing their personal weapons. There is a door on each side of the cabin, split so that the top half hinges upwards and the bottom half downwards. In the front cockpit of the A model sits the gunner behind a small-calibre bullet-proof windshield, very gently sloping to minimise optical distortion. Behind him sit side-by-side the pilot and co-pilot; and behind them the observer/crewchief.

Although the same fuselage has been retained, the D and later models are not intended to carry troops. The cabin area is, nevertheless, ideal for carrying a ferry tank, camouflage nets, crew kit and ancillary equipment, or extra ordnance in the shape of missiles, rockets or bombs. Readily apparent in these models are the completely redesigned nose sections which incorporate improved target acquisition and fire control systems and new weapons. The cockpit in the A model does not provide particularly good lookout for the flight crew. To cater for the change to a more aggressive role the opportunity was taken to rearrange the cockpit to improve visibility and enhance survivability by reducing the frontal profile and introducing armour protection. The Hind-D and later models have a two-man cockpit crew with the gunner sitting in front. Directly behind and at a higher level so that he has an unobstructed view forwards, sits the pilot. Both have individual canopies which are curved and flatplate windscreens which are almost certainly resistant to fire up to 12.7 mm calibre. An engineer who doubles as a crewchief is located in the cabin. Although the Hind has not been seen flying with its cabin doors open one of the two perspex windows is often removed, allowing the engineer to observe to the rear for flight safety or combat purposes.

One of the major areas for speculation since the appearance of the Hind has been the extent of armour protection provided for the crew and vital components. The Hind-A does not have much armour protection but the D and later models are thought to have an armoured undersurface and cockpit sides. Key components, such as the engines, fuel tanks, gearboxes, hydraulic and electrical systems, probably have some armour plating. In certain cases aluminium may well have been superseded by steel with titanium for the main rotor assembly.

Mounted level with the top of the cockpit and above the main landing gear are the tapered planform stub wings. With experience gained from the Hook, the Mil OKB examined in depth the use of wings on helicopters to augment lift and stability in forward flight, and extend the performance envelope. In this particular instance, by off-loading the rotor by perhaps as much as 25% at cruise speed and more at maximum speed, payload/range and speed can be raised and radius of turn reduced. The angle of incidence is about 18°, giving an angle of attack in forward flight of perhaps 2° or 3° – the minimum drag angle.

In the hover, however, the wings interfere in the rotor downwash and some lift is lost. To compensate for this about 16° of anhedral is built in to reduce the flat plate drag area and the wings are of minimum planform and maximum camber. Nevertheless, more power is needed and this leaves less available for acceleration. On each wing are mounted two pylons for carrying various armaments or fuel tanks and, at the tips, two rails for anti-tank missiles or other devices.

The swept fin, offset a few degrees, is mounted at the end of the tail boom. It is quite large, probably to reduce the power consumed by the tail rotor. In the early copies of the A model (and all the B models) the three-bladed tail rotor is mounted on the starboard side. But in 1976 later A models were seen to have the tail rotor transferred to the port side of the fin, becoming a 'puller' rather than a 'pusher' as in previous Mil designs. All models since have followed this example. This modification sought to improve yaw control by reducing interference to the airflow caused by the fin, which is much larger than the Hip's, and was further associated with the installation of new, more powerful, engines. The horizontal stabiliser is all-moving, being linked to the cyclic and collective to help provide the best fuselage/wing attitude. Below the fin is a protective tail skid.

Standard fuel carried by the Hind probably amounts to about 1,550 kg (3,417 lb). Two rubber tanks are located beneath the cabin floor, two collector tanks aft of the main rotor gearbox and one behind the cabin. Instead of carrying troops part of the cabin space may be used for a ferry tank that is left in place most of the time: whether it is filled or not would depend on range/endurance and armament load requirements. It would supplement the normal fuel load by perhaps another 1,200 kg (2,645 lb). The Hind does not use strap-on external fuel tanks – the first Soviet helicopter to dispense with this measure – as they would create extra and unwanted drag and, in any case, are not needed. Four drop tanks with a capacity of perhaps another 300 kg (660 lb) each can, however, be attached to the wing pylons. Such tanks, together with the ferry tank, give the Hind the ability to deploy self-contained over long distances – from the western parts of the Soviet Union into East Germany. It is highly likely that all these tanks are self-sealing.

The search for high speed and therefore streamlining has led to another Mil OKB innovation: retractable landing gear. The twin nose wheel unit and single main wheels all retract rearwards. They do not in fact fully retract into the fuselage. The nosewheels are still visible; fairly conspicuous blister fairings protect the main wheels which rotate rearwards and inwards into the aft end of the fuselage. Apart from the sleek shape of the Hind and the measures to reduce parasite drag noted above, the surface finish of the helicopter has been much improved to minimise skin friction drag. Performance is thus enhanced and fuel consumption decreased.

The articulated main rotor system was developed from that of the Mi-8 but it is of smaller diameter (17.3 m; 56 ft 9 in) and chord (58 cm; 1 ft 11 in) and has a higher rpm (240), enabling flight speeds thereby to be higher. The five blades with aluminium spars, honeycomb-filled sections and glassfibre skins have flapping and drag hinges, drag dampers, and automatic droop stops. This rotor system should be relatively insensitive to turbulence and give a relatively low vibration level but response to control inputs is slower than with semi-rigid or rigid rotor systems. TV films have shown that in the hover the rotor downwash causes a significant signature from dust clouds and blowing leaves. This strong downwash also would make hovering close to trees most uncomfortable. The rotor head is made of titanium. Electrical de-icing is built into the blade leading edges and into those of the three aluminium alloy tail rotor blades. According to Lev Chaiko, a fenestron tail rotor with more than 12 small blades built into the fin was designed for the Mi-24 along with the tail rotor actually adopted. Anti-icing for the engine air intakes is achieved by re-routing warm air from the compressor.

A Czechoslovak Mi-24 Hind-D. The redesigned front fuselage section and the tail rotor on the port side of the fin clearly distinguish the D model from earlier models.

To speed development and reduce risk Tishchenko elected to use the well-tried engine and dynamic components of the Mi-8. Mounted side-by-side above the cabin, two 1,500 shp Izotov TV2-117 turboshaft engines powered the first A and B models. It was soon realised that the power available was insufficient, particularly in hot and high conditions and at low speed and in the hover. Thus later A and subsequent models were given the 2,200 shp Izotov TV3-117, not an uprated version of the TV2-117 but a completely new engine. All models from the D onwards sport engine air intake debris guards probably to prevent the ingestion of foreign objects, sand and ice that may form and later fly off the cockpit canopies. Both TV2 and TV3 turboshafts are certainly very reliable, flat-rated to altitude, and, although rather heavier and less fuel-efficient than comparable Western engines, run at lower turbine entry temperatures. Exhaust gas temperatures are therefore lower with a consequently reduced infra-red (IR) signature. This is further reduced by the installation of box-like suppressors over the engine exhausts – as seen for example on some Hinds in Nicaragua and in Afghanistan. Above and between the engines is the cooling air intake to cool the main gearbox oil and paradoxically to prevent ice forming on the main rotor head. The large capacity of this intake suggests that it may also be used to lower the temperature of the surrounding hot metal and the engine exhaust plume which also helps to reduce the IR signature, and to prevent hot spots. Inside the fairing to the rear of the rotor is mounted an APU for engine starting.

For a battlefield helicopter the Hind is rather large with the consequent penalties of a large radar signature and loss of agility at low speed. It is 3.97 m (13 ft 3 in) high and has a side aspect 25% greater than that of the AH-64; frontal area is, however, only 2% greater although the Hind's wingspan is 1.34 m (4 ft 5 in) longer at 6.57 m (21 ft 7 in). Its engines are unexpectedly noisy. Its disruptive pattern camouflage is quite effective but it is still prone to acquisition visually, aurally and on radar, if not so much by IR devices. But by being large the Hind has the payload capacity to carry some armour

A Libyan Mi-25 Hind-D captured at Ouadi-Doum airfield, Chad in March 1987.

plating and other survivability measures thus lessening its overall vulnerability. The antennae for the passive radar warning receiver can be seen on the wing end plates facing forwards and to the rear on the outboard pylons. 360° coverage is thereby achieved.

Photographs have been published showing later model Hinds, even ones in Nicaragua, with what appears to be an IR jammer mounted on a plinth on top of the rear part of the cabin. The beacon emits modulated IR energy several times greater than that of the Hind itself, thus producing false information as to the real position of the helicopter and confusing the IR seeker in the attacking missile. A chaff or flare dispenser pack has been seen strapped below the tail boom just forward of the tail skid. If the Press reports are anything to go by these devices to counter heat-seeking missiles have not been particularly successful against the American Stinger missile in Afghanistan but more effective against the Russians' own SA-7 missiles. Other measures to enhance survivability include bullet-proof canopies for the separate cockpits, duplicated flight controls in both cockpits, systems redundancy and IFF. The distinctive aerials of the Odd Rods IFF or sometimes a small fin IFF antenna have been positioned above the root of the low airspeed probe and below the tail fin. The main and tail rotor systems are possibly the most vulnerable parts of the Hind but in general terms this helicopter is probably more or less immune to 7.62 mm calibre fire and can accept a degree of 12.7 mm fire. Its own weapons have a major defensive role besides their more obvious aggressive purposes.

At the top of the starboard corner of the gunner's windscreen in the D and later models is a conspicuous probe, or air data sensor, used for measuring the helicopter's attitude in pitch, roll and yaw at low airspeed. Such information is fed into the fire control computer, principally to help when firing unguided rockets at these speeds or when in the hover. Some D and all later models have moveable vanes on their probes.

In the nose of the A model is a single-barrelled, flexibly-mounted 12.7 mm machine gun which has a probable maximum effective range of between 1,000 and 1,500 metres and a high rate of fire. In the D and E models, however, there is a massive turret under the nose which contains a stabilised four-barrel Gatling-type gun of 12.7 mm calibre, specially designed for the Hind. The gun's azimuth range is about 70° either side of the direction of flight and it may be depressed to -60° and elevated to about +15°; it can undoubtedly be fixed in the forward position for the pilot to fire. It is a high velocity gun with a very high rate of fire of about 4,000 rounds a minute and a maximum range, one may estimate, of about 1,500 metres. The ammunition drum contains some 1,500 armour-piercing or high explosive incendiary rounds. During Exercise *Druzhba-82* a few Hinds appeared with a fixed twin-barrel cannon mounted on the starboard side of the fuselage instead of the nose-mounted four-barrel gun. The calibre of the twin cannon was hard to assess but most experts now agree that it is 30 mm. Obvious advantages are increased range, to a likely effective maximum of 2,000 metres, and destructive power but the fixed installation means that the entire helicopter must align itself with the target before opening fire, a manoeuvre which could take precious seconds.

Under the nose of the A model is a small pod which incorporates the radio command link antenna for the Swatter missiles. This antenna is housed in a small pod, able to rotate horizontally, on the port side of the undernose turret in the D model; in the E and F models this pod is fixed, is longer and larger, and is located slightly further forward and outboard. The bigger fixed pod to starboard has armoured hinged doors in the D model and sliding doors in the E and F models. This pod probably contains stabilised optics with two different magnifications for target acquisition and tracking purposes and an IR goniometer for missile tracking. This pod is not thought to contain night

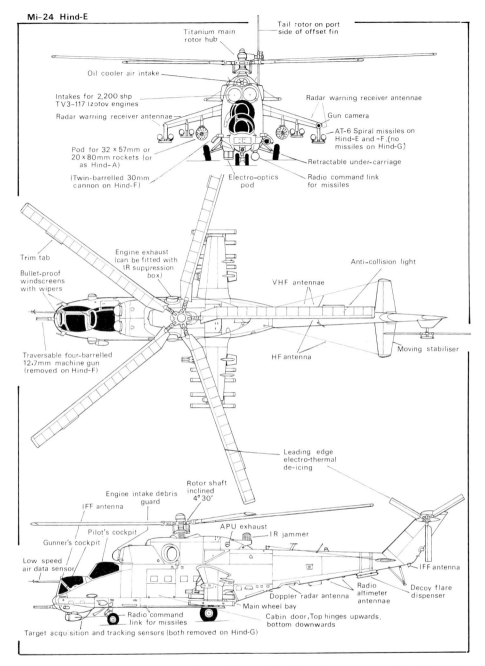

Tail rotor on port
side of offset fin

Titanium main
rotor hub

Oil cooler air intake

Intakes for 2,200 shp
TV3-117 Izotov engines

Radar warning receiver antennae

Radar warning receiver antennae

Gun camera

AT-6 Spiral missiles on
Hind-E and -F,(no
missiles on Hind-G)

Pod for 32 × 57mm or
20 × 80mm rockets (or
as Hind-A)

(Twin-barrelled 30mm
cannon on Hind-F)

Electro-optics
pod

Retractable under-carriage

Radio command link
for missiles

Trim tab

Engine exhaust
(can be fitted with
IR suppression
box)

Anti-collision light

VHF antennae

Bullet-proof
windscreens
with wipers

Traversable four-barrelled
12·7mm machine gun
(removed on Hind-F)

HF antenna

Moving stabiliser

Leading edge
electro-thermal
de-icing

Rotor shaft
inclined
4° 30'

Engine intake debris
guard

IFF antenna

APU exhaust

IR jammer

Pilot's cockpit

Gunner's cockpit

Low speed
air data sensor

IFF antenna

Decoy flare
dispenser

Radio
altimeter
antennae

Doppler radar antenna

Main wheel bay

Radio command
link for missiles

Cabin door,Top hinges upwards,
bottom downwards

Target acquisition and tracking sensors (both removed on Hind-G)

vision devices, the Hind usually using rockets to illuminate its targets at night. The sight
in the starboard pod is very close to the ground which means that practically the whole
aircraft has to expose itself above cover before the gunner has an uninterrupted view
through it. In Western circles this is considered to be a tactical shortcoming (3).
Initially this was immaterial for the Hind because it relied more on speed than stealth to
execute its attacks; technical rather than tactical considerations therefore dictated the

127

A Nicaraguan Mi-25 Hind-D. Of particular note are the infra-red jammer just above the roundel, the flare dispenser strapped below the aft end of the tailboom and the 23 mm gun pod on the inner pylon.

location of the sight. Now, however, as Hind crews adopt more frequently the Western technique of hovering or moving slowly forward behind cover and then ascending to observe and fire, they are more vulnerable. In the G model, which carries no anti-tank missiles, both pods have been removed; however, a new cylindrical pod can be seen under the fuselage on the port side about as far back as the pilot. Its purpose and that of the G model itself is unknown; although seen in the open Press fitted with rocket pods, it is likely to have a less aggressive role than that of the D, E and F models. As Soviet TV revealed it at Chernobyl it may be associated with nuclear radiation monitoring.

With greater emphasis now being placed on flight at low level the need for a tactical navigation aid or moving map display, and good target acquisition and tracking devices becomes more pronounced. In the Hind the pilot has a moving map display. As increasingly sophisticated close air support aircraft the Hind-D, E and F may be expected to incorporate many features to aid accurate weapons delivery and even to have systems to be found in the more modern Soviet tactical fixed-wing aircraft. *Soviet Military Power* 1983 (4) included an excellent head-on view of a Hind-E in which the rocket and gun sight could be seen quite clearly in the pilot's cockpit.

The later models of the Hind must have at least three computers for navigation, gun-aiming, and rocket and bomb delivery. The crew are also aided by the helicopter's four-axis autopilot and instrumentation in both cockpits. On the A model the gun camera is mounted at the top of the inboard pylon on the port wing; in the D, E and some F models it adorns the port wing tip. Other F models and the G model, however, seem to have had the installation removed. Externally visible antennae indicate the installation of a Doppler radar driving the moving map, two radar altimeters, HF, VHF and UHF radios.

All A, D, E and F models can carry a heavy weapons load, estimated at up to about

750 kg (1,653 lb) on each wing. On the two pylons on each side may be mounted a variety of stores: two UB-16 or UB-32 57 mm rocket pods, each holding 16 or 32 unguided rockets respectively and which are capable of penetrating up to 200 mm (8 in) of armour. The effective range of these rockets is estimated to be about 1,200 metres. They may have any selection of warheads such as high explosive (HE), HE anti-tank (HEAT), illumination and so on. Larger calibre rockets can also be fitted. The 80 mm, the pod for which carries 20 rockets, is being installed more frequently. Alternatively, each of the four pylons can carry a variety of stores to give an enviable flexibility to cater for most targets: a general purpose, fragmentation or cluster 250 kg (550 lb) bomb, a twin-barrelled 23 mm cannon in a pod (although no great accuracy can be expected), maybe an air defence suppression or air-to-air missile, or a fuel drop tank.

On two rails at each wing-tip can be attached two anti-tank missiles. On the Hind-A and D these are usually AT-2 Swatter-C with a maximum range of 4,000 metres and said to be capable of penetrating up to 500 mm (20 in) or so of armour under ideal conditions. Introduced in the late 1960s, for launch from ground vehicles, they were subsequently adapted for helicopter use. Unlike the wire-guided systems of the West, radio-command guidance is used. The obvious advantage of a wire link is that it is more or less immune to countermeasures but its major disadvantages are that missile range and speed are limited due to the weight and length of wire required and the need to unwind it very quickly from the back of the missile. Swatter-B/C has a semi-automatic command to line-of-sight, known as SACLOS, guidance system which means that, for the missile to achieve a hit, the gunner has only to maintain the sight's cross-hairs on the centre of the target.

The Hind-E and F normally carry four AT-6 Spiral missiles on H frames at the wing tips although more can be installed on the outboard pylons. These missiles, which entered service in about 1975, are tube-launched, SACLOS radio-command guided

Two East German Mi-24 Hind-Ds in formation. Note the exceptionally good view for both crew members.

and have a reported range of about 5,000 metres which they can reach in about ten seconds.

Visual acquisition of targets at such a range will rarely be easy and some degradation of missile accuracy – if only visual tracking of the target is possible – is inevitable. Films indicate quick acceleration off the launcher and a flight speed significantly faster than that of the Swatter. In addition there is less flame at launch and armour penetration must be better. So far the Spiral is the only Soviet missile specifically designed for helicopter use – but it is unlikely to be the last. The next may well have characteristics similar to those of the American Hellfire anti-armour missile: a fire-and-forget missile with a laser seeker and capable of direct and indirect fire.

It would be reasonable to expect that the gunner in the D and E models has at least separate sights for the 12.7 mm machine gun and the anti-tank missiles. It may be assumed, therefore, that he is responsible for acquiring targets and engaging them with the gun in the flexible mode or with missiles and for helping to navigate and look out for enemy threats. The pilot flies and navigates the helicopter using the moving map display and, with help from data from the various sensors and computers and a simple sight, fires the rockets, the gun in the fixed mode and releases the bombs. In the F model it is the pilot who probably fires the 30 mm cannon.

The Hind's flight performance and weights are a matter of conjecture and only estimates may be given. Designed for high speed flight, maximum speed at sea level is thought to be about 335 kph (208 mph) and cruise speed about 295 kph (183 mph). Maximum vertical take-off weight is assessed at about 11,500 kg (25,353 lb) and combat weight is likely to be between 11,000 kg (24,250 lb) and 11,500 kg. At the higher figure about 3,000 kg (6,614 lb) of fuel and armaments may be carried. For rolling take-offs maximum weight could be as much as 12,000 kg (26, 455 lb). The extra 500 kg (1,102 lb) of useful load available could be taken up with more fuel or a different combination of armaments; possibly some weapon reloads in the cabin. It is almost certainly true that the Hind's hover and low speed performance is better than originally thought. It was considered then that the helicopter was quite severely limited in this flight regime but this assessment has given way to the view that the Hind can hover with a full fuel and armaments load at least in average European conditions of wind, temperature and altitude. However stability is likely to be poor due to the rotor downwash over the stub wings. Vertical rate of climb from the hover at this weight is estimated to be about 150 m (500 ft)/min. Radius of action and mission time are estimated at about 160 km (99 miles) and some two hours with a weapons load comprising four missiles, four rocket pods with 80 or 128 rockets and full ammunition load for the machine gun or 30 mm cannon.

The Hind-D is clearly an attack helicopter, albeit not purpose-designed, while the E and F models could be classed as low speed ground attack fighters. The A model should probably be seen as an armed assault and anti-tank helicopter, supplementing the Mi-8 Hip. The Hind-A is now obsolescent and is no longer to be found in Soviet forces deployed in East Europe although it may well be present in other parts of the world.

It is clear that the Hind is a most versatile helicopter and its roles can be summarised as armed assault, anti-tank, close air support and anti-helicopter. Most of its weapons can be used for both air-to-ground and air-to-air attack although they are more effective in the former. While some foreign countries which operate the Hind may use it in the armed assault role it is used most sparingly by the Russians in this manner. The A, D, E and F models are all effective in the anti-tank role; attacks, however, would not be confined to tanks but would also include all kinds of armoured fighting vehicles with mobile air defence systems a high priority. Not only can the Hind carry four anti-tank missiles and up to 128 rockets with HEAT warheads (the Hind-E and F more missiles at the expense of rockets) but also, instead of some of the wing armaments, ground-based teams equipped with manportable anti-tank missiles. Hinds have a leading role in supporting *desant* operations by providing an armed escort and laying down suppressive fire around the landing zones. Other close support tasks include observation and protection of the flanks of an advance and on-call fire support to advancing armour. The use of bombs, particularly in a strong air defence environment such as Europe, will presumably be infrequent since their application necessitates overflying the target which should make the helicopter itself a comparatively easy target. Suppressive fire would probably be needed first. Elsewhere, participating in 'Wars of Liberation' or in 'peace-keeping' operations, Hinds could achieve a certain psychological effect against lightly-armed opposition with the use of bombs. These have certainly been used to considerable effect in Afghanistan. With its speed, armour protection and armament the Hind could be employed in air-to-air combat but its size, weight and manoeuvrability would impose limitations.

Countering enemy airmobile operations is an important element of this role as is the engagement of enemy anti-tank helicopters opposing an armoured advance. If it is to be specially tasked to seek and engage enemy helicopters then it might well be armed with some new air-to-air missile designed purely for helicopters. In giving the Hind a high speed the designers have accepted relatively poor low speed handling qualities. This would be a serious disadvantage if the Hind were to become embroiled in close range, highly manoeuvering air-to-air combat. Not only might it not be able to get itself into a position to fire on its adversary but it could find itself outperformed and either shot down or crash out of control.

The Russians also write of suppresssing surface-to-air missile sites. This would, however, involve deep penetration of enemy-held territory and thus presumably would not be undertaken lightly or without fixed-wing aircraft support. It should be noted that Hinds also played a role, monitoring radiation and chemical levels, in the aftermath of the Chernobyl disaster; according to details published in *Red Star*, one Hind apparently made some 50 flights in a single day. The Hind enjoys flexibility and versatility not matched by any other Soviet weapon system. Therefore many a commander will be tempted to hold a proportion of those available to him as a significant component of his mobile reserve able to respond quickly and intervene anywhere on the battlefield.

According to the *Military Balance* 1987/88 1,080 operational Hinds of all models are in service in the Soviet Air Forces. Perhaps some 2,500 have been built so far and production is continuing. The production rate at its peak was thought to have been close to one Hind a day but this has probably now slackened off to one every two days or so, or about 200 machines a year. D models have in most cases being upgraded to the E standard and some Es to the F standard. All the member states of the Warsaw Pact, less Romania, operate the Hind and these countries are also in the process of converting their D models into Es as well as equipping them with some of the devices already noted to aid survivability. The number of Third World countries to have received the Hind is growing and this helicopter is now to be found in Central America, Africa, the Middle East and Asia, in addition to Europe.

Some 14 Third World countries are now the proud possessors of some Hinds. Those belonging to Afghanistan, Angola, Ethiopia, Iraq, Libya, Mozambique, Nicaragua, Syria and Vietnam have all seen combat action although details have been scarce. In the hands of the Iraqis they have allegedly made some impact on the fighting – at least to the extent that 27 October is marked as the 'Day of Helicopter Gunships'. Encounters between Iraqi Hinds and Iranian Cobras have been infrequent and probably by chance. The achievements of Libyan Hinds in the fighting against Chad

An Hungarian Mi-24 Hind-E at the Budapest Air Display in 1986. Besides the IR jammer and flare dispenser it is also possible to see brackets below the exhaust for the installation of a suppressor. Also visible, just are the Spiral missile rails on the outer pylons, thus allowing this aircraft to carry eight of these missiles.

and Angolan Hinds (flown mainly by Cubans and East Germans) against the Unita guerrillas apparently have been negligible – due largely, it is presumed, to the lack of expertise of the crews. Cuban pilots are also said to have been flying Nicaraguan Hinds, at least in the first months after the initial delivery in late 1984. In Nicaragua, the Sandinistas have formed special forces battalions which operate in conjunction with Mi-8 and Mi-17 Hips and Mi-25 Hinds to make co-ordinated attacks on Contra rebel positions. A small number has been lost to Contra fire.

Soviet Hinds participated in the invasion of Afghanistan in late December 1979 and have been used in significant numbers ever since. Unless they concentrate to attack a Soviet and Afghan government target the Mujahideen are so inaccessible in their mountains that aircraft are the only means, apart occasionally from heavy artillery and

A pair, the standard grouping, of Mi-24 Hind-E dive onto their targets while another pair turn away having completed their task.

132

The smooth nose and twin-barrelled 30 mm cannon mounted on the starboard fuselage denote the Mi-24 Hind-F.

A Mi-24 Hind-F in Afghanistan. The flash eliminator on the cannon are conspicuous.

special forces, by which they can be attacked. Fast jet aircraft have found it difficult to manoeuvre in the mountains and so very often it has been left to the Hinds and armed Hips to attack the guerrillas whenever they can be found. And there is no doubt that the tribesmen fear aircraft more than any other equipment used against them. Indeed, it is probably true to say that the Hind is the most flexible and effective, and the most feared, weapon system in Afghanistan. It was the achievements of the Hind that prompted the Mujahideen to ask for Stinger and Blowpipe shoulder-launched SAMs and there is little doubt that these have been successful in bringing down some Soviet and Afghan helicopters, forcing a change in tactics and encouraging the installation of devices to counter these missiles. Very often now, Hinds fly very low or very high, both of which reduce vulnerability to SAMs, but increase it to machine gun fire at low level. An earlier modification to Hind tactics had been to operate sometimes in groups of three rather than pairs or two pairs. Two of the aircraft remain at low level, mutually supporting each other, and being directed by the third which stands off much higher out of small arms range observing the sources of ground fire. If one is shot down, a second Hind can land nearby in an attempt to rescue the crew while the third gives covering fire. Such small groups have sometimes been concentrated into larger formations of up to 15 or more helicopters to attack certain targets. As the British and French discovered during various desert wars rocket fire is particularly effective for shooting into caves.

The roles of the Hind in Afghanistan contain no surprises: general fire support, escorting vehicle convoys and other helicopters involved in airborne assaults, patrolling overhead routes and base camps, bombing and strafing tribal villages, destroying crops, attacking Mujahideen groups whenever found, casualty evacuation under fire, and armed reconnaissance and observation before a Soviet or Afghan cordon and search operation or attack begins. The complete range of Hind weaponry is used. Since the range and explosive power of the 57 mm rockets have not always been equal to the task 80 mm and even larger calibres have sometimes been employed.

Action in Afghanistan where Soviet helicopters are operating in extreme climatic

A formation of Mi-24 Hind-F helicopters. They are all carrying a fuel tank on the inner pylon.

A Mi-24 Hind-G, first seen at Chernobyl. Note the device at the wing tips in place of the missile rails.

conditions, both in winter and summer, has apparently led to a refreshing degree of improvisation. It is likely that some equipment judged to be superfluous has been removed, and local modifications incorporated. Some Press reports have indicated that a machine gun has been installed in the cabin floor with the barrel facing downwards and to the rear. Like all other helicopters it may be expected that the Hind's engines are susceptible to erosion of the turbine blades because of the very dusty conditions in Afghanistan. Apart from the increased maintenance there is also a danger of loss of power. In mountainous terrain often above 1,800 m (6,000 ft), and in temperatures above 25°C (77°F), any loss of power, even in one engine can be critical. In such an eventuality Soviet Hind pilots have few options. No doubt time in the hover is kept to a minimum to try and avoid stirring up clouds of sand which adversely affect rotor blades and may clog up other moving parts, particularly those of machine guns.

We may expect to see Hinds appear in more and more countries around the world. They are certain to continue as the backbone of the Warsaw Pact attack helicopter fleet until well into the 1990s. In the words of the late Marshal Grechko, Minister of Defence until his death in April 1976, the Russians have developed "a powerful combat aircraft which can carry out a broad range of missions, including hitting enemy personnel and equipment on the battlefield and in the enemy rear. . . ." The Afghan Mujahideen have been quoted as describing the Hind as a 'flying tank' – a *Shturmovik 2* – and, more graphically, the 'Devil's Chariot'.

It is indeed a formidable machine. It has been continually upgraded and there is no reason to suppose that it will not benefit from further modifications. It has proved itself in combat in various trouble spots around the world. More than just a fast-moving platform carrying a comprehensive array of armaments, it has mightily impressed its opponents who have quickly learned to respect its capabilities and fear its firepower.

135

For operations on the Central Front in Europe doctrine and tactics are assuredly under constant review. New concepts on the tactical co-operation between advancing armour and attack helicopters may emerge; its capabilities in the defence and in adverse weather and darkness will not be neglected.

While the effectiveness of the Hind has not been tested against sophisticated opposition it could certainly be argued that the deployment of several hundred Soviet and Warsaw Pact D and later models in Eastern Europe represents a small but significant change in the tactical military balance in favour of the Warsaw Pact. It would be wiser perhaps to think of the Hind-E and F now as modern V/STOL day/night close air support aircraft rather than as attack helicopters. The distinction may be subtle but it may open the mind to the potential capabilities of the Hind.

During July and August 1975 a female crew flying what was reported to be a Mil A-10 claimed two general and six female world records. Details are to be found in Appendix 3. The A-10 has since been confirmed as an Mi-24, stripped down for record attempt purposes. The crew in all records consisted of Galina Rastorgueva and Ludmila Polyanskaya, an Aeroflot navigator. On 21 September, 1978 an Mi-24/A-10, powered by two 2,200 shp TV3-117 engines, set a new absolute world speed record for helicopters: a speed of 368.4 kph (228.9 mph) was achieved over a 15/25 km (9.32/15.53 miles) course by Gurgen Karapetyan. (5)

Notes

1. Sometimes known as the BSh-2 (*Bronirovannyi Shturmovik-2*, Armoured Attack Aircraft) or *Ilyusha*, this aircraft is believed to have been produced in greater numbers than any other aircraft in the world; 36,163 are thought to have been built. *Shturmovik* is a generic term used to describe any low level ground attack aircraft.

2. Between 1 January, 1962 and 31 December, 1972, for example, 13,477,430 hours were flown by helicopters in Vietnam. They were hit 31,170 times by ground fire but only 5,604 helicopters were shot down. Of these only 2,033 were lost, the balance of 3,571 being recovered and repaired. Thus one helicopter was shot down and lost every 6,629 flying hours. The French Army in Algeria lost one helicopter to ground fire every 9,250 flying hours.

3. The American Cobra has its sight in the nose as does the AH-64 Apache. The British Lynx/TOW has the same sight as the Cobra but it is located in the roof of the cockpit. It is recognised, however, that for tactical purposes the best place for a sight, laser rangefinder/designator and so on is above the mast. Many manufacturers are now working on mast-mounted sights.

4. *Soviet Military Power* was originally a report prepared by the Pentagon for issue to NATO officials. It has since been declassified and issued to the Press as an annual analysis of the Soviet Union's Armed Forces.

5. This record was finally broken on 11 August 1986 when a Westland Lynx achieved a speed of 400.87 kph (249.09 mph).

CHARACTERISTICS

Designation	**Mil Mi-24 (Hind-E)**	**Bell AH-1F***
Engine	2 × Izotov TV3-117	Lycoming T53-L-703
	2 × 2,200 shp	1,800 shp
Rotor diameter	17.3 m (56 ft 9 in)	13.41 m (44 ft 0 in)
Fuselage length	17.0 m (55 ft 9 in)	13.59 m (44 ft 7 in)
Height	3.97 m (13 ft 3 in)	4.12 m (13 ft 6¼ in)
Empty weight	8,400 kg (18,519 lb)*	2,993 kg (6,598 lb)
Max gross weight	11,500 kg (25,353 lb)	4,536 kg (10,000 lb)
Max speed	335 kph (208 mph)	227 kph (141 mph)****
Range	600 km (373 mls)?	507 km (315 mls)*****
Service ceiling	4,480 m (14,700 ft)	3,660 m (12,000 ft)
First flight	1969?**	1979

Designation	**McDonnell Douglas AH-64**
Engine	2 × GE T700-GE-701
	2 × 1,696 shp
Rotor diameter	14.63 m (48 ft 0 in)
Fuselage length	14.97 m (49 ft 1½ in)
Height	4.22 m (13 ft 10 in)
Empty weight	4,881 kg (10,761 lb)
Max gross weight	9,525 kg (20,999 lb)
Max Speed	296 kph (184 mph)******
Range	482 km (300 mls)
Service ceiling	6,400 m (20,997 ft)
First flight	September 1975

---

* Operating empty weight less crew
** Hind-A; first flight of Hind-D 1974; of Hind-E 1977; of Hind-F 1980
*** Previously designated as Modernised AH-1S
**** With TOW missiles carried
***** With 8% fuel reserves
****** At 6,552 kg (14,444 lb) take-off weight

A Halo
for the Communists

Virtually two years to the day after it first lifted into the hover in December 1977, the existence of the Mi-26 Halo was revealed by the Soviet Press. It was by then entirely predictable that a replacement for the Mi-6 Hook, first flown in September 1957, was forthcoming. But it was not until June 1981 that a pre-production version (SSSR 06141) of the machine was unveiled for the first time in the West at the Paris Air Show. Many months of intrigued speculation could then give way to a comparatively detailed inspection of the helicopter. This opportunity was seized all the more avidly perhaps because it was ten years since a new helicopter, the Mi-12 Homer, had been exhibited at Paris.

According to the Mil design bureau the Soviet government ordered the development of a new heavy lift helicopter in 1970 to assist in the exploration for, and exploitation of, natural resources in the wastelands of Siberia and Central Asia. A requirement to lift heavy oil drilling and construction equipment into areas beyond provincial airports and railheads was stated. An analysis indicated that this equipment would often consist of outsize cargoes of between 15,000 and 20,000 kg (33,069 and 44,092 lb) which could not be broken down into smaller components or 20 tonne ISO containers; these cargoes would have to be carried over distances up to 800 km (497 miles) and be loaded or unloaded at heights up to 1,500 m (4,920 ft) above mean sea level. The possibility that the new helicopter might have military applications was studiously ignored and it was not until the second half of 1983 that public admission of a military role appeared in the form of photographs in Soviet military magazines. It is now known that the military requirement was at least as important as the civil requirement, a helicopter able to lift the 12,700 kg (28,000 lb) BMP infantry fighting vehicle, its crew and ammunition, being sought.

Given these requirements, and a decree that the empty weight should represent no more than 50% of the maximum take-off weight, Marat Tishchenko, who had taken over the OKB when Mikhail Mil had died on 31 January 1970, was faced with a daunting problem: starting with known cargo hold dimensions, useful payload and weight ratios, he had to design and develop what would be the biggest helicopter ever to go into production. Furthermore, given that it would often be operating in the Siberian wilderness low fuel consumption, robustness, a day/night adverse weather capability and a very high degree of reliability would be major factors. Although technical risk would be inevitable in trying to minimise structure weight, tried and tested technology would be preferable to the use of advanced technology.

Initially three configurations were studied: single rotor, tandem rotors and side-by-side rotors. The latter was quickly rejected but work continued with the first two. A tandem rotor configuration seemed to offer a good solution: the diameter of the main

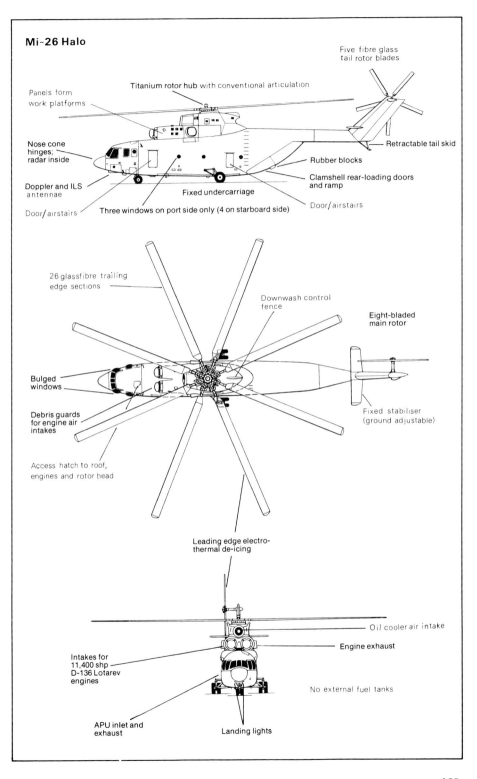

Mi-26 Halo

Five fibre glass tail rotor blades

Titanium rotor hub with conventional articulation

Panels form work platforms

Retractable tail skid

Nose cone hinges; radar inside

Rubber blocks

Clamshell rear-loading doors and ramp

Doppler and ILS antennae

Fixed undercarriage

Door/airstairs

Door/airstairs

Three windows on port side only (4 on starboard side)

26 glassfibre trailing edge sections

Downwash control fence

Eight-bladed main rotor

Bulged windows

Debris guards for engine air intakes

Fixed stabiliser (ground adjustable)

Access hatch to roof, engines and rotor head

Leading edge electro-thermal de-icing

Oil cooler air intake

Engine exhaust

Intakes for 11,400 shp D-136 Lotarev engines

No external fuel tanks

APU inlet and exhaust

Landing lights

rotors needed to be no more than 28 m (91 ft 10 in), each main rotor gearbox would have to transmit only 10,000 hp and the complications associated with a large tail rotor would not arise. After some study, however, and no doubt reference to the design of the Mi-12, it was decided that such a helicopter would be more complex, heavier and more susceptible to vibration than a conventional helicopter with a single main and tail rotor. Why the Mi-26 succeeded where the projected single rotor design of the Mi-12 did not was due principally to the use of advanced materials and vastly improved gearbox and engine technology. Improved methods of analysis and design and lighter and stronger materials helped the Mil OKB to take a major stride forward in large helicopter design. A comparison with the Hook and Sikorsky CH-53E is interesting:

	Halo	**Hook**	**CH-53E**
Empty weight percentage of maximum take-off weight	50.36	64.09	45.2
Useful payload percentage of maximum take-off weight	35.71	28.23	48.98
Useful payload percentage of normal take-off weight	40.4	29.63	

The interrelation between empty weight, take-off weight and payload is crucial and the improvements in weight optimisation between the Hook and the Halo are noticeable, even if the latter's do not compare favourably with the American helicopter which, it should be remembered, has a maximum take-off weight 22,661 kg (49,958 lb) less.

Operating empty weight of the Halo is 28,200 kg (62,170 lb) which is just under 1,000 kg (2,205 lb) heavier than the Hook; yet the Halo can carry, underslung or internally, a 20,000 kg (44,092 lb) load comfortably compared to the Hook's maximum load of 12,000 kg (26,455 lb). The Halo is also a replacement for the Mi-10 and Mi-10K Harke since it can undersling 12,000 kg more than the -10 and 6,000 kg (13,228 lb)

In military service the Mi-26 can carry two BMD or well over 100 combat-equipped troops. (Author)

more than the -10K. The Halo's maximum weight for vertical take-off is 49,500 kg (109,129 lb) and for running take-offs 56,000 kg (123,459 lb). Nevertheless, in February 1982, a Halo took off at 56,768.8 kg (125,154 lb) with a payload of 25,000 kg (55,115 lb) and took it up to 4,100 m (13,450 ft) to set two new world records. Although the empty weight of the aircraft was probably reduced for the record attempt to maximise the payload/altitude combination this seems to provide evidence that the Halo can exceed its stated payload limit of 20,000 kg. Retaining 5% fuel reserves at a 56,000 kg take-off weight the range is quoted as 800 km (497 miles). No other helicopter can carry more than a token part of its maximum load over such a distance. With a vertical take-off, at 49,500 kg, the same load can be taken 500 km (311 miles). Currently there is no provision for external fuel tanks; ferry tanks would probably be installed internally if required at all.

More important for a weightlifter is productivity and in this respect the Halo outshines the Hook and the CH-53E. Able to carry 20,000 kg over 800 km at a cruising speed of 255 kph (158 mph), the Halo has a payload/range more than three times greater than that of the Hook and CH-53E.

So that it may meet and take on board the complete load of a fixed-wing aircraft a heavy lift helicopter should have the same, or larger cabin volume and payload capacity. The Halo is complementary to the An-12 Cub four-engined turboprop transport in both respects although the Halo's cabin volume is slightly larger. The dimensions are 3.25 m (10 ft 8 in) wide, between 2.95 m and 3.17 m (9 ft 8 in and 10 ft 4½ in) high and, with the ramp up, 12 m (39 ft 4½ in) long. These figures are also very similar to those of the C-130 Hercules.

The fuselage is an all-metal, semi-monocoque structure of the pod-and-boom type. The unpressurised cabin itself, perhaps better called the freight hold because the carriage of large numbers of personnel will be rare, is austere. The aircraft is clearly optimised for cargo-carrying in so far as no concessions towards passenger comfort have been made but, more importantly, there is simply not enough space for passengers to

Gentlemen in the trade dwarfed by the Mi-26 which stands 8.05 m (26 ft 5 in) high. (Author)

absorb the available payload; given an average passenger weight of 90 kg (200 lb), 220 passengers could be carried within the Halo's payload. If the need arose, as it did during the Falklands War in 1982 when a Royal Air Force Chinook carried 81 British parachutists (1) over a short distance, perhaps as many as 150 lightly-armed troops could be crammed into the hold. The standard load, however, is probably about 80 combat-equipped troops or 40 stretcher cases.

The Paris aircraft had 36 uncomfortable tip-up seats along the hold walls (19 on the starboard side and 17 on the port side), none with the luxury of a seat-belt. Three further columns of 21 seats each could be installed giving a total seating capacity of 99. The reason for these odd numbers is the location of three doors, all with built-in steps, two on the port side and one, opposite the rear port door, on the starboard side. Any passengers would have their discomfort aggravated by a high noise level for there was no sound proofing; and they would be sitting in Stygian gloom since the minimal lighting was mounted in the roof of the hold and appeared insufficient to make good the ambient light filtering in through four small round windows on the starboard side and three on the port side. At the forward end of the hold is a seat for a loadmaster, a normal member of the five-man crew.

At the aft end of the freight hold are two large clamshell doors which hinge upwards and outwards to each side, an hydraulic ramp which forms part of the freight floor and which lowers to the ground to rest on two bumpers, and two extensions to this ramp which permit vehicles to be driven on board. These doors can be opened by a hand wobble pump located close to the port side rear door, in addition to the normal hydraulic system. In the military version of the Halo each door has a small rectangular window for observation to the rear. The ramp can be locked in the horizontal position to facilitate the carriage of excessively long loads within the fuselage and also at any other height to assist in loading and unloading from the backs of lorries. Visible in the roof is the large tail rotor drive shaft. On each side of the roof runs a gantry rail along which moves an electric winch capable of pulling forward loads up to 2,500 kg (5,512 lb). On the cockpit bulkhead is a ladder which allows access through a hatch in the roof to the engines and main rotor head.

It would seem that an underslung load would be suspended from underneath the main rotor gearbox with the strop dangling down through a hole in the floor. Oscillation of any load can be damped.

The spacious cockpit is pressurised, air-conditioned and may be protected by removable armour plating up to shoulder level. Behind the pilot on the port side sits the flight engineer and to starboard sits the navigator behind the co-pilot. There is a jump-seat level with the engineer's and navigator's forward-facing instrument panels. At the rear of the flight deck is another row of four tip-up seats; to their right is the door leading to the freight hold. Lookout, particularly downwards and to the rear, is good and this is achieved by each of the four crew stations having prominent bubble windows. The flight instrument panel in the Paris aircraft, which like any other part of the flight deck may not have been representative of production aircraft, was quite conventional if somewhat haphazardly laid out. In the centre at the top was the caution panel with space for 30 captions, some warning and some advisory. It is understood now that the Halo incorporates the RI-65 voice warning system which automatically advises the crew if engines, gearboxes and other items approach their limits. Both pilots had large flight directors; the captain had a Doppler hover indicator and radar altimeter while the co-pilot had Doppler drift, groundspeed and distance gone indicators as well as the digital fuel contents gauge. The central console incorporated the Doppler, moving map display, four-axis autostabiliser and autopilot controls. The Doppler navigation system can be pre-programmed and is said to have an accuracy error of no more than 2% to

3% an hour which, although not of the highest standards, is adequate for the distances likely to be flown. The Doppler also provides drift indications in the hover, a useful facility when the ground may not be visible due to blowing snow or sand. Coupled with two radar altimeters and the Doppler, the autopilot offers an automatic transition from the cruise to a pre-selected hover height – as low as 1.5 m (5 ft) wheel height.

The navigator seems to be almost completely responsible for the navigation of the helicopter. Besides having all the necessary controls and indicators, on the side wall of his panel is the display for the weather/mapping radar which is not repeated for the pilots. The flight engineer's panel contains mainly vertical scale instruments concerned with the helicopter's fuel, hydraulic and electrical systems.

The monitor for the closed circuit TV is on the captain's panel. One camera is mounted at the forward end of the hold pointing to the rear – very useful for watching loading operations in very cold temperatures or in a chemical environment as the crew sit in a pleasantly warm cockpit. A second camera gives a view downwards onto the underslung load while a third, mounted under the tail boom, points forward.

The phrase 'double bubble' has been used to describe the Halo's nose section. The upper half comprises the cockpit while the lower half contains the APU on the starboard side and much of the avionics, all of which can be inspected at chest height. The air intake for the APU can be recognised by some shutters just forward of the exhaust outlet. The APU can start the engines, and run the hydraulic and electrical systems including air-conditioning and heating for the flight deck before engine start-up.

Forward of the APU in the nose radome, which hinges to starboard, is the weather radar antenna. It is obvious that much thought went into deciding the best location for the auxiliary systems and how the helicopter could be maintained and serviced at

A military Mi-26 helping to clean up Chernobyl in April 1986.

remote sites without the need for special work platforms and support facilities. Thus all the systems are accessible either from the ground or from within the fuselage. The Halo has a non-retractable tricycle undercarriage with twin castoring wheels mounted on a single oleo under the nose; the twin main wheel units are mounted very close to the side of the fuselage and have a single oleo pneumatic shock absorber.

Why titanium was not used in their construction to save weight is not known but maybe it was due to the characteristic brittleness of titanium. Nonetheless, thanks to the cockpit's bubble windows and a slight tapering of the fuselage the crew can see the main wheels, a distinct advantage when trying to land on uneven or soft surfaces. They are certainly crude and may in due course be encased in a fairing of some sort to reduce drag. However, the length of the main legs may be adjusted hydraulically to ease landing on slopes and loading through the rear doors.

Below the floor of the hold are eight main fuel tanks from whence fuel is pumped up to two tanks above the engines. Should the pump system fail fuel can flow by gravity to the engines for a short period as an emergency supply. According to a Czech source, fuel capacity is estimated at between 7,683 kg (16,938 lb) and 9,220 kg (20,325 lb) but it might be as much as 12,000 kg (26,455 lb).

The tail boom with its flat undersurface has a large fin which is cambered and offset so as to unload the tail rotor during forward flight. Almost at the base of the fin and mounted on its leading edge is a large graphite composite horizontal stabiliser, adjustable only on the ground. Underneath the tail boom at the rear is a tail skid which can be retracted to facilitate the loading of outsize cargo.

The tail rotor has five fibreglass blades with leading edge electro-thermal de-icing. It is mounted on the starboard side of the fin as a 'pusher'. Its diameter is 7.61 m ($24 \, \text{ft} \, 11\frac{1}{2} \, \text{in}$). The Halo's main rotor head and blades superficially resemble those of the Hook's but on closer inspection the similarity recedes. Most obvious of all is that the Halo has eight main rotor blades – the first helicopter ever to have this number. With so many the rotor diameter can be less than that with fewer blades, and the rotor rpm and blade tip speeds can also be reduced. Indeed, the Halo's rotor rpm are 132 and its blade tip speed is 220 m/sec (722 ft/sec). Another advantage is much reduced vibration and lower noise levels. In fact the Halo's rotor diameter at 32 m (105 ft) is 3 m (9 ft 10 in) less than that of the Hook's. The Hook's rotor downwash is quite strong enough to blow people some distance away off their feet and the Halo's appears no more gentle. The rotor system has a traditional configuration although it is of advanced design.

Tishchenko initially considered the use of titanium spars and fibreglass ribs and skin for the main rotor blades but decided against titanium for the good reasons that qualifying such spars would have delayed the project, was of higher technical risk and would have cost more. He positively did not want the weight saving inherent in titanium because he required the centrifugal force necessary to prevent the blades coning at high aircraft weights and greater inertia in the event of autorotation. He thus elected to follow the less adventurous path of having torsionally rigid blades with simple tubular steel spars similar to those of the Mi-6. There is a difference, though: the Halo's spars are manufactured as a single piece whereas the Hook's spars have a separate end-piece connecting the spar to the hub; construction is simplified, weight reduced and strength and reliability increased.

The narrow and constant chord (about 1 m, 3 ft 3 in) blades consist of 26 glassfibre-covered and honeycomb-filled segments, bonded to the spar, and a blade tip. The twist is moderate and the blade tapers in thickness towards the tip. The aerofoil section, which starts very close to the hub, appears to be optimised for the cruise – like the tail fin. Each blade has electro-thermal de-icing at the leading edge. The main rotor hub is a work of art, the first Soviet hub to be made of titanium alloy. Special measures were

The cavernous interior of the Mi-26 Halo – very similar to that of the C-130 Hercules in dimensions. The mechanism to help in loading can be seen clearly.

taken to enhance fatigue strength. The conventional flapping, drag and feathering hinges are present together with droop stops and hydraulic drag dampers. Conventional it may be but in terms of size and weight it is superb: slim, compact and light. Indeed, the eight-bladed main rotor system of the Halo weighs 2,000 kg (4,400 lb) less than the five-bladed system of the Hook – a major saving in weight. To reduce drag in the cruise there is a neat rotor pylon fairing, parts of which hinge downwards to form working platforms.

Two 11,400 shp Lotarev D-136 triple shaft turboshaft engines power the Halo. This engine is derived from the D-36 high bypass turbofan which powers the An-72 and the Yak-42 and most of the gas generator components are common; the technology therefore dates back some years. Nevertheless, these engines use new materials and techniques to allow much higher pressure ratios and temperatures compared to other engines installed in Soviet helicopters. For the Halo the pressure ratio is 18.3 and the power turbine inlet temperature is 1,205°C. Dry weight of the D-136 is 1,050 kg (2,315 lb), 150 kg (330 lb) lighter than the Soloviev D-25V in the Hook, yet it offers more than twice as much power. Specific fuel consumption at maximum power is quoted as 0.198 kg (0.436 lb)/shp/hr.

Maximum continuous power at 7,500 engine rpm is 11,100 shp. The D-136 underwent unprecedented testing during development and consequently it is now an efficient and reliable engine which complies with British Civil Airworthiness Requirements and American Federal Aviation Regulations. The two engines, modular in design, are located side-by-side above the fuselage with their cowlings able to let down hydraulically to form work platforms. The engine intakes are heated and protected by deflectors against ice, sand and foreign object ingestion – essential if the Halo is to operate from unprepared landing sites. Further protection is afforded by

145

centrifugal particle separators inside the engine intakes. Between and above the engines, and set well back, is an air intake to provide fan-driven cooling air for the gearbox.

Of the 22,800 shp available from the two engines the VR-26 transmission can only take 20,000 shp so maximum engine power output may only be tapped if one engine fails. This, what might be called, power reserve is useful in the event of a loss of power due to high temperatures or altitudes when the extra 2,800 shp can be brought in to compensate. In the event of an engine failure the other engine is brought up automatically to full power. Operating on one engine, the Halo can continue to fly and can even hover at a gross weight of over 40,000 kg (88,183 lb) – much the same weight as the maximum take-off weight of the Hook. Perhaps the key to the success of the Halo design is the main rotor gearbox. The Hook was probably as big as a single rotor helicopter could be, given the technology of the 1950s. In the intervening years the advance in technology has included main rotor gearbox design, perhaps the single most important component of large helicopters. So the most intriguing aspect of the Halo is this gearbox. After enterprises specialising in the design of gearboxes had failed to design one capable of transmitting the torque from two 11,400 shp engines within the specified weight limitations, the Mil OKB took on the task itself, an unprecedented step. Prototypes were built, using mainly Western equipment, and successfully tested. One of the ways to reduce weight is to minimise the number of gear tooth engagements through which torque is transmitted. The R-7 gearbox of the Hook has 18, weighs 3,200 kg (7,054 lb) and transmits 11,000 hp; the Halo's VR-26 has only eight engagements, weighs 3,500 kg (7,716 lb), transmits 20,000 hp and is some 5.9 cu. m (208 cu. ft) bigger. The improvement is obvious. At 3,500 kg the VR-26 alone represents 12.4% of the empty weight of the Halo. But the mighty power of the engines coupled with the weight-effectiveness of the VR-26 gives an impressive power-to-weight ratio. Nevertheless, it would be fair to deduce that the VR-26 was not initially trouble-free in service. Given the comparatively urgent need to replace the Hook, the Halo's rate of production appears to have been disappointingly slow – probably due to technical difficulties associated with the helicopter's design – and what more likely assembly than the gearbox?

The Hook has been used in military and civil guise all over the USSR, Eastern Europe and a few countries elsewhere. The operating costs of the Halo are not known but a substantial number are in Aeroflot service adding a new dimension to the capabilities of the Hook. Reports of the helicopter being used in the Siberian gas and oil fields have become frequent with credit being given to its vast lift capability. However, complaints have been voiced about the need for ordinary workers having to supervise the pick-up and release of underslung loads and the lack of instructions about the strength of the rotor downwash. In 1986 a Czech paper reported the existence of the Mi-26T, modified for operations in extreme weather conditions and due to enter service with Aeroflot in Siberia and the Far East.

Militarily, the Halo offers a significant improvement in lift capability by means of its much increased payload and huge freight hold. It is therefore able to carry many weapon systems that the Hook and Harke cannot. Helicopter-portable systems now include such equipments as the SA-9 SAM, the MTLB tracked combat transport vehicle and variants of it, the ASU-85 assault gun, the BMP and BMD infantry fighting vehicles, the PT-76 amphibious tank and the self-propelled 122 mm 2S1 and 120 mm 2S9 howitzers; indeed, two BMDs or 2S9s, their crews and ammunition, can be accommodated in the hold. With this lift capability and a radius of action of 400 km (248 miles) heliborne operations have entered a new era: whereas the Hook is confined, in practical terms, to the tactical arena, the Halo can go further afield into the operational area.

146

Following the example of the Hook it can act as a flying fuel tank with up to 20,000 kg (44,092 lb) of fuel carried in palletised tanks in the fuselage. Able to refuel at least four vehicles simultaneously and quickly, Halos can make a significant contribution to maintaining the momentum of an advance.

Together with other helicopters, military Halos played an important role in the aftermath of the Chernobyl explosion. Time and again – it is said that crews carried out up to 22 missions each – Halos hovered over the smouldering reactor dropping sacks of boron, dolomite, lead, sand and clay onto the burning graphite. From Soviet films it would seem that the crews did not wear special protective clothing.

The Halo first lifted into the hover on 14 December, 1977 and on 21 February, 1978 made its first full free flight. It is thought to have entered production in 1981, the biggest helicopter ever to do so. Even before it became operational in the V-VS in 1985 it had been offered for export. The first foreign country to procure the Halo was India which took delivery of the first two of ten for her Air Force in June 1986. These two were used for operational trials in mountainous and desert terrain. Bristow Helicopters of the UK apparently began negotiations for three or four in 1988.

The Halo is aerodynamically attractive, apart from its rather crude undercarriage; gone are the Hook's glazed nose, stub wings, external fuel tanks and long main landing gear struts. Although there may have been initial production difficulties the Halo now seems well able to cope with the civil and military demands likely to be made upon it in any kind of hostile environment. The cautious approach using available technology whenever possible and eschewing high technical risks has paid off. And the Mil OKB will have been pleased at the success of their and others' efforts to save weight by means of light, fuel-efficient engines, a unique main rotor gearbox, the use of titanium alloys in the rotor system and other measures.

Note

1. The normal passenger load is 33 troops.

CHARACTERISTICS

Designation	**Mil Mi-26**	**Sikorsky S-65A (CH-53E)**
Engine	2 × Lotarev D-136	3 × GE T64-GE-416
	2 × 11,400 shp	3 × 4,380 shp
Rotor diameter	32.0 m (105 ft 0 in)	24.08 m (79 ft 0 in)
Fuselage length	33.73 m (110 ft 8 in)	22.35 m (73 ft 4 in)
Height	8.06 m (26 ft 5 in)	5.66 m (18 ft 7 in)
Empty weight	28,200 kg (62,170 lb)	15,071 kg (33,226 lb)
Max gross weight	56,000 kg (123,459 lb)	33,340 kg (73,500 lb)
Useful payload	20,000 kg (44,092 lb)	16,330 kg (36,000 lb)*
Max speed	295 kph (183 mph)	315 kph (196 mph)**
Range	800 km (497 mls)	500 km (310 mls)
Service ceiling	4,500 m (14,760 ft)	5,640 (18,500 ft)
First flight	December 1977	March 1974

 * Maximum external payload
** At 25,401 kg (56,000 lb) take-off weight

The new Mil helicopters

Probably some time during the second half of the 1970s the Mil Design Bureau began work on a number of different designs but, by the end of 1987, not one had entered series production. These designs vary greatly in size and capability. The two-seat Mi-28 Havoc is an attack helicopter while the four-seat Mi-34 Hermit is destined to become a trainer and sports helicopter, at least initially. The Mi-30 and Mi-32 are reported to be tilt rotor transport aircraft to carry 15 and 30 troops respectively but, according to Lev Chaiko, further development of these aircraft may well depend upon the success of similar Western aircraft, notably the Bell/Boeing V-22 Osprey which is due to make its maiden flight in September 1988. Another idea that may be under active consideration is a twin rotor heavy lift helicopter which would use the rotor system of the Mi-26 Halo as a starting point; such a helicopter would be able, in theory, to lift some 50,000 kg (110,229 lb). We shall have to wait and see what transpires with the latter three types and maybe other types as well about which we know nothing. Some details are available, fortunately, on the Mi-28 and Mi-34.

Mi-28 Havoc

The shortcomings of the Hind as an attack helicopter have already been noted. In many respects it compares unfavourably with the American AH-1 Cobra and the newer AH-64 Apache attack helicopters. Furthermore, experience in Afghanistan and

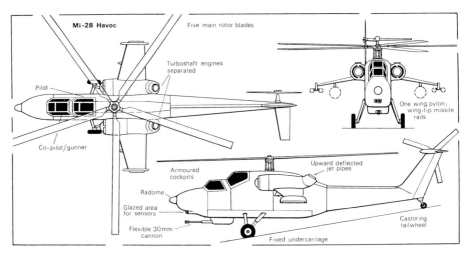

The Mi-28 Havoc is the first Soviet two-seat specialist attack helicopter. It resembles the US Army's AH 64A Apache but is not expected to enter service before 1990. (US DoD)

improvements in NATO's anti-helicopter defences have made the need for a new Soviet attack helicopter increasingly urgent. It thus came as no surprise when it was learned that the Mil OKB had embarked on the first ever purpose-designed Soviet attack helicopter. It is not clear when work actually began but it may have been in about 1977 or 1978. The 1984 edition of *Soviet Military Power* confirmed the existence of the Havoc by which time it had been in flight test for some time.

The roles of the Havoc will probably not differ much from those of the Hind and the Apache: namely, anti-armour and close air support, escort and armed reconnaissance, and probably anti-helicopter. It will, of course, have to fly and fight in adverse weather by day and night over all types of terrain and in all climates. Thus it requires a comprehensive array of weaponry, avionics and night vision systems together with various measures to reduce its vulnerability to the most likely threats against it. These measures include a high degree of manoeuvrability at low and high speed and good acceleration and deceleration. Such flight characteristics demand a healthy power-to-weight ratio and, because of the necessarily sturdy airframe structure, from this follows the need for comparatively powerful and heavy engines.

An artist's impression of the Mi-28 appeared in the 1985 edition of *Soviet Military Power*. It depicted a helicopter very much like the Apache with a streamlined fuselage able to take only a crew of two in tandem, the pilot sitting behind and well above his co-pilot/gunner. A conventional semi-monocoque structure is used with the cockpits probably having substantial armour protection. In the nose is a radome containing an unidentified radar and under it is a glazed area which probably contains various sensors such as a FLIR or low light level TV, a direct view sight and a laser designator.

With the sensors in this location no improvement has been made in comparison with the Hind, the entire helicopter having to be exposed before the sensors can be used effectively. The Apache's sensors are in the nose. Short stub wings, apparently with only a few degrees of anhedral, are mounted centre-fuselage and have two weapon pylons each, one of which is at the tip and able to take two missiles. The leading edges of the wings are swept back and the wings themselves seem to have no movable surfaces. Their span is in the order of 5 m (16 ft 5 in). The tail fin is also swept back and there is a small horizontal stabiliser at the top on the port side. Like the early Hinds the three-bladed tail rotor is mounted on the starboard side, either at the top of the fin or on the stabiliser itself.

The main rotor has five blades – more than is usual for a helicopter of this size and weight – and may well be of a new design, using composites. Blade chord can be smaller with a five-bladed rotor. The Mil OKB has probably taken advantage of its expertise and followed previous practice in making the rotor head of titanium. It is impossible at this stage to do more than estimate the diameter of the main rotor but it is probably slightly less than that of the Hind: say, 15 m (49 ft 3 in). For the first time the two turboshaft engines are front drive, rather than rearward, and they are separated to increase aircraft survivability; they are now located one on each side of the fuselage above the stub wing roots. They are unidentified as yet but, given the estimated weight of the Havoc and its power-to-weight requirements, are possibly new and in the 1,800 shp class. They have debris deflectors in the intakes and the exhaust jet pipes are turned upwards to reduce the IR signature by mixing the hot air with the rotor downwash. There is no sign yet of IR suppressors for the engine exhausts but production aircraft are almost bound to have something of this sort. The undercarriage is fixed with two main wheels forward and a castoring tail wheel under the fin. The undercarriage has probably been designed to withstand substantial impact loads to save the crew and limit damage to the helicopter in the event of a crash.

Now that a number of Warsaw Pact countries have the Hind-E with the AT-6 Spiral missile it is more than likely that a new anti-tank missile is in existence and that it will equip the Havoc. Its details are not known but it could be similar to the Spiral in terms of range and flight speed but have in addition terminal homing to improve accuracy at long range and better penetration of armour. Under the fuselage and level with the front cockpit is installed a single-barrelled cannon which probably has a calibre of 30 mm, useful in both air-to-ground and air-to-air roles. The four wing pylons can take, it may be estimated, up to 1,500 kg (3,307 lb) of armaments which could include unguided rockets and missiles of different types. It is clear that the Havoc is not as heavily armed as the Hind though the quality of its weapons is almost certainly better.

To enhance further its combat capability the Havoc will undoubtedly have various protective devices such as a radar warning receiver, an IR jammer and flare dispensers. Besides the cockpits other key areas assuredly have armour protection and the fuel tanks are self-sealing. The angular flat-plate canopy is certain to be armoured.

Every effort has been made to keep the Havoc as small and light as possible and to give it a better overall performance than the Hind and one that more or less matches that of the Apache. However, if this is the case then the Russians have missed an opportunity to leapfrog ahead of the Americans in helicopter attack capability. Dimensions, weights and performance may only be estimated at present. The Havoc appears to be a little shorter than the Hind and less high. Maximum vertical take-off weight could be about 8,000 kg (17,637 lb) and with a rolling take-off perhaps 8,500 kg (18,739 lb). Of this 1,500 kg (3,307 lb) might be ordnance on the wings with a further 300 kg (661 lb) of ammunition for the cannon. Maximum speed may be about 300 kph (186 mph) with a cruise speed of about 270 kph (168 mph) – roughly similar to the

Apache. Where the Havoc almost certainly outshines the Hind is in its hover and low speed performance.

It is too early to say whether the Mil OKB has developed a helicopter which in terms of firepower, survivability and flight performance can surpass the Apache. It was forecast by the aviation Press at one time that entry into operational military service would be in 1983 and there have even been 'sightings' in Afghanistan and Eastern Europe. However, bar further unforeseen technical or production difficulties the Havoc could begin series production sometime during 1988 and enter service from 1990. It is not expected to replace the Hind on a one-for-one basis; rather, to complement it for some years until the Hind begins to be withdrawn from service perhaps some ten years from now.

Everything about the Havoc suggests that the Russians have come to the conclusion that their traditional attack helicopter tactics will result in unacceptable losses in any future war in Europe and that NATO-style tactics are likely to be more effective. However, at this stage, nothing is certain and any such change would indicate a major variation in doctrine. If there is indeed to be a doctrinal change then we may see other changes concerning Soviet helicopter tactics right across the board.

If there was a competition with the Hokum then it seems as though the Havoc won – at least to provide an attack helicopter to support the ground forces.

Mi-34 Hermit

In its issue No. 49 of 8 December 1985 the Polish aviation periodical *Skrzydlata Polska* gave a few details of the new Soviet light helicopter which it claimed was designated the Mi-34. This has since been confirmed and the Mi-34 has been given the NATO name Hermit. According to the paper, the first flight of the prototype was expected to take place in 1986 – and this is what happened. By mid-1987 two prototypes were flying.

In June 1987 the Mi-34 appeared as a static exhibit in the Soviet pavilion at the Paris Air Show. It could be seen to be the lightest Mil helicopter ever to have been built – at least of those of which we have knowledge. Whereas the Mi-1's maximum take-off weight was 2,550 kg (5,620 lb) the Mi-34's is only 1,250 kg (2,756 lb). According to

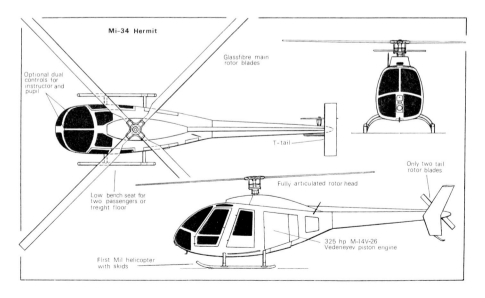

Marat Tishchenko it has been designed as a primary trainer and sports helicopter in place of the aged Mi-1 for Aeroflot pilots, DOSAAF and competition flying. It could also be used for a myriad of other tasks such as light utility, and forest, highway and border patrol. Tishchenko did not of course mention any military interest but it must be assumed that the Mi-34 will also replace Mi-1s and Mi-2s as training helicopters in the Soviet Armed Forces as well as possibly undertaking other roles such as reconnaissance and observation, target acquisition and forward air control and assisting in command and control.

The Mi-34 has space for four seats: two in the front side-by-side and room behind for two passengers on a bench seat, or freight. Its external appearance resembles that of the French AS 350 Ecureuil. However, there are in fact many differences. Perhaps surprisingly the Mi-34 has a single nine cylinder radial piston engine – the well-tried 325 hp Vedeneyev M-14V-26 – mounted in the rear fuselage. With its reduction gear this engine weighs 245 kg (540 lb), a significant proportion, 19.6%, of the maximum take-off weight and this gives the helicopter a comparatively low ratio of payload to maximum weight; the specific weight, more importantly in this case, is high at 0.75 kg (1.65 lb) per hp, some three or four times higher than a comparable turboshaft engine. Indeed, the option to replace this piston engine with a turboshaft probably exists and may well be taken up at a later date. Avgas for piston engines is becoming less plentiful and this factor would be significant when contemplating exports. The light alloy pod and boom fuselage is pleasantly streamlined and well finished; visibility from the cockpit seems to be good. The tail fin, mounted on the port side of the tail boom, is swept with a horizontal stabiliser at the top forming a T; both the leading and trailing edges of these stabilisers are made of carbon fibre composite material. A tail skid is fitted at the bottom. In tanks in the fuselage may be carried up to 120 kg (265 lb) of fuel but with a crew of two the normal amount is 85 kg (187 lb); in the sports role only 30–40 kg (66–88 lb) will be carried. Fuel consumption is advertised as 45 kg (99 lb) per hour at a weight of 1,200 kg (2,645 lb).

The four-bladed composite main rotor has a diameter of 10 m (32 ft 10 in) and a fully-articulated metal hub. This combination of composites and full articulation offer good flight performance and manoeuvrability. The two-bladed tail rotor is also of composite construction and is mounted on the starboard side of the tail boom level with the fin. For the first time the Mil Bureau has gone for a skid undercarriage with curved support tubes. Ground handling will therefore pose new problems for the Russians both on and off airfields in civil and military service.

The normal take-off weight is 1,200 kg (2,645 lb) at which the cruising speed is 180 kph (112 mph), the maximum straight and level speed is 210 kph (130 mph) and the hover ceiling 1,500 m (4,920 ft). The recommended weight for sporting manoeuvres is 1,020 kg (2,249 lb) at which the Mi-34 can sustain a load factor of 2.5 g for a limited time and a minimum of 0.5 g. It is hard to see when the maximum backwards speed of 130 kph (81 mph) may be used except during some spectacular aerobatics manoeuvre. At the maximum take-off weight of 1,250 kg (2,756 lb) and with a load of 90 kg (198 lb) a range of 450 km (280 miles) is given; 180 km (119 miles) with a 165 kg (364 lb) load. With instructor and student and a fuel load of 85 kg (187 lb) a training sortie could last as long as one hour and 40 minutes with 10% fuel still remaining in reserve.

The future career of this helicopter will be carefully watched as it could take some unexpected directions. It would not be a great surprise, for example, if it were to be re-engined with a turboshaft and if this were so the Mi-34 would come close to the Polish turbine-engined SW-4. Could the two projects merge with production being undertaken in Swidnik? The precedent has been set with the Mi-2. Could production be undertaken in both countries? There are many factors to be considered, not least other Polish helicopter programmes. Unlikely though it is production might just

The Mi-34 is not yet in production but is intended for training and competitive flying. It may in due course be re-engined with a turbine. It was demonstrated in the USA in May 1988 when Tishchenko said the minimum production run would be for 1,000.

possibly be carried out elsewhere: the Romanians and Yugoslavs both build helicopters under licence now. If and when production will start is not known but, if the decision to proceed is taken, then it could be as early as 1989. Thereafter the Mi-34 will no doubt make its presence felt at World Helicopter Championships.

The future

The first edition of this book suggested that the Mil and Kamov OKBs could be working on four new types: a cheap basic trainer, an 8–12 seater to replace the Hoplite and Hound, a replacement for the Hip and an attack helicopter. The Mi-34, Mi-30/32 and the Mi-28 and Hokum seem to meet these forecasts fairly well. If the tilt-rotor Mi-30 and Mi-32 do not proceed into production, and perhaps even if they do, a conventional replacement for the Mi-8/17 Hip can be expected. This would probably have a single main rotor/tail configuration, be more steamlined and have a retractable undercarriage.

On the basis of the inadequate information so far made available it may be concluded that the Mil Bureau is still well behind the West in the design of light helicopters while it maintains its lead in heavy lift helicopters. The neglect of light helicopters seems at long last to have ended.

Further development of the new Mil and Kamov types, the heavy lift helicopter and perhaps helicopter drones together with improvements to existing types will keep both bureaux busy for some time to come. The use of new materials for the manufacture of such items as rotor blades and hubs, fairings, control surfaces and primary structural elements is certainly being studied and put under test. Within the next ten years the use of composites may reduce the overall weight of a helicopter by up to 20%, significantly lowering empty weight. The improved efficiency of main and tail rotors is now beginning to allow take-off weights to rise for a given engine power. Improved rotor and fuselage profiles will further reduce the decreasing specific fuel consumption of new engines. The Mil and Kamov OKBs are sure to take advantage of all available technological advances in concepts, materials and engineering. It would be reasonable to expect combat effectiveness to be enhanced with improved sensors, avionics and weapons systems and better systems integration.

CHARACTERISTICS

Designation	Mil Mi-28 Havoc*	Mi-34 Hermit
Engine	2 × ?	Vedeneyev M-14V-26
	2 × 1,800 shp	325 hp
Rotor diameter	15 m (49 ft 3 in)	10 m (32 ft 10 in)
Fuselage length	16.5 m (54 ft 2 in)	8.71 m (28 ft 7 in)
Height	3.9 m (12 ft 9 in)	2.8 m (9 ft 2 in)
Empty weight	?	?
Max gross weight	8,500 kg (18,739 lb)	1,250 kg (2,756 lb)
Max speed	300 kph (186 mph)	210 kph (130 mph)
Range	480 km (298 mls)	450 km (280 mls)
Service ceiling	?	4,500 m (14,765 ft)
First flight	1982?	1986

* All characteristics estimated

Design,
development and production

The design, development and production of helicopters in the Soviet Union are quite unlike those procedures in the West. The principal reason for this fact is simply the lack of a true competitive element in the Soviet system. Helicopters are ordered for the Armed Forces (only the Ka-26 was built as a civilian machine) and then adapted for commercial or civil use. With the closed society and rigid bureaucracy that prevails in the Soviet Union the Ministry of Defence, as the customer for practically every new type of helicopter, relieves the defence industry sector of the Soviet economy of any need to conduct market research or to seek out new contracts. The Soviet economy is centrally planned and organised in such a way that each element has a specific task and duplication is reduced to a minimum. National goals are set by the Communist Party using a system of Five Year Plans which are implemented in annual stages. The overriding importance of adhering to these Plans is made abundantly clear to all and ostentatiously reinforced by the issue of awards and penalties.

The Ministry of Aviation Industry (MAI)

The Ministry of Aviation Industry directs research, design, development, testing and production of all aircraft. It is one of nine industries in the defence sector of Soviet industry, all of which are controlled by the Military-Industrial Commission (*Voenno-Promyshlennaya Kommissiya*) of the Council of Ministers which also includes representatives from the industries, the Ministry of Defence and *Gosplan* (the State Planning Commission). This Ministry has three main customers: the Military Air Forces (V-VS), the Naval Air Arm (AV-MF) and the Civil Air Fleet (*Grazhdanskii Vozdushnyi Flot*, GVF), known, world-wide, as Aeroflot. Aeroflot conducts all civil operations, including passenger, cargo and mail flights, and agricultural, fishery and forestry patrols. The Ministry of Defence, which naturally controls the V-VS and AV-MF, also directs the activities of DOSAAF (*Dobrovolnoe Obshchestvo Sodeistviya Armii, Aviatsii i Flotu*, Voluntary Society for Assistance to the Army, Air Force and Navy) which is responsible for recreational aviation, including gliding.

MAI controls all aviation research establishments, such as TsAGI and TsIAM (*Tsentralnyi Institut Aviatsionnovo Motorostroeniya*, Central Aero-engine Institute), the various design bureaux and production plants.

Scientific-technical committees

All nine defence industry ministries have a Scientific-Technical Committee concerned with technical advice, directing research and development (R & D) and examining

155

GOVERNMENT – PARTY – ARMED FORCES

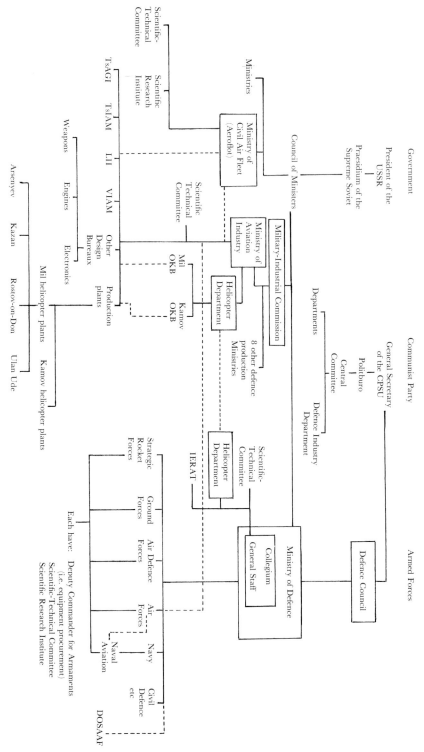

proposals for new equipments. The Soviet General Staff, much concerned with equipment procurement, also has a Scientific-Technical Committee which is thought to have close links with *Gosplan* and to co-ordinate, if not plan, all military R & D. It can provide advice to the General Staff on the technical feasibility of new proposals and act as a monitoring authority. The five branches of the Armed Forces each have their own Scientific-Technical Committees which, besides planning research, also review all technical projects within their Service. They are well able to alert their Services' armaments directorate to technical opportunities.

Scientific research institutes

There is no shortage of Scientific Research Institutes (*Nauchno-Issledovatelskii Institut*, NII). The nine ministries, and indeed Aeroflot, possess their own and each branch of the Armed Forces has more than one. They are supported by various institutes in the Academy of Sciences and some higher education laboratories. They deal in pure and applied research with the emphasis on the latter. Research is not confined to theoretical work but embraces also the development of hardware.

A variety of research organisations study different elements of helicopter design. The Moscow Aviation Institute has a small helicopter section devoted to theoretical research. Materials, specifically aluminium alloys, are studied at the VILS (*Vsesoyuznii Institut Legkikh Splasov*, All-Union Light Alloys Institute) while research into transmissions is conducted by the Zhukovsky Air Academy. IERAT (*Institut Ekspluatatsii i Remonta Aviatsionnoy Tekhniki*, Institute of Aviation Equipment Operation and Maintenance) studies the repair and maintenance of aircraft and helicopters.

The design bureaux rely heavily on the work of these institutes which publish the results of their research and tests for the benefit of the bureaux. The bureaux are not often permitted to disregard the advice, techniques and procedures offered. TsAGI is of course the best known of all the aviation research institutes and is, together with TsIAM and others, directed by the Scientific-Technical Committee of the MAI.

Design bureaux

As the demands made on TsAGI proliferated and became more complex in the early 1930s so special departments were established: the Section of Special Constructions in the case of helicopters. In due course the fixed-wing specialist design groups separated from TsAGI to form OKBs but helicopter R & D, still in a comparatively embryo stage, was retained within TsAGI; the first helicopter OKBs were not established until after the Second World War. They then became, to a greater or lesser degree, semi-autonomous organisations each headed by a Chief Designer, the first letters of his name being used to identify his machines (Mi, Ka, Yak).

Soviet helicopter design bureaux have a clear and simple aim: to design and construct new experimental systems and improve existing ones. They are responsible for neither pure research nor production and are quite independent of the research institutes and factories. They lie in between, accepting the findings of the institutes and passing their approved designs to the production plants. In general they can be expected to have three departments: design, prototype construction and testing. Both the Mil and Kamov bureaux are in Moscow.

This central position confers great influence on the Chief Designer and his OKB. While in close touch with his customers and aware of their needs he can provide guidance to the research institutes in the direction their activities should take. He has the twin advantages of an independent budget and a stable workforce (unlike Western firms which often have to 'hire and fire' as new contracts are awarded or cancelled). He is thus free from the worry of having to recoup R & D and production costs, or indeed make a profit and he therefore has no reason to embellish his designs with perhaps desirable but not essential attributes. The result is comparative simplicity – the first principle of Soviet weapons acquisition. Furthermore, because design teams stay together over many years great continuity is enjoyed and a high level of expertise and experience built up. This is not surprising because those involved in military R & D and production earn more and receive perks that those in the civilian sector do not. They also enjoy the use of better and more equipment with which to carry out their work.

Despite their considerable stability, OKBs are never in a position to rest on their laurels. Chief Designers are continually concerned with getting their designs accepted for production. The Soviet system, whereby prototype hardware actually exists, permits easier decision-making than in the West where the decision to proceed with a project is sometimes made on the basis of paper proposals. Chief Designers also set great store by a second principle – evolutionary change – by refining and developing existing hardware.

In general terms the helicopter OKBs are not known for their design creativity and initiative which is not encouraged as it is in the West. Chaiko, an engineer of the Mil OKB, claims that new projects usually start as a result of the General Staff's fear of falling behind, presumably the West, or the desire to imitate what has already been demonstrated successfully elsewhere. Western ideas, therefore, often confirm a particular line of R & D or cause new research to be started up. The Mi-24 is a good example of the General Staff wanting to follow the lead of the USA. With the appearance of the HueyCobra in Vietnam Mil was ordered to develop a similar machine very quickly and regardless of cost. To design from scratch would have taken a long time and so Mil was directed to base the new helicopter on the Mi-8 with the consequences that we have seen.

Production plants

Production plants, scattered all over the USSR, are merely given work by MAI. Concerned with meeting schedules they are generally resistant to change. This is something of a hangover from the last war when Stalin insisted on continuity of design so as not to disrupt production lines. It is also an expression of the overwhelming conservatism present in the Soviet system where there is no enthusiasm for change unless it is ordered by a superior. Initiative was generally suppressed by Stalin and only in recent years has it been moderately encouraged, more so now under Gorbachev's reform programme. It is therefore easy to see why evolutionary rather than revolutionary change is preferred in the defence industry. These plants may build aircraft designed by different bureaux but in general terms will stick with a particular type, e.g. fighters, transport aircraft or helicopters. There are thought to be ten plants devoted to helicopters and light aircraft of which at least four – at Arsenyev, Kazan, Rostov-on-Don and Ulan Ude – produce only the Mi-8/17 and Mi-24/25/35.

A major difference between Western and Soviet production lines is the use of labour. In the West labour is expensive and becoming ever more so. Thus it makes sense to invest in machines and keep labour to the minimum. In the USSR the position is reversed due to the large numbers of skilled workers available at a comparatively modest cost. Labour-intensive manufacturing procedures are used and every effort made to reduce to a minimum special tooling and materials.

Helicopter procurement

A new helicopter usually originates from a request from the V-VS, AV-MF or, possibly,

158

THE PROCUREMENT OF A V-VS HELICOPTER

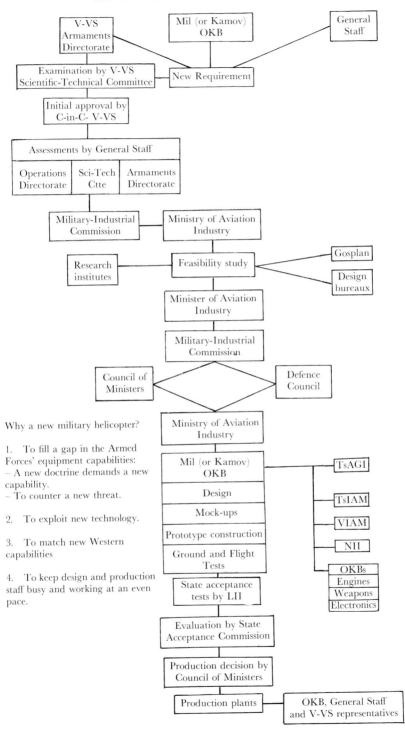

Why a new military helicopter?

1. To fill a gap in the Armed Forces' equipment capabilities:
– A new doctrine demands a new capability.
– To counter a new threat.

2. To exploit new technology.

3. To match new Western capabilities

4. To keep design and production staff busy and working at an even pace.

Aeroflot. For a military helicopter the V-VS armaments directorate would issue a document setting out the tactical and technical requirements. The Mil and Kamov design bureaux, keen to get more work or to exploit technology for which they see military value, may also put forward proposals. An example of this was the Mi-6, which was proposed by Mil who was keen to take advantage of the new turboshaft engine and build a very large helicopter. Occasionally the higher reaches of the military or even political leadership may demand a new design. These distinct divisions are in fact probably blurred with the armaments directorate being well aware of the results of the research institutes' work and how the design bureaux can turn them into advanced hardware. Designs and drawings may be available.

Procurement is characterised by a secretive, rigidly bureaucratic and lengthy process. It is thought that as soon as the requirement has been drafted, probably with the help of the Helicopter Department in the General Staff, it is reviewed by the Scientific-Technical Committee of the V-VS or AV-MF. Once the Commander-in-Chief has approved the proposal it is passed to the General Staff for its armaments and operations directorates to assess its place in future organisations and plans, and likely costs. The General Staff's Scientific-Technical Committee also examines the proposal from a technical standpoint. If it clears this hurdle the requirement is submitted to the VPK which commissions a feasibility study. This is probably conducted by the Scientific-Technical Committee of the MAI with help from research institutes and design bureaux; it includes an examination of project milestones. The Minister himself may also review the proposal before it is submitted to the VPK for final examination and its recommendations. These go to the Defence Council and the Council of Ministers for joint clearance. If the proposal, unusual in the case of a helicopter but perhaps becoming more likely in the future, requires large resources or is politically sensitive, it is then put before the Politburo.

During this whole process the mission capability of the proposed helicopter, once agreed, is sacrosanct. While the Helicopter Department of the General Staff and other military authorities will concede on qualitative characteristics such as payload ratio, survivability, reliability etc, they will not budge on mission capability, regardless of cost. The date for the start of production and the number of helicopters to be built are also critical issues and the Ministry of Defence and MAI usually argue their case before the Council of Ministers. The military requirement is carefully balanced against the state of the domestic economy and many other factors.

Once the decision to proceed with the project has been made one or more design bureaux are given the task of preparing detailed designs, mock-ups and prototypes. It is unlikely now that all the aviation bureaux would be invited to participate in a helicopter design as they were in 1951 for the Mi-4 and Yak-24. But it may be thought worthwhile at this stage to involve both the Mil and Kamov OKBs (and just possibly the Yakovlev OKB) as a form of insurance. Because of high R & D costs it is less usual now for the competition to continue up to and including the building of prototypes (1). Competition for assemblies and components such as engines, gearboxes, weapons systems and avionics may be normal.

The Soviet system is not so bureaucratic that it cannot react to new tactical requirements and technological advances during the design, prototype construction and flight test stages. Indeed, changes are often made even during series production. Such modifications are facilitated by having representatives of the General Staff Helicopter Department working in the design bureaux, other R & D organisations and in the production plants.

It is the Preliminary Design Department which proposes the configuration of the new helicopter, usually in two or more variants. Designs of the components and assemblies for the different variants are prepared by different teams within the bureaux and in this way an element of competition is introduced. During this stage all the sub-contractors (engine, gearbox, hydraulics, electronics etc.) are involved. After careful examination of all the options a variant is chosen and work begins on a full-scale, normally wooden, mock-up. The design is then discussed by a special commission of engineers drawn from the OKB, the General Staff, TsAGI and other R & D organisations, the production plant and the sub-contractors. Modifications are suggested and agreement is reached eventually on the final design.

Even while the design of components and assemblies is being finalised production tooling begins. This, of course, entails some risk as more modifications may be forthcoming but timescales are considered more important than any financial losses that may result from re-tooling. Production of these components starts even before the first flight and the first few examples are subjected to bench tests.

Aircraft models undergo wind-tunnel testing at TsAGI before the building of prototypes is begun. Three are almost invariably constructed and one of these is used as a ground test vehicle. The Mil and Kamov OKBs share an airfield at the intersection of the Moscow Ring Road and the Lubertsy Highway but their flight test facilities are quite separate. According to Chaiko all flight tests are carried out above the Ring Road with rescue vehicles stationed along it.

As soon as the flight tests are completed State acceptance tests take place. These are undertaken by the LII and the results are given to the State Acceptance Commission which is nominated by the Council of Ministers. The Commission's job is to examine the results and decide whether the helicopter should go into production. By this stage this is virtually a formality. Also reviewed by the Commission are the results of component and assembly bench tests completed by the Helicopter Research Section in TsAGI. In attendance at the Commission meetings are the Chief Designer of the OKB concerned and the Head of the LII. If production is to go ahead resources will have to be made available and co-ordinated with the annual and current Five Year Plan. The General Staff and the Military-Industrial Commission will already have assessed the economic and military implications of making materials and labour available. Once the production decision is made, and this would include which plant or plants are to undertake the work, plant representatives are called in to discuss details. Production quantities and the schedule are geared to the current and future Five Year Plans. The production run may extend over ten or 15 years. Once a helicopter is authorised for production there are no annual budget reviews. The next five years at least are assured and thus significant reductions in unit costs are possible. Any Western firm would be mightily relieved to work on such a basis rather than the present Western system whereby funds for military helicopters are voted only one year ahead.

The OKB despatches an advisory team to the chosen factory or factories to help set up the production line and to ensure compliance with specifications. The customer also has representatives on site and together they and the OKB team supervise quality control. They have considerable authority and are able to refuse the finished product if not satisfactory. According to Tishchenko the process now takes between ten and twelve years from the drafting of the requirement to the start of production.

The Soviet and Warsaw Pact domestic and military markets are so large that production runs of two, three or more thousand helicopters (Mi-1, Mi-2, Mi-4, Mi-8/17 and Mi-24/25 for example) are not unusual. Helicopter production really began to grow in the late 1960s and a high and level rate was sustained throughout the 1970s; from 1977 to 1986, according to *Soviet Military Power 1987*, 4,650 military helicopters were produced. During the mid-1980s the annual production rate was close to 600, a decrease from over 700 in earlier years. This fall is not surprising given Halo production

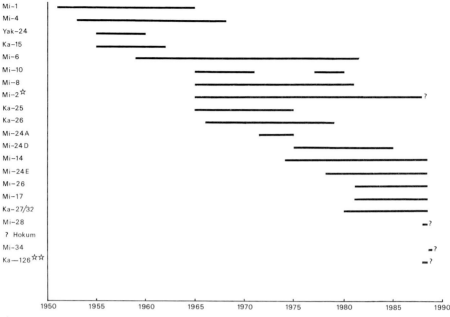

Soviet Helicopter Production Runs

| | 1950 | 1955 | 1960 | 1965 | 1970 | 1975 | 1980 | 1985 | 1990 |

Mi–1
Mi–4
Yak–24
Ka–15
Mi–6
Mi–10
Mi–8
Mi–2 ☆
Ka–25
Ka–26
Mi–24 A
Mi–24 D
Mi–14
Mi–24 E
Mi–26
Mi–17
Ka–27/32
Mi–28
? Hokum
Mi–34
Ka—126 ☆☆

☆   Produced in Poland
☆☆ Production planned in Romania

difficulties and the need for some plants to tool up for the Havoc and possibly the Hokum. Long production runs and relative unsophistication help to keep costs down. With the establishment of Aviaexport in 1964 more importance is now given to the export potential of new designs.

The Soviet procurement system within a planned economy cannot be compared with those pertaining in the West. Lack of innovation, secrecy, frequent reviews, reluctance to make decisions and a rigid bureaucracy all characterise a system which upholds the view that military might has more than just a deterrent effect. Defence expenditure is necessary and well-spent. If a new type of helicopter is required then one will be developed and it will be the best that the OKB can manage. Cost overruns are less important than keeping to development and production schedules which are geared to Five Year Plans. The greater the technical risk the higher may be the cost but, once the decision to proceed has been taken, money will be made available; time generally will not. The Soviet programme manager is not concerned with sales or profits, merely schedules. Stalin's order in October 1951 to Mil and Yakovlev each to build and fly their new designs within 12 months is an example of the time constraints imposed. It is clear then that Soviet programmes are time-oriented rather than cost-oriented. It was principally excessive cost which put the Boeing Vertol XCH-62A Heavy Lift Helicopter project into suspended animation before the first prototype was even assembled. Such a course is unlikely in the USSR.

To achieve maximum military cost-effectiveness, and there are signs that greater priority is now being given to keeping costs down, it is not always necessary to produce a brand-new helicopter. As in other armies, if it is believed that a potential threat is not being adequately catered for, then changes to doctrine and tactics, organisation or training are considered first. If such changes are unable to match the new threat then product improvement is the next option – the many variants of the Mi-8 and the Mi-24 are eloquent proof of upgrading. Only when improvements are deemed insufficient is a new machine proposed.

While competition may not be the driving force that it is in the West all countries outside the Soviet bloc which are not client States are still free to choose the helicopter best suited to their needs. So far there has been little inclination to buy Soviet equipment and thus, to some extent, the Russians are forced to compete if they wish to sell worldwide. A notable Third World customer has been India which operates significant numbers of Mi-17 and Mi-25 and also a few Mi-26 and Ka-28. Between 1981 and 1986 over 1,000 Soviet helicopters are thought to have been exported and a few given away to selected countries in the Third World. A case in point is the presentation of a single Hip-C, with outrigger pylons for armaments, to Guinea-Bissau in West Africa. Mainly because Soviet helicopters are produced in such large numbers extremely attractive prices (2) and credit terms can be offered to prospective customers, although these vary depending upon national identity and political affiliation. Soviet helicopters have often been offered at around £50 per kg (2.2 lb) of empty weight in comparison to Western prices at least four times higher. Despite fears in the West, however, this price-cutting exercise has not resulted in any significant Soviet penetration of the helicopter market due to high operating costs and general frustration with the inefficient aftersales arrangements.

Where the Russians enjoy a major advantage over other manufacturers is in delivery times where the average time from contract signature to delivery is sometimes less than 12 months. There is a reverse side to the coin. The US State Department is of the view that "The world market operates under certain 'laws' which conflict with traditional Marxist-Leninist economic principles. Unwillingness to adjust to changing market conditions would diminish the comparative advantage of the Soviet Union, making it less competitive with other suppliers in the Third World market." Other trends likely to result in a diminishing export market include competition with an increasing number of Third World countries now establishing their own helicopter production capability and the desire of previous customers and potential new ones to procure the most modern technology, something the Russians have been unwilling to offer in the past. Another factor gaining in importance is that of counter-trade and other offset agreements.

It is almost certainly true to say that there is more to the export of helicopters than simple economics. They provide a seemingly innocuous way of inserting a Soviet presence into the country concerned. Either before or with the helicopters go instructors, technicians and other operational personnel – some who are only very loosely concerned with the machines themselves. Soviet methods and practices are adopted and, if for military use, some penetration of the country's armed forces is achieved. This may eventually lead to overflying rights, maintenance arrangements for visiting Soviet aircraft and eventually even the establishment of a Soviet base or at least enclave on an airfield.

Great influence over target countries can be achieved by the export of aircraft and this fact goes some way to explaining why certain Third World countries are possessors of Soviet helicopters. Countries of particular interest to the Soviet Union can expect to be approached with enticing offers: some because they pay in much-needed hard currency and others for political reasons. It is interesting to note that the Mi-24/25 Hind was exported to Libya before all the Warsaw Pact countries except East Germany.

The contention that Soviet helicopter technology is behind that of the West does not mean that Soviet technology in general is lagging. It certainly is not. Given the unwavering commitment to achieving military superiority, the Soviet Union now has the most comprehensive and expensive military R & D programme in the world, greatly exceeding that of the United States. The Communist Party gives a very high priority to military R & D and controls it carefully at all levels of activity right down to individual research establishments. Vast capital investments have been made and the most highly qualified scientists and engineers are allocated to this programme.

The traditional American lead in technology is thus being systematically eroded. Every effort is being made to acquire Western advanced technology through overt trade agreements (where it can be adapted for military purposes) and by covert operations. Soviet technology is already ahead in such fields as air defence missiles, artillery and rocket launchers, chemical warfare and cold weather equipment. For the moment the Soviet leaders do not choose to put much of their advanced technology resources into helicopter development although there are signs that this policy is changing.

Notes

1. It is not yet clear whether the building of the prototypes of the Havoc and Hokum is an example of direct competition.

2. The reported price of the Mi-34 in 1987 was 150,000 roubles (approximately £150,000).

Design philosophy

Since the helicopter design bureaux work primarily to satisfy military requirements their designers are conscious of the need to develop equipment that will be available, that is to say not unserviceable, when required in battle; and that can be operated and maintained without difficulty by officers and soldiers in the field at night and in bad weather and harsh climates. Thus simplicity is the key design factor: whereas in the West the aim is to maximise equipment performance, the Soviet intent is to develop a system that offers ease of operation, maximum reliability and minimum maintenance over a relatively short period of time. The difference between American and Soviet design philosophy was neatly summed up by an Israeli general when he said: "American weapons are designed by engineers for engineers, whereas Soviet weapons are developed for the combat soldier." While he may be guilty of a degree of exaggeration, the gist of what he said is indisputable. If Soviet helicopters are generally less sophisticated and capable than Western helicopters – and the gap continues to narrow – they are generally easier to operate and maintain. Thus they can almost certainly reach the same level of battlefield performance as their more advanced Western counterparts, any shortfall in flight performance being offset by higher reliability and availability. This comparative lack of sophistication is attractive to many countries in the Third World where technical skills are lacking.

Hard facts concerning Soviet helicopter design philosophy are not easy to come by. Little is known of R & D programmes and even less of accident statistics. Such is the closed society of the USSR that information on new equipments is extremely sketchy until they are revealed to the public or specific claims made for them. Nevertheless it is possible to make certain deductions concerning Soviet design philosophy in general and that pertaining to helicopters in particular. It is certainly true that personnel stability is a feature of the Mil and Kamov OKBs. Engineers and design staff are respected and not subject to the "hiring and firing" policies so commonplace in the West. Such stability offers experience, team work and a long and broad OKB memory. Unproductive designs and mistakes repeated should be rare.

Following closely behind simplicity as a major design consideration comes standardisation. Standardisation of components, configurations and operating procedures produces many benefits: simpler logistic support, greater availability, reduced training requirements, lower risk, less time spent in development and longer production runs to name just a few. All this adds up to enhanced effectiveness and lower costs. Components can be scaled up or down if necessary as evidenced by the commonality between the Mi-8, Mi-14, Mi-17 and Mi-24 and between the Mi-6 and Mi-26. A perfect example is engine standardisation. Many types of Soviet turbine-powered helicopters have either the Izotov TV2-117A or the more powerful TV3-117A which can be installed in its place with comparative ease; the only other turbine engine in full production as far as is known is the Lotarev D-136 for the Mi-26. The TV3-117, for example, powers the Mi-14, Mi-17, most Mi-24, the Ka-27 and Ka-32; it may also be the powerplant for the Mi-28 and the Hokum. Where standardisation of a complete assembly is not feasible then interchangeability of parts, such as rotor blades, oil filters etc is the aim.

Highly desirable though it is, this drive for standardisation is partially an inevitable result of Soviet technological caution. In a system where the fear of failure is paramount it is logical to pursue a conservative approach, taking as few technical risks as possible and using well-tried technolgoy if it meets requirements – quite the reverse of Western practice where the emphasis very often is on employing new technology. The Soviet view persists that there is no need to re-invent every nut and bolt each time a new helicopter is designed. Indeed the history of Soviet helicopter developments abounds with examples of new aircraft substantially using components of the aircraft that they are replacing. The prototype Mi-2 consisted of an Mi-1 with only a new fuselage and engines. Another example among many is the use of the Mi-6's main rotor system on the Mi-12. An excellent example of this philosophy of 'step-by-step upgrading' is the Mi-17 derivative of the Mi-8. It is hard to distinguish them and both are called the Hip. The transition from production of the Mi-8 to the Mi-17 must have been very smooth, the same facilities and personnel being used with no upheaval and with the minimum of re-tooling and re-training. It would be unthinkable for the Russians to undertake a project like the American LHX with a new airframe, new engine and new avionics involving a host of advanced technologies in a single new package. In other words, the Russians are not slaves to advanced technology. If a 25 or 30-year-old design can still do the job it is not replaced. The result seems to be that Soviet aircraft, fixed and rotary-wing, are not retired; they simply go on flying until they eventually become worn out. The Mi-1, now celebrating the 40th anniversary of its first flight in 1948, was still good enough to win the men's and women's individual titles in the Second and Third World Helicopter Championships in 1973 and 1978 respectively (1).

Because of the reluctance to take technical risks, to have equipment that can absorb the wear and tear of intense combat operation – ruggedness and the desire to keep to engineering simplicity – it is commonly the case that Soviet helicopters are some 5% to 10% heavier than their Western equivalents. A stronger and heavier structure is therefore necessary and this meets safety and reliability standards that are considered excessively high in the West. Flight performance is almost bound to suffer. Less attention is paid to the insatiable Western demands to reduce weight and size. Thus heavier and stronger components can be, and are, used and they should be relatively trouble-free. The massive R-7 gearbox in the Mi-6 and Mi-10 is virtually leak-free. Such a 'brute force' technique results in fewer maintenance-man-hours per flight hour and helps to mitigate the consequences of insufficient and inadequately trained maintenance personnel and shortages of spare parts. On the other hand, in the two decades after the war, the somewhat unadventurous approach led to an acceptance of quite low time between overhauls (TBO). Although scheduled maintenance was thus increased, unscheduled – and therefore inconvenient – maintenance was significantly reduced. Now, this situation has changed and TBOs have been lengthened. Despite this, it is believed that the maintenance policy for military helicopters calls for a higher degree of minor preventive maintenance than is the case in the West. For some unexplained reason, possibly political for prestige purposes, some exported helicopters have been half-lifed. Every effort is made to improve component life: during manufacture, and during flight when Soviet pilots tend to operate at no more than 80% of available power. Operating limits are frequently set substantially below design

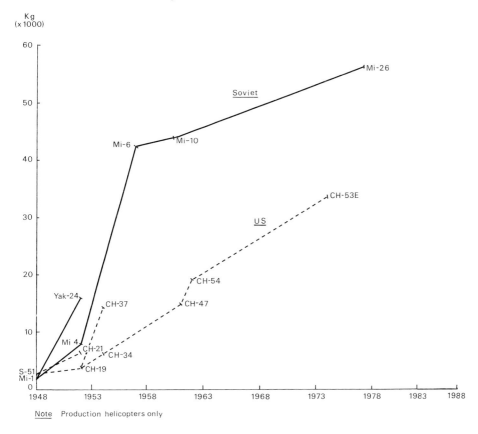

Growth in Maximum Take Off Weights

Kg (x 1000)

Soviet

Mi-26

Mi-6

Mi-10

Yak-24

CH-37

CH-53E

US

CH-54

CH-47

Mi 4

CH-21

CH-34

S-51
Mi-1

CH-19

1948 1953 1958 1963 1968 1973 1978 1983 1988

<u>Note</u> Production helicopters only

limits. Modifications are retro-fitted or incorporated during the later stages of the production run. The initial blade life of the Mi-1 was under 200 hours in 1953; by 1966 it was 2,000 hours. Service life of the Mi-6 was planned at 12,000 flying hours but now this has been raised to 20,000 hours in steps of 1,000 hours subject to the satisfactory state of certain components.

Combat equipment is meant for fighting and therefore is not likely to last long before it is destroyed or badly damaged. There is no point then in wasting resources by designing components with lives of 2,000 or 3,000 flying hours which need extensive maintenance. Instead, high levels of reliability and availability and low and simple maintenance requirements have become design factors and, if achieved, will result in high sortie rates. The West has a different view: designing for protracted service in peacetime with long TBO to reduce life cycle costs. The Soviet view tends towards building helicopters that are simpler and cheaper than those of the West but more rugged and in much greater numbers. Large quantities are, of course, another form of redundancy and compensate for inferior quality and the need for anything but basic maintenance in the field.

Even though a particular design appears to meet the specifications laid down as far as combat operations and its technical support are concerned, yet one more factor has to be considered. How easily and cheaply the helicopter may be produced is crucial to the project. Any design that demands high levels of skilled manpower, a high degree of

167

special materials or sophisticated tooling will be minutely scrutinised to see if it is cost-effective. Long, trouble-free and inexpensive production runs are the aim.

It is because Soviet helicopters are usually designed with the military forces in mind that tactical considerations govern such design factors as flight performance, survivability, payload/range and therefore cabin dimensions, loading arrangements, engine self-starting capability and ease of maintenance. But most of these characteristics are also of extreme importance for Aeroflot helicopters given the rugged climate and terrain of the Soviet Union which demand a robust and reliable aircraft that is easy to maintain. Because of the enormous expanses of the USSR payload/range is a key factor and to enhance the range capability most Soviet helicopters have the ability to carry external fuel tanks.

It is not unknown in the West for a new weapon system to be developed without there initially being a role for it. This is not mirrored in the Soviet Union where weapon systems are produced for one or more good reasons.

What seems to be clear is that military helicopters are usually designed with a single mission in mind rather than having a multi-role capability. The fact that the Hip is very heavily armed has not changed its role; its armament merely assists in the successful completion of its troop-carrying role. But the Russians have always been keen to maximise the potential of their helicopters and the Hind can be regarded as a truly multi-role helicopter. It was not designed as such, however, and its new roles emerged during the development process when its potential as a 'gunship' was recognised. It remains to be seen whether the Russians will continue with their single-role philosophy. It is likely that they will; the Havoc is certainly a more specialised helicopter than the Hind. It should be recognised that the mere arming of a helicopter does not automatically signify a change of role. Practically all Soviet military helicopters, if not actually armed, have the fittings and wiring to take weapons. They may, however, only be installed to enhance the helicopter's self-defence capability.

Two trends can easily be distinguished in the development of the helicopter: first, what might be called the quantitative trend which has been concerned with the size of the machine and thus its payload capacity; and second, the simultaneous qualitative trend which involved improvements within a certain size and weight class. Militarily, this would mean enhanced flight performance and tactical characteristics; commercially, lower operating costs. Superficially, it would appear that Soviet helicopter developments have been marked by a remorseless evolution from small (Mi-1) to medium (Mi-4) to large (Mi-6 and Mi-10) to massive (Mi-26) helicopters.

It is, however, true to say that increases in size and weight are virtually impossible without qualitative improvements in transmissions and engines. Here a reduction in weight per unit horsepower and decreased fuel consumption are possibly the most important. The 240% increase in payload of the Mi-2 compared to that of the Mi-1 is a case in point and due almost entirely to the installation of two free turbines which generated 40% more power while weighing only half that of the Mi-1's single piston engine.

The development of the Mi-6 would have been unthinkable without the appearance of turboshaft engines. The belated recognition that helicopters perform better with engines designed for them was a far cry from the early days before and after the Second World War when helicopters had to make do with any engine available in the appropriate class.

Apart from the Mi-1, Mi-4, Mi-34 and Ka-26 all Soviet helicopters in service today employ turboshaft engines. Except for the Lotarev D-136 in the Mi-26 these engines are all based on 1950/60s technology, however, and their performance in general terms is below that of comparable Western engines. Power-to-weight ratios, not unexpectedly, do not match modern Western designs. Transmissions are much heavier and specific fuel consumption is about 25% higher. The principal reason for this is lower turbine inlet temperatures. The 11,400 shp D-136 is more modern and efficient. Using high temperature-resistant metals, it is light and has a low fuel consumption. As has already been noted the Mi-26's VR-26 transmission is a major improvement on the R-7 of the Mi-6. A conspicuous feature of Soviet helicopters is the auxiliary air intake above, between and behind the engine intakes. This is for cooling transmission oil and is not found on Western helicopters. The location of powerplants favoured by both the Mil and Kamov OKBs, side-by-side over the forward fuselage, was long ago discarded by Western designers. Side-mounted and well separated engines offer greater survivability and it would seem that this layout has been adopted by both the Havoc and Hokum. Furthermore, the auxiliary transmission cooling intake is no longer evident.

By increasing rotor span the size and weight of a helicopter may also be raised but the ratio of useful load to take-off weight will decrease if there is no simultaneous improvement in blade design and reductions in the weight of engines, transmissions and other assemblies. Indeed, in the 1930s it was thought that there was no point in developing helicopters with a power greater than 500 hp since any further increase in power would not lead to a higher useful load. At that time if power was increased the weight of the rotors, reduction gears, and in fact the whole machine rose more rapidly than that of the useful load. This, of course, is quite unacceptable and thus simultaneous qualitative improvement is necessary to achieve increases in useful load. Western designers had generally agreed that seven blades were the maximum for a rotor head even though Mil had suggested in his text book that eight was the limit. Then the Halo appeared.

In the 1950s as helicopters became more reliable and able to lift productive loads, so their potential both in the civil and military fields came to be recognised. Despite the fact that there is no real helicopter development in the Soviet Union for purely civil purposes economic considerations have become of major concern. The operating cost per hour is the decisive factor in whether to employ a helicopter for agricultural purposes, and for passenger and freight carrying. Costs per passenger mile and per ton mile are of particular interest to all countries but specially to those outside the Soviet bloc. These figures must be competitive with Western helicopters if the Soviet Union is to succeed in selling its helicopters in the world market.

The Soviet helicopter industry still has close technical links with its fixed-wing counterpart. Indeed, helicopters are generally built to complement fixed-wing aircraft, if not actually compete with them. Speed and payload/range are important and this is well demonstrated by the Mi-6 Hook, the first helicopter to exceed 300 kph while, at the same time, being easily the biggest in the world. In the early days the Ka-8 and Ka-10 had pontoons but no Soviet helicopter ever had skids rather than wheels until the recent arrival of the Mi-34. The reason for wheels was the preference for a short take-off and landing (STOL) capability rather than a purely vertical capability with its lower payload. Soviet helicopters are thus often described as having two take-off weights: a maximum for rolling take-offs which is higher than the normal weight which allows vertical take-off. Speed, in the dive and in the cruise, is more highly prized than good hover performance. Evidence of this is the generally poor hover and low speed performance of the Hip and the Hind, the latter having particularly good high speed characteristics. These are further enhanced by having a retractable undercarriage; only the Mi-14 Haze and Hokum join the Hind in having this feature. As battlefield tactics and techniques evolve it may be expected that the next generation of Soviet military helicopters including the Havoc and Hokum will have a better hover/low speed performance with improved agility and acceleration/deceleration.

169

As in fixed-wing aircraft the pilot always sits in the left-hand seat with the co-pilot on the right whereas in Western helicopters the pilot often sits in the right-hand seat. In single rotor helicopters the blades always rotate clock-wise when viewed from above so that torque reaction is always anti-clockwise – the same as in Soviet single-engined fixed-wing aircraft. All tail rotors, with two exceptions, have been 'pushers' rather than 'pullers'; the exceptions are the Mi-17 Hip and the Mi-24 Hind. Some early A models and the B models have a pusher. More recent A models, and all others have a puller. Flight decks are usually more spacious in Soviet helicopters despite the fact that crew numbers are higher. Less attention, however, is paid to crew comfort and cockpit ergonomics. The Mi-8 Hip has a crew of three while the S-61 only has a two-man crew. The bigger helicopters of course have even larger crews and outnumber the flight crew of most Western transatlantic jets. One reason may be that all types of helicopter will surely have to operate in remote and climatically harsh regions of the world. On these occasions a navigator and also a flight engineer have proved of inestimable value. They reduce pilot workload, contribute to the operations' cost-efficiency and allow the pilots to look out more. Again the economic aspects of bigger flight crews are of less importance than in the West.

It is probably foolhardy to state that Soviet helicopter technology is behind that of the West in most departments. There can be no doubt that this is true as far as small helicopters are concerned despite the advent of the Mi-34. Light helicopters do not seem to have been of much interest to the Mil OKB. In 1964 responsibility for the production of the smallest helicopter then in the Mil range, the Mi-2 Hoplite, was passed over to the Poles. Throughout the 1970s and most of the 1980s the lightest Mil helicopter to enter production has been the 11,500 kg (25,350 lb) Hind; the lightest Kamov military helicopter, the 7,485 kg (16,500 lb) Hormone. The Western countries have devoted much of their development efforts to helicopters with maximum take-off weights below 10,000 kg (22,046 lb) – there has, of course, been a number of successful machines above this weight – and in this sector is many years ahead. Notable exceptions to this Western superiority, however, are in the heavy lift field and in certain disciplines such as the arming of many different types of helicopter and the use of electrical de-icing systems where the position is reversed. In the former there seems to be a trend towards larger calibre machine guns; in the case of the latter the rigours of the Russian winter no doubt helped to concentrate the minds of the designers. Furthermore, operating in extremely cold conditions raises special problems: the congealing of lubricants, the cracking of metals, the loss of elasticity in rubber etc. Thus the Russians have been forced to develop materials, lubricants and other items capable of withstanding excessively low temperatures. But it is not really profitable or fair to compare technologies due to the different emphasis placed on them.

Yet there is no doubt that the Russians are always on the lookout for Western technology and are prepared to go to great lengths to acquire it. They are not averse to filling operational capability gaps by simply copying Western ideas, attack helicopters for example, and designs; the Su-25 Frogfoot and the Mi-28 Havoc are fairly recent copies of the American A-10 Thunderbolt and the AH-64 Apache respectively (2).

The Soviet philosophy is to produce a helicopter able to do the job. It must do it cheaply; it must be able to go on doing it for years – therefore it must be simple and robust; production must be uncomplicated. The Mi-6 and Mi-24 are good examples: both production runs lasted over 15 years with the Mi-24s still continuing. The Mi-8 prototype first flew in 1961 and the production line is still running, albeit in the modified form of the Mi-17. Over 10,000 Mi-8 and Mi-17 Hips have now been built.

It should never be thought that to bring a new helicopter into service as quickly as possible corners may be cut in the testing of components and the helicopter itself. Mil

170

once said that his newest helicopters underwent at least 1,000 hours of field tests and that any design shortcomings had to be sorted out before series production began. What a change from the days when production began shortly after the machine took to the air for the first time.

There is no evidence to suggest that the Soviet Union is likely to change dramatically her present philosophy of low risk evolutionary, rather than high risk revolutionary, design work. Under Mikhail Gorbachev the clamp on creative initiative may be relaxed but a new generation of bold and imaginative, and untypical, technocrats and engineers will be needed to take advantage of new opportunities.

For the reasons we have seen greater numbers of simple, rugged helicopters are preferred to fewer, more sophisticated machines. This is not to say that the Russians cannot, or will not, develop very sophisticated helicopters or components if necessary, but their actions tend to support the well-worn phrase that "the best is the enemy of the good". Soviet helicopters may be slower, they may vibrate more, they may look less attractive, they may have higher operating costs, they may not compete well with Western helicopters world-wide, but they fulfil the jobs for which they were built – jobs, military and civil, which range geographically from the freezing temperatures of the Arctic to the searing heat of the desert. It is Mikhail Mil who is reputed to have coined the admirable slogan: "Make it simple, make it reliable, make it rugged and make it work."

Notes

1.   The Russians did not enter a team for the First Helicopter World Championships in 1971.

2.   The Russians have bought some Western helicopters, notably American and French. The Vietnam War was invaluable as a source of downed American helicopters which were shipped back to the Mil plant in Moscow for thorough examination.

The evolution
of Soviet helicopter tactics

The Soviet Armed Forces consist of five main Arms of Service which come under the direct operational control of the General Staff and which are ranked in the following order of precedence:

Strategic Rocket Forces (*Raketnye Voiska Strategicheskogo Naznacheniya*)
Ground Forces (*Sukhoputnye Voiska*)
Air Defence Forces (*Voiska Protivo-Vozdushnoi Oboroni* – VPVO)
Air Forces (*Voenno-Vozdushnye Sily* – V-VS)
Navy (*Voenno-Morskoi Flot* – VMF)

These Services each have their own Deputy Minister of Defence who is responsible to the Minister of Defence, Army General Dmitri Yazov, who is also Chairman of the Military Council. The first four branches, historically, are described as the Soviet Army. The Air Forces have undergone a major reorganisation during the last decade and now comprise:

Five Strategic Air Armies (still sometimes known as *Dalnyaya Aviatsiya* – Long Range Aviation – DA)
20 Air Forces of Military Districts and Groups of Forces (still sometimes known as *Frontovaya Aviatsiya* – Frontal Aviation – FA)
Transport Aviation (*Voenno-Transportnaya Aviatsiya* – V-TA)

Aircraft are also to be found in:
Air Defence Forces (*Aviatsiya PVO*)
Naval Aviation (*Aviatsiya Voenno-Morskogo Flota* – AV-MF)

Helicopters are principally to be found in the Air Forces of the Military Districts and Groups of Forces (AFMD/GOF) with a few serving in the V-TA. AV-MF also operates a sizeable number of helicopters, a significant proportion of them in the ASW role. The majority of helicopters in an AFMD or GOF are allocated to its combined arms and tank armies and thus the term army aviation (*armeiskaya aviatsiya*) is applied to them. Although flown by air force personnel the crews of these helicopters are known, confusingly, as 'army aviators'. This concept of army aviation is perhaps best explained by examining the most important GOF, the one stationed in East Germany and known as the Group of Soviet Forces Germany (GSFG). GSFG, which might form one or conceivably two Fronts in the event of war, has five armies which between them have 19 divisions. The HQ has almost certainly retained operational control of certain helicopter assets such as Hip electronic warfare (EW) helicopters and a regiment of

172

Hips and the larger Hook transport helicopters; it has also no doubt a few Hooks in the airborne command post role. Army aviation is to be found in the armies and divisions. The commanders of these formations exercise operational control of their helicopters while the V-VS remains responsible for all other aspects: doctrine and tactics, procedures and techniques, the manning and training of air and ground crews and support in all its forms. Such a system is at odds with most of those in NATO where it is generally believed that battlefield helicopters should be flown by Army crews because they should have a better understanding of the needs of the ground forces and be more able to make good use of the terrain. It was the need to reduce the time to respond to calls for air support, to allow better integration with the ground forces and to give army and divisional commanders greater tactical flexibility that led to the decentralisation of operational control of helicopters and the establishment of army aviation. In the second half of the 1970s complaints of lack of flexibility and initiative appeared regularly in the military press and this criticism, the example of most NATO countries and the dawning realisation that the helicopter's potential influence on battlefield activities may previously have been underestimated were enough to initiate action.

Each army has an attack helicopter regiment, usually commanded by a colonel but sometimes by a lieutenant colonel, with some 60 helicopters possibly organised like this:

ATTACK HELICOPTER REGIMENT

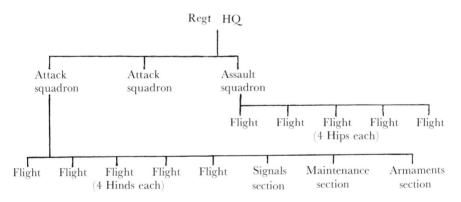

It would be no surprise if each army also has a separate squadron comprising a few Hoplites, Hip and Hook airborne command posts, and probably a few simple transport versions of the latter two types as well.

In 1979 the first division in GSFG began to receive its own helicopters and probably by 1985 all 19 divisions had a squadron each, typically of 18 helicopters. These consisted of six Hind-D, six Hip-C, and six Hoplites, a handy and varied little force under the direct operational control of the division commander. It also meant that an army commander with four divisions could count on the support of some 130 helicopters.

Thus, by the mid-1980s, in terms of helicopter types, GSFG could boast possession of over 320 Hind-D, E and F, about the same number of Hip-C, D, E, G, H, J and K, over 140 Hoplites and about 40 Hooks – a total of not less than 820 helicopters – a fourfold increase in ten years. However, once all 19 divisions had formed their squadrons the number of Hinds in them began to be increased and so the total number of helicopters in GSFG continues to rise inexorably. Besides its highly potent force of attack helicopters the GSFG has the capability to lift its air assault brigade, less its heavy equipment, in a single lift. The GSFG commander can, of course, concentrate army and divisional helicopters for specific operations if he so desires. Available as an addition to this massive force are the helicopters of the East German Air Force, Aeroflot reinforcements and others from nearby AFMD or GOF.

The Great Patriotic War, devastating as it was yet to the Russians intensely heroic, has eclipsed without question any other episode in Russian or Soviet history (with the possible exception of the Revolution!). Although losing some 20 million people, the Soviet Union became the greatest power in the Old World. Small wonder then that, in searching for a new way ahead, recourse should always be made to the lessons learned during that war. Perhaps the greatest was that the Red Army was not ready for war and that is why today combat-readiness is rated so highly. GSFG's divisions are all classed as 'ready', almost fully manned and equipped to their war establishment. The exploits of the Red Army Air Force during the war have been the source of constant inspiration for those responsible for devising new concepts and procedures.

Only now is the influence of this war beginning to diminish but it is likely to be many years yet before it ceases to be the primary influence on those responsible for combat development. Long before the war, however, the attractions of offence rather than defence had been clearly recognised. One of the Bolshevik leaders during the Revolution, M. V. Frunze, who in 1925 became Commissar for Military and Naval Affairs, declared that year: "The victor will be the one who summons the determination to attack; the side which only defends is doomed to inevitable defeat."

Nearly 65 years on this philosophy still holds good as an expression of Soviet military thinking: offensive action throughout the enemy's tactical and operational depth using surprise, deception, mobility and speed of manoeuvre is the key to victory. As Colonel General M. A. Gareyev wrote in *M. V. Frunze – Military Theorist* in 1985 – "The modern offensive is a composite of strike actions, a swift penetration of tanks and mechanised infantry supported from the air by aviation and attack helicopters and by bold airborne actions inside the enemy's defence and on the flanks of opposing groups."

From 1945 until Stalin's death in 1953 the Soviet Armed Forces remained slaves to the military doctrine and procedures developed during the Great Patriotic War. Firepower, mobility and shock action on a continental scale were the keystones and the introduction of more sophisticated weapons and equipment made no more than a minor impression. But in 1954 a dramatic transformation was put in hand as the Armed Forces began to train for war under nuclear conditions. At this time a global mission was given to Soviet strategic forces but it was not really until 1960 that the Russians had enough strategic and battlefield nuclear weapons to consider them the primary weapon in their inventory; in 1959 a completely new and independent arm of service, the Strategic Rocket Forces, was formed. The introduction of nuclear weapons inevitably had major repercussions, not least in the conduct of the land battle. As the new nuclear doctrine was being developed and refined for this particular arena, the NATO doctrine of a massive nuclear response to any aggression against it was superseded in 1967 by the strategy of forward defence and flexible response whereby aggression might be met initially with conventional weapons. At much the same time the Russians began to appreciate that any nuclear war would result in the destruction of Europe and key centres, at least, in the Soviet Union. Such a war must therefore be avoided and it followed that the Soviet Union must win any war in Europe before the Western Allies resorted to nuclear weapons. Victory would be assured only if Soviet forces could penetrate deeply into Western Europe, rout NATO forces and bring about a political collapse so quickly that the Western governments would not have time or the will to make the all-important decision to "go nuclear". The ability to fight a nuclear war, however reluctant the desire, it was essential to retain. By the time the 1960s were drawing to a close the Soviet General Staff under Marshal Grechko, who took over as Defence Minister in 1967, had become embroiled in a modernisation programme to meet the political requirement to be able to win a conventional war in Europe within a few days. New, more suitable equipment was subsequently issued and tactics refined with the result that now the Soviet Ground Forces are organised, equipped and trained for a lightning offensive war using conventional weapons only, though still under the constant threat of the use of nuclear weapons by NATO. What effect the elimination of intermediate range nuclear weapons will have on the strategies of NATO and the Warsaw Pact remains to be seen. Whatever measures are necessary for NATO's policy of flexible response to remain credible will, no doubt, be taken.

The Operational Manoeuvre Group (OMG)

As Warsaw Pact capabilities in firepower and mobility grew during the 1970s the shortcomings of NATO's static defence concept began to appear more and more obvious. While maintaining the principle of forward defence, a concept of more active defence was studied and then adopted. This was seen by Warsaw Pact planners as a concept combining the best features of both static and truly mobile defence and one that might prevent Warsaw Pact forces achieving the military and political collapse of the NATO Alliance before it was able to resort to nuclear weapons. Thus a good deal of thought was, and still is, devoted to the problem of how to destroy NATO's nuclear capability before it can be used while simultaneously destroying or neutralising NATO's conventional fighting forces. Success would depend, in the view of many Soviet writers, on the speed and destructive power of the initial offensive which would involve deep thrusts into NATO territory by air and ground forces. These might result in encirclement of NATO forces or be followed by much deeper penetrations by armoured forces in conjunction with airborne and air assault units. It is this second stage of the attack which is now considered to be the answer to NATO's active defence and would be carried out by a force known as the Operational Manoeuvre Group (OMG). This Soviet concept is not, however, completely new, merely an updated version of the Great Patriotic War Mobile Group which was essentially a tank-heavy force of about divisional size which had much the same function. The activities of OMGs would constitute an important element of the ground forces operation which, in turn, is part of the principal triad for a strategic offensive: the air, anti-air and ground force operations (1). Without the success of the first two, OMGs would be at the mercy of enemy air power and would have little chance of success themselves.

The OMG does not have a standard organisation like a tank or motor rifle division. However, after some ten years or more of theoretical study and many field exercises it would seem that, according to the 1986 edition of *Soviet Military Power*, independent army corps, between two and three times the size of a tank division, have been formed; these are well suited to act as an OMG for a Front with a reinforced tank division being the OMG for an army. Nevertheless, in general terms, an OMG comprises those units which are considered necessary to carry out its mission. The aim of any OMG is simply to penetrate to the enemy's rear areas as quickly as possible, to attack important targets, particularly nuclear weapon systems, left unscathed by the initial air attack; to isolate the forward defences and disrupt any reorganisation of the defence in depth and the movement of reinforcements; and to capture vital ground and terrain features, such as airfields, bridges, and road junctions, with a view to maintaining or even increasing the momentum of the advance of the main forces. Indeed, Lt Gen V. G. Reznichenko, in the 1984 edition of his book *Taktika* (Tactics), writes of the previous method of attack whereby succeeding echelons had to grind their way through the defences; now, highly mechanised forces in smaller numbers can penetrate to a much greater depth much more quickly.

On 20 September 1981 Colonel General Sukhorukov wrote in *Red Star* of "vertical envelopment" which was considered to be "an important manoeuvre without which modern offensive operations are not possible". Other writers have stressed how essential is the role of airborne, heliborne and helicopter units in deep penetration operations by OMGs. Helicopters obviously have a key role to play: transport helicopters for the carriage of troops and equipment, for resupply and casualty evacuation, attack helicopters to act as mobile weapons platforms to provide close air support and to engage enemy combat helicopters, reconnaissance helicopters to acquire targets and watch the flanks, gaps and the rear, airborne command post helicopters, and EW helicopters to jam and suppress enemy radars and communications. In this way helicopters can contribute to the combat potential of the OMG and thus increase the momentum of the advance of the main forces. There is no denying that all these helicopters will be very vulnerable when operating behind enemy lines and they will need a good deal of protection. Another major problem will be their rearming, refuelling and minor maintenance. Difficult decisions will centre around the choice of sites for these activities: within the area held by the OMG, inevitable if the OMG is already beyond reasonable flying range of the main ground forces, or just behind the leading elements of the main force? Both have their obvious disadvantages as does any compromise between the two.

At a lower tactical level ground-air raiding groups can be formed temporarily for specific hit and run tasks, both in attack and defence. These groups differ from an OMG, not only in scale but also in concept: they raid – they do not capture and hold ground but return to their own lines once the mission is complete. Helicopters from the divisional squadrons would form part of the ground element – an interesting indication of the level of integration envisaged – while more helicopters and fighter aircraft would comprise the air element. Attack helicopters would be vital for armed reconnaissance and close air support while other types would carry out command, control and communications (C^3) duties, EW and troop lift tasks. Helicopters may also be used to insert small teams of special forces behind enemy lines to attack specific targets.

Early tactical employment

As we have already seen, for the two decades after the Second World War, the helicopter was regarded as a useful vehicle for troop lift and administrative and logistic tasks but hardly as a weapons platform. Although with only the Mi-1 Hare in service, Soviet interest in the tactical use of helicopters was quickened by their employment in two small-scale assaults by the Americans in the Korean War. In using helicopters with spectacular success for evacuating casualties and rescuing downed airmen behind enemy lines, the Korean War's place in aviation history was won by the demonstration of the military potential of the helicopter rather than by the contest between the MiG-15 Fagot and the North American F-86 Sabre.

The Soviet view in the early 1950s was that helicopters could be employed in the tactical delivery of troops (*Vertoletnyi Desant*, heliborne assault) in certain circumstances. The need for a troop-carrying helicopter was quickly appreciated and in October 1951, fifteen months after the outbreak of the Korean War, Stalin gave his famous and chilling order to Mil and Yakovlev to build the Mi-4 Hound and the Yak-24 Horse respectively. One role for the new helicopters was envisaged as lifting airborne troops ahead of the main body to capture key objectives such as bridges, road junctions and even airfields. This had the further advantage of carrying these troops over natural obstacles and forward areas likely to be mined. This new concept was practised on exercises and proved to be successful. The desire for an even larger helicopter to help in opening up the more remote regions of the USSR coincided with the military requirement for a heavy lift helicopter. The Mi-6 Hook, with its maximum payload of 12,000 kg (26,455 lb) or 65 lightly-armed troops, entered service in the early 1960s. Now large numbers of troops together with a wide variety of equipment, including assault and anti-tank guns, could be delivered simultaneously onto tactical objectives provided that they were not too heavily defended. Thus before the Vietnam War had even begun the Russians had accepted the potential of the helicopter as a battlefield vehicle, if not an armed one. With the possibility that any war in Europe might start or "go nuclear" the Russians had also turned their attention to nuclear war and developed a doctrine which included very rapid rates of advance and the by-passing of nuclear-contaminated areas. And in assisting the momentum to be maintained heliborne troops had a clear and positive role.

The extensive use of helicopters in Vietnam during the 1960s was very closely monitored by the Soviet military hierarchy. Publicly, the Russians were somewhat reticent about their judgements as to the viability and survivability of the helicopter on the battlefield. Privately, it now transpires, they were quickly becoming convinced of the potential of both armed and unarmed helicopters. The major reason for this conviction was the prominence attached to mobility. By the late 1950s it had become the most important principle. But the Russians, according to Colonel V. Ye. Savkin in his authoritative and much quoted book *The Basic Principles of Operational Art and Tactics*, published in 1972, "understand troop mobility to be their high manoeuvrability and their capability for full use of combat power for the rapid achievement of their assigned mission with maximum effect and for the immediate and most expedient reaction to any events or changes in the situation." Mobility is thus seen not purely as an ability to cross terrain easily but also what we in the West would term flexibility. It embraces a commander's flexibility of mind, his use of firepower, his command and control, and his ability to outperform his adversary at any chosen place and time. Superior mobility allows a Soviet commander to create favourable circumstances before his attack, to concentrate superior forces, to achieve surprise, to sustain his combat activity, and to disperse his troops before they can constitute a nuclear target.

A number of methods of enhancing the mobility, in the Western sense of the word, of Soviet ground forces was studied including their total motorisation and the conversion of towed artillery to self-propelled. The prospect of a significant level of airtransportability was closely examined. The Soviet General Staff was well aware that increased mobility could help to offset the growing lethality of the battlefield. Fire and movement has always been the fundamental principle of combat but whereas the effective ranges of weapons and their probabilities of hit and kill had improved dramatically, the speed of movement had increased by only a few kilometres per hour. Air transport, however, could make possible a quantum jump and help to redress the balance. Modern combat, it was thought, would henceforth be characterised by operations of great ferocity and rapidity. Airmobility would become an integral part of modern warfare and would "permit a reduction in the gap between the power and mobility of troops."

Three aspects were studied. First, the development of fixed-wing transport aircraft permitted not only the mass use of parachutists but also the rapid deployment of ground forces and their equipment; furthermore such activities could be conducted on an operational and strategic scale and not just at tactical levels (2). Second, the use of helicopters allowed tactical redeployment to make the most of any combat opportunity. Finally, armed helicopters, integrated into combined arms formations, enhanced those formations' flexibility and ability to achieve surprise. It was not long before these concepts were being tried. And in 1967 the first film of Soviet armed helicopters taken during Exercise *Dnepr* was released to the West (3). Three years later on Exercise *Dvina* Hares were filmed firing Swatter anti-tank missiles. The success of these exercises confirmed the requirement for an armed assault/anti-tank helicopter and to meet it the Mi-24 Hind-A was already under development.

Besides the perceived need for helicopters to attack specific ground targets, the arming of helicopters in general fulfilled also a deep-seated psychological need: soldiers are more confident and will go forward to meet the enemy if they can pull a trigger. Similarly, the crew of a helicopter is less likely to hold back if it can fire on the enemy. Furthermore, ground troops will not fire so resolutely at a helicopter that is spewing lead at them. For this reason the decision was taken to arm all helicopters likely to be involved on the battlefield, even some Hooks.

At the same time as greater numbers of larger helicopters, principally the Mi-6 Hook and Mi-8 Hip, were becoming available so troops other than airborne were given the chance to participate in heliborne assaults. Writing in *Voennyi Vestnik* (Military Herald) in January 1968, Colonel Ya. Samoylenko first made it clear that: "The introduction of helicopters has brought the practice of the aircraft landing method of airborne assault, which has great advantages over the parachuting method: the landing force is set down compactly, as a sub-unit, together with its arms and equipment. This makes it possible for the force go to into action immediately." (4) Army General V. F. Margelov, at one time Chief of Airborne Troops, added three years later: "But perhaps the main distinction of the helicopter landing is that personnel who have been trained for just a few hours can be used in it. Thus marines, combat engineers, mortarmen, and motorised riflemen, that is, representatives of the various arms of troops, can readily be moved to the enemy rear using helicopters and begin active combat operations there." The unit most suited to this role was considered to be the motor rifle battalion (MRB) (5) – any MRB – whose equipment is all airportable. It is well supplied with transport and firepower and could be further reinforced with extra anti-tank and anti-aircraft weapons, medium artillery, combat engineers, chemical troops and others. Various Soviet articles have suggested that such a reinforced MRB could operate effectively behind enemy lines for an extended period of time although this is in fact probably limited to 24 hours at the most with a more normal time of perhaps 8–12 hours before help would be needed. The key factor will clearly be how far in advance of the main force the MRB is expected to operate and this will in turn depend on the operational or tactical need to capture the vital ground, estimates of enemy resistance on the objective and the rate of the main Soviet advance. Very often helicopter-borne assaults are likely to be restricted to objectives which are within reach of Soviet artillery. No mention is made of how this force, consisting of perhaps 30 large helicopters, would actually cross the front lines and under what circumstances. Little is written of how troops may be extracted and it must therefore be assumed that plans will rarely be made for such an eventuality. Instead the force holds on until it can link up with the main body or it is destroyed.

There may, however, be occasions when a heliborne force is employed purely on a specific raid of very limited duration in which case extraction will be as important as insertion. According to Major General Belov the aim of such raids is "to penetrate quickly by air into the enemy position, destroy important objectives there, take prisoners, capture documents and samples of weapons and return immediately to the positions of the friendly troops."

As the 1970s dawned so the Soviet military press began to print more and more articles on airmobile tactics (6) although the authors still tended to value the helicopter more highly in its pure assault role. Major General Belov was the most prolific but he was followed closely by a number of others, notably Colonel Savkin who tended to write on a wider variety of subjects. But because of the helicopter's limitations, seen by Major General Belov mainly as its lack of an all-weather capability and vulnerability to all battlefield weapons (7), few of the articles in the early 1970s discussed offensive operations; although the Hind had flown its existence had not yet been publicly revealed. Yet there were signs in these articles that some writers felt that the mobility of the helicopter did not go far enough to counter the growing lethality of the modern battlefield in terms of ground-based weapons. Strap-on armaments were quite effective but they did limit the performance of the helicopter to which they were attached. What was needed was a multi-role helicopter with integral weapons capable of carrying out armed assaults and the destruction of tanks. The basic Soviet tenet that victory goes to the side with the greatest firepower demanded that all battlefield vehicles, including helicopters, had to be able to move across country without difficulty and be able to fire on the enemy.

The influence of US airmobile doctrine is conspicuous in Soviet writing on the subject. By 1974 the stream of articles had become a flood and due emphasis was being given to the helicopter as a tank destroyer and also as complementing the tank in combined arms actions. The main purpose of these articles may well have been part of a propaganda campaign to sell the idea of airmobility with all its implications to the military population in general and to the old and doubting diehards in particular. Major General Belov considered that "the development of modern military science and technology has made helicopters a formidable weapon, no less effective than winged aircraft. In certain tactical situations they are virtually indispensable." One of the characteristics of the Soviet military system, though, is its conservatism. There was no question of allocating resources to build up airmobile forces until it had been proved that they could survive in a mid-intensity or nuclear environment in Europe.

Soviet airmobile forces are tasked with a variety of missions but many are connected in one way or another with helping to maintain the momentum of an advance. In 1971 *Voennyi Vestnik* published an article entitled 'The Battalion of an Air Assault Force' which included the following extract: "The importance and significance of tactical (heliborne) landing forces have greatly increased in modern combat. These forces may be assigned various tasks: delay the entry of the enemy's reserves; destroy nuclear attack weapons; occupy and hold (until the arrival of advance units) water crossings and sections suitable for crossing in force; destroy command posts in the rear; hold mountain passes, gorges, road intersections and other important tactical areas or facilities of the enemy. In addition, they can seize sections of a shoreline and thus contribute to the landing of marines."

Air assault forces

While selected MRBs became more adept in the execution of the airmobile role the development of the OMG concept soon served to emphasize their major shortcoming: their inability to operate as part of an OMG engaged in deep penetration. Despite claims that an MRB could be landed up to 50 km (31 miles) ahead of the forward edge of the battle area (FEBA), in practice they rarely went beyond 20 km (12 miles). The reason was almost certainly inadequate mobility and firepower and therefore their need for artillery and aviation fire support. For army and front level OMGs to succeed, and succeed they must if the war is to be won quickly, they must make incisive and deep penetrations. But with only heliborne MRBs at their disposal army and front commanders were hamstrung: they could not reach forward far enough and therefore had to ask for the help of parachute forces. These might not be forthcoming or be allocated too late. Thus, a strong case could be made for an air assault force, more powerful and with a longer reach than a heliborne MRB, that was organic to both armies and fronts. The creation of airmobile brigades of three battalions each began in the early 1970s to be followed by air assault battalions at army level and air assault brigades at front level in the late 1970s. According to *Soviet Military Power 1987* seven air assault brigades have been formed so far. If more are formed could we see brigades grouped together to form air assault divisions at front level?

From various articles in Soviet magazines it seems that an air assault brigade might be expected to operate in excess of 100 km (62 miles) ahead of the FEBA while a battalion can probably reach out to 70 km (43 miles) or so. A brigade has some 2,500 men and seems to consist of three parachute battalions, one assault battalion equipped with the BMD airborne amphibious infantry fighting vehicle, an artillery battalion with the 122 mm D-30 or the newer 120 mm 2S9 self-propelled howitzer and various smaller units to provide anti-tank, air defence, engineer, signals, chemical defence, medical and transport support. An air assault battalion has about 500 men and consists of a BMD company, three parachute companies, an artillery battery and other smaller sub-units. Powerful as these organisations are they have, nevertheless, a significant weakness and that is the lack of organic helicopters. This shortcoming results inevitably in less joint training and therefore lower standards and the all-important camaraderie and common purpose generated by belonging to the same unit. It is of course easier to convert motor rifle troops into full-time air assault troops and to give them the appropriate equipment already in service than it is to provide them with their own helicopters – there simply are not enough to go round. To lift an air assault brigade, complete with BMDs, artillery, mortars etc, in a single lift would require over 100 Hooks or at least 50 Halos and not less than 50 Hips. While there are more than enough Hips in GSFG to undertake such a commitment, prior to sustaining any losses and at the expense of other tasks, not enough Hooks or Halos are currently available. Were the brigade to operate without its BMDs and similar sized vehicles, and thus be less mobile and effective, then it could be transported by GSFG's own helicopters with the Hooks undertaking two sorties rather than three or four.

Given its composition an air assault brigade or battalion is capable of carrying out a number of important tasks in support of an OMG. Whether a brigade would be targetted against nuclear weapon sites is open to discussion, there being other means more likely to achieve success. But without doubt the destruction of headquarters, command posts and communications centres would be a high priority. Another important task would be the capture of ground which dominates routes forward or terrain on which the defence hinges. A particularly important aspect of the terrain are rivers which present a formidable obstacle to advancing forces. Ideally, bridges should be captured intact but when this is impossible river crossing sites, suitable for armoured vehicles to get into and out of the water or for bridges to be built, must be seized. Such sites are likely to be hotly defended. Other targets for air assault units might be airfields, mountain passes, key road junctions and beachheads – indeed, any feature, natural or man-made, which might expedite the advance of the OMG or other forces for which the unit is working.

The disruption of enemy reserves and blocking the movement of reinforcements follow a precedent set during the Second World War; Lieutenant General Reznichenko has written approvingly of units which attack targets in enemy rear areas to "destroy personnel and equipment, deny the enemy rest and to sow panic". Furthermore, attempts to encircle the enemy could be very much assisted by hindering their withdrawal.

Advancing forces are always hungry for information as to what is ahead of them and in this respect BMD-equipped air assault battalions can do much to help. By inserting such units at intervals along the projected axis of advance invaluable information on routes and enemy deployments and movements could be collected.

The Russians pay a good deal of attention to deception to try to achieve surprise and air assault units can help in being landed in places chosen to confuse the enemy's perception of Soviet plans. While reserves are moved to counter the force other Soviet units fill the gap. On Exercise *Zapad-81* (West-81) a heliborne force was landed in the enemy rear to cause as much disruption as possible. While reserves were rushed to contain and destroy it another heliborne force was sent in to seize a river crossing site.

The creation of air assault brigades and battalions has made a significant contribution to the combat effectiveness of those armies and fronts which now possess them and would probably use them as part of OMG operations to help maintain the momentum of the advance. Their creation is a further sign of Soviet willingness to exploit the potential of the helicopter and not be deterred by the probability of heavy losses.

They have been used extensively and effectively in Afghanistan where their operations first came to notice. The war will have been a useful proving ground to test and check organisations, equipments, techniques and procedures.

Despite the establishment of air assault units some MRBs in selected divisions are still trained for a heliborne *desant* role; it is thought that they would be used against certain specific targets or to capture a piece of key terrain. An article entitled 'A Tactical Airborne Landing' written by Colonel Yu. Chernyshov which appeared in the May 1980 edition of the Soviet *Military Review* gave an interesting account of a heliborne *desant*. After listing the possible missions for a heliborne motorised infantry unit the Colonel described the factors to be considered in planning a heliborne assault. Such an operation is always bedevilled by uncertainties and therefore extremely meticulous and thorough planning is essential. This planning however is based on well-rehearsed drills and tactics known to all. What has to be decided is which drill is to be applied to the assigned mission. By Western standards, a lesser degree of planning is required and the attack can be launched more quickly. The composition of the assault force depends to a large extent upon the mission assigned to it. For the seizure of a river crossing, for example, the force might consist of:

One MRB
One or two 122 mm artillery batteries
An additional anti-tank platoon
A combat engineer platoon or section
A chemical reconnaissance team
Forward observation posts for the main force artillery
Tactical air control party
Underwater demolition teams
Appropriate helicopter units.

The force is organised on functional lines with each group having a well-defined task: a seizure group, a covering group, a support group and a reserve. The seizure group's task is to capture the crossing site, its composition depending upon the enemy's strength and the physical nature of the objective; if a bridge, this group will include combat engineers and demolition teams to prevent its destruction by the enemy. The covering group is the largest element of the force and has the task of providing all-round defence for the bridgehead and supporting the link-up with the main advance. The support group of one or two motorised rifle platoons and some engineers carries out deeper reconnaissance of the enemy and the local terrain as a form of early warning. The reserve, held under the battalion commander's control, is available to help any of the other groups although it is not much more than a reinforced platoon.

Once the two major decisions have been made the battalion commander and the helicopter unit commander can deliberate upon the many matters involved in the troop lift. The most important of these will include timings for all phases; the allocation of troops and equipment to helicopters and where the embarkation and loading will take place; order of fly-in; routes and heights to fly; location of landing sites; artillery, helicopter gunship and fighter support; briefings for all participants to include political and psychological preparation; and rehearsals if deemed necessary.

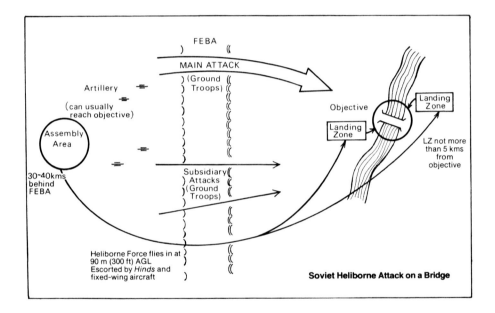

Soviet Heliborne Attack on a Bridge

During the planning and briefing process very tight security is maintained. Every effort is made to keep this time to no more than a few hours and a number of events take place concurrently. Helicopters and ground troops begin to concentrate and start their preparations before final briefings are given. With political exhortations ringing in their ears the troops begin loading their equipment under the supervision of the flight crews. Troops embark in order to ensure unit integrity so that the force can start to fight straight after landing.

Various Soviet films have shown heliborne forces being flown in to an objective. Fixed-wing aircraft first of all started the suppression of air defence weapons along the fly-in route. The transport helicopters were preceded by attack helicopters with others flying above them to provide flank protection and to engage any enemy helicopters that might have appeared. Usually a forward air controller flew with the leading attack helicopters to co-ordinate strikes by close air support aircraft and an artillery officer controlled the guns. When the artillery fire lifted with about three minutes to go to landing the attack helicopters strafed the area.

The formations were tight with transport helicopters being about three or four rotor diameters apart: close enough to simplify control and to allow the use of comparatively small landing sites yet far enough apart to reduce the risk of a mid-air collision and the possibility that enemy surface-to-air weapons might hit one aircraft having aimed at another. Normal heights to fly are about 90 m (300 ft). The choice of landing sites for a battalion is not easy as the hope remains that one suitable for the entire battalion formation can be found close to the objective. For a river crossing landing zones on both sides of the river are preferred.

A MRB without its BMPs requires about 20 Hips; if in a single lift and landing virtually simultaneously an area, free from obstacles, of at least 500 metres by 500 metres would be necessary. The five Hooks or three Halos carrying the heavy equipment usually land as a second wave, time on the ground being kept to a minimum.

Having landed the force unloads its equipment and should be ready to attack or begin its approach march to the objective within 10 or 15 minutes. Standard ground force tactics are now adopted as the objective is further blasted by air and artillery attack. Armed helicopters will continue to give support to the Hook/Halo fly-in and once the site has been captured Hips may undertake aerial minelaying along likely avenues of enemy approach.

One of the main advantages likely to be enjoyed by Soviet air assault and heliborne forces is that they will often operate in conditions of air superiority and under a formidable array of air defence weapons which, on the other hand, pose a substantial threat to NATO airmobile forces and close air support aircraft. Without attendant local air superiority heliborne forces are extremely vulnerable to attack from the air and the ground as soon as they approach the FEBA. Indeed, it is unlikely that heliborne operations would even be attempted without such superiority except in cases where the ground forces commander considers the risk worth taking. Fighter aircraft would be tasked to keep the skies clear to the depth judged necessary while attack helicopters would probably be ordered to take care of any intruding enemy armed helicopter. Both would attack ground targets and help to provide suppressive fire around landing zones.

A *desant*, to be successful, also relies heavily on ground-based fire support and in this context multi-barrelled rocket launchers such as the 220 mm BM-27 with its long range and area coverage are well suited to preparing the way.

A Polish commentator has written that "an airborne tactical assault should be given protective fighter cover during the entire process. This threat (of enemy intervention) will increase as the assault force approaches the landing area. This can be prevented by assigning a maximum number of fighter aircraft to provide air cover during the final assault stage." Once landed, the troops are responsible for their own air defence. All Soviet troops are taught how to fire their personal weapons at enemy aircraft. In addition, air assault units have their own complement of man-portable SA-7 and SA-14 surface-to-air missiles and they may well be reinforced with anti-aircraft artillery.

Helicopter roles

As the Russians watched American progress and became themselves more adept at moving troops by helicopter so they became more innovative. It was felt that combat in the early 1970s had indicated that modern defensive techniques had achieved a clear superiority over offence. Major General Belov believed that "the success of offensive operations of the land forces was doubtful unless mass use is made of helicopters. . . ."

Thus vertical manoeuvre was a necessary capability for modern forces. As the 1980s dawned the importance of the helicopter for combat and logistic support continued to grow and greater efforts were made to integrate the activities of mechanised infantry, tanks, artillery and helicopters.

So far has the concept of the battlefield helicopter advanced in Soviet eyes that it is now considered an important means of increasing the pace and widening the scope of ground force operations, principally at the operational level. While the attack helicopter has not superseded the other fighting arms the Russians now appear convinced that it can provide unequalled support (by being able to move forward at the same speed as the ground forces) and at times actually play the leading role both by day and night. Providing close air support has become the primary role but other uses, besides troop lift, to which the helicopter can be put on the battlefield have received much attention. Exercise activity confirms the Soviet determination to realise the potential of this three-dimensional machine.

Nor has the attack helicopter superseded fixed-wing close air support aircraft such as the Su-25 Frogfoot. The strengths of one largely cancel the weaknesses of the other and, working in tandem, they may be said to be complementary and very effective.

Close air support

Despite enormous efforts to modernise their artillery in terms of range, mobility and logitistic support, the Russians recognise that it will not be able to provide continuous support for a high speed offensive. The only weapon system that has the necessary flexibility is the helicopter. As a form of airborne self-propelled assault gun it is able to respond to calls for close air support very quickly in those areas for which there is no or insufficient artillery. In giving this support helicopters follow the same three phases as artillery: the preparatory phase (*podgotova*) which is preplanned and delivered before the attack starts; supporting fire (*podderzhka*) during the attack; and accompaniment (*soprovozhdenie*) when helicopters are available for opportunity targets within enemy rear areas. Cannon, rocket fire and guided missiles would be quite effective in providing suppressive fire to support the ground assault and against tanks, helicopters, multi-barrelled rocket launchers, strong points and other targets. Forward air controllers would almost certainly help in target acquisition and engagement of point targets. More and more of these controllers are themselves in helicopters.

Not surprisingly, Hind attack profiles initially reflected the design characteristics of the aircraft and the Soviet offensive doctrine; they thus resembled those of fixed-wing aircraft with the accent on speed. The basic grouping was a pair of helicopters, the tactical unit being two pairs – a *zveno* (flight). Flying towards the combat area at perhaps 250–300 m (820–1,000 ft), the Hinds would then descend as they approached the target only to 'pop up' to 150 m (500 ft) to fire their weapons in a shallow dive. Such tactics involved considerable exposure to enemy observation and fire but to minimise vulnerability engagements were begun at maximum weapon range and disengagement initiated as soon as possible at low level. Hovering in ambush positions was, and still is, not favoured because the gun and fire control systems are located very low on the fuselage and to use them entails exposing the entire helicopter, stationary, before they can be brought into play; furthermore, the Hind has a strong downwash and the debris and dust kicked up by it would almost certainly give its position away as well as obscuring the weapons sights. The rotor downwash in the hover also exacerbates the inevitable descent of a missile directly after launch due to gravity. Unless the hover is conspicuously high missiles might strike the ground. As familiarity with the Hind grew and training improved so did the flight profiles get lower and lower until sometimes there is no 'pop up' at all now, the helicopters remaining at just above tree top level. This development in tactics was followed by a new technique: Soviet films showed Hinds moving slowly forwards at speed of perhaps 50 kph (31 mph) into ambush positions. With this method concealment is still jeopardised but such a manoeuvre allows quick evasive action, minimises the effects of downwash and fire is from a relatively stable platform. It is rarely used, however.

The Havoc will surely have a good hover capability at maximum take-off weight and a reduced downwash; then attack from concealed ambush positions will be possible and no doubt will be used whenever Soviet forces are conducting defensive operations, perhaps when an OMG is under counter-attack, or when their helicopters are stalking enemy armour during an advance.

In 1983 a new three-helicopter tactical formation was proposed. In an article entitled 'The Quest for New Techniques' in the June 1983 edition of *Aviatsiya i Kosmonavtika* Colonel B. Nestrov wrote: "In that variant, the formation would include a two-helicopter search and attack element, and a single helicopter to provide cover. The attack element would fly in open formation, parallel to the battle line. The wingman would be positioned slightly rearward and slightly higher than the leader. The third helicopter would bring up the rear at a distance ensuring good visual contact and mutual fire support. They would fly nap-of-the-earth and at optimum speed. The commander of the section mans the cover helicopter. His principal task is tactical control." So far it is not thought that this formation has been accepted as standard, the pair or two pairs still being preferred.

One of the aspects of the NATO opposition that most concerns Soviet commanders is its tightly-knit anti-tank defence. To ensure a rapid victory all types of anti-tank weapons must be destroyed or at least suppressed. Most of these weapons (guided missiles, rockets and grenade launchers) are small and easily moved. They are easy to camouflage. The modern tank is a more formidable anti-tank weapon than ever with its accuracy, long range, rate of fire and ability to fire on the move. Dug-in and camouflaged it is indeed a potent anti-tank weapon. So predictably anti-tank tactics have received a great deal of attention. Writing in *Red Star* on 5 October, 1976, Lieutenant General Reznichenko gave his views on the value of anti-tank helicopters; "They are superior to other anti-tank weapons in terms of field of vision, manoeuvrability and firepower; they are capable of hitting enemy armoured targets while remaining out of reach of anti-aircraft weapons. The correlation between tank and helicopter losses is 12:1 or even 19:1 in the helicopter's favour, according to practical experiments."

The normal Soviet practice is to task fixed-wing aircraft against targets in depth and to use helicopters in the battle area to engage small targets such as individual tanks and air defence weapon systems. In particular, Hinds and Havocs when they enter service may be tasked to fly top cover to large tank formations literally to blast enemy tanks and anti-tank helicopters out of the way. On other occasions they may be held as a mobile anti-tank reserve. Occasionally they may be used in multiple pairs or flights of four to quarter the battlefield and seek out enemy armour.

As the first Hind units began to form, Colonel Savkin was writing that armed helicopters can and should provide air support for tanks and motorised infantry. Integrated into the combined arms group, these helicopters can attack enemy defensive areas holding up the advance, protect flanks, disrupt the movement of enemy reserves and destroy enemy reconnaissance units. Thus while NATO's armed helicopters are employed, first and foremost, in the anti-tank role, bolder use is being made of attack helicopters within the Warsaw Pact.

Helicopter air combat

A future European battlefield is not going to lack helicopters and there is no reason, therefore, to suppose that those that do meet will ignore each other. If they do not fight by design in helicopter hunter/killer teams, then chance encounters must be anticipated while they carry out other tasks – particularly on the fast-moving battlefield confidently expected.

Only a helicopter can match the speed range, manoeuvrability and firepower of another helicopter. For this reason it is fair to draw the conclusion that an armed helicopter is the best means to defeat another helicopter. It can then be argued that, in addition to being inevitable, helicopter combat may also be desirable. Major General Belov agrees. In an article entitled 'How to Fight Helicopters' printed in the Soviet *Military Review* in September 1979 he wrote that "Use of helicopters by both warring sides will inevitably lead to clashes between them. Like tank battles of past wars, a future war between well-equipped armies is bound to involve helicopter battles."

For helicopter air-to-air engagements it is now generally agreed that no single weapon is suitable. A stabilised machine gun or cannon for the closer ranges supplemented by a 'fire and forget' missile for the longer ranges would be ideal. Major General Belov writes of a 20–30 mm automatic cannon; anything less than 20 mm is not really suitable to engage aerial opportunity targets that can manoeuvre violently.

As has been noted the Hind-F sports a twin-barrelled 30 mm cannon instead of the four-barrelled 12.7 mm gun under the nose in the earlier models. However, the new weapon is fixed and it follows, therefore, that the aircraft itself must be manoeuvred to face its target. The rationale for this may be that there simply will not be much opportunity for the pilot to look anywhere but in a narrow arc forwards, particularly if he is flying at very low level.

Any purpose-built missile must be simple, light, supersonic, highly manoeuvrable and lethal with a minimum range of not more than 500 metres. Needless to say, sophisticated target acquisition and fire control systems are necessary. The Hind's armaments do not prohibit or even inhibit engagements. It is believed that the 57 mm rockets were originally designed for an air-to-air role and they, the 12.7 mm machine gun of the Hind-D or -E, the 30 mm cannon, and the Swatter and Spiral missiles could all be utilised now for the engagement of enemy helicopters. The Havoc is expected to have a better anti-helicopter capability than the Hind but, best of all in this role, if and when it comes into service, will be the Hokum, possibly designed to be a dedicated fighter helicopter with specialised weapons, great agility and high speed.

Various options are open to Soviet ground force commanders when it comes to using attack helicopters in the air-to-air role. An advancing commander may, for example, on occasion be sorely tempted to launch these helicopters against enemy missile-armed helicopters which are delaying his armoured thrust by standing off in ambush positions and engaging his tanks. At the very least the defenders will have their attention diverted from the advancing armour. More positively still, attack helicopter sub-units could be specifically tasked to seek out and attack NATO helicopters wherever they are and whatever they may be doing. More and more likely is it that Soviet crews will be given freedom to attack NATO armed helicopters whenever they are encountered. Defensively, when NATO forces counter-attack, Soviet attack helicopters will be earmarked to intercept and destroy the opposing helicopters.

Helicopter air combat will almost certainly start as group combat with substantial numbers being involved. Pairs, threes, or groups of pairs and threes will provide mutual support in terms of lookout and fire. Eventually one-on-one helicopter duels may emerge from the melée. The combat will be characterised by tight manoeuvering in an effort to get into a position in which to open fire or to prevent the enemy getting into a similar position. The freedom of manoeuvre vertically because of the presence of air defence weapons and fixed-wing aircraft will be rare and ground obstacles will offer another major hazard as the machines twist and turn at very low level. Speed margins will not be great and it will be almost impossible to disengage by accelerating away.

The advantage will nearly always lie with the crews which see their opponents first, thus being able to achieve some degree of surprise. The Russians therefore envisage 'long-range' combat when they acquire their targets beyond weapon range and close in for the kill and meeting engagements when both sides have a chance encounter. The struggle here will be to gain the initiative. Before battle is ever joined, however, much can be achieved. Rate of turn and the ability to change the mode of flight very rapidly have now become crucial performance characteristics for combat helicopters. These will have been features to which the designers of the Havoc and Hokum will have paid due attention. Another critical element will be crew and sub-unit co-ordination and expertise and high standards can only be achieved by continual and realistic training. In recent years the Russians have carefully studied the whole topic of helicopter air combat and started training their attack helicopter crews.

General support

The second area where the role of helicopters has been expanding is that of general support, a miscellany of functions, old and new.

While NATO helicopters include reconnaissance and observation as an important role, this aspect of helicopter operations has until recently been neglected by the Russians. But now interest is being shown in using helicopters to gather essential information on enemy deployments and movements and the terrain so that commanders can take correct and timely decisions on the concentration of their forces on the axes most likely to allow the desired rate of advance. Reconnaissance in contact with the enemy is an extremely difficult and demanding task. To do it stealthily without the enemy being aware is probably beyond Soviet crews at the moment, given their lack of training in such techniques and a helicopter type suited to reconnaissance. The Hoplite is the helicopter usually employed in this role but it does not compare with any of the NATO reconnaissance helicopter types, such as the Gazelle, OH-58C and D or the Bo 105, in its ability to acquire and designate targets without being seen: its performance is poor, it is too noisy and it is too big, its empty weight being more than the maximum take-off weight of the Anglo-French and US helicopters and only just less than that of the Bo 105.

Behind the leading elements of their own forces they can, however, be especially useful in finding good artillery fire positions and communication sites, carrying commanders to give them a view of the terrain ahead and providing some security on the flanks.

Target acquisition from the air is becoming more favoured and this is closely linked to the subsequent engagement of targets. The practice of correcting fire from the guns is growing, an artillery officer riding in a Hoplite for the purpose. NATO aircrew are trained to fly and adjust fire simultaneously but the Russians clearly feel that their Air Force pilots are not yet able to adjust gunfire adequately.

Another aspect of reconnaissance is chemical contamination and nuclear radiation monitoring.

Command, control and communications has long been an important role for Soviet helicopters, the Hip-D and G and the Hook-B all being used as airborne command posts. The Hips are usually used at divisional level and the Hooks at army level. They are fitted out with a wide range of C^3 equipment and, besides providing greater mobility and flexibility for the commander and his close staff, are useful as airborne relay stations. Heliborne command posts would play a crucial role in OMG operations.

The Hound-B was the first helicopter used for EW but this role is now thought suitable for battlefield helicopters in a wider variety of tasks. EW includes the interception and analysis of radio communications, and the location and jamming of enemy transmitters; it is in this sphere of radar and communications jamming that the Hip-J and K would be most active. This role is likely to grow in importance with more and more helicopters being earmarked for it.

Pictures of a Hound laying mines by means of a chute protruding from the rear have been published; more usual now is a pair of Hips each hover taxying at about 30 kph (19 mph) and laying up to 400 anti-tank mines at a rate of one a second. Laying smoke screens is also considered appropriate from a helicopter, either by means of a smoke generator or by dropping smoke pots. As more medium and heavy lift helicopters become available so will greater emphasis be put on their logistic support role, particularly to assist in deep penetration operations.

Air space control

With the Soviet emphasis on high speed and unrelenting offensives, two potential headaches for Soviet planners are the control of the low-level air space and the provision of logistic support. A large number of projectiles of various shapes and sizes and moving at different speeds in different directions will be competing for air space: rifle and machine gun bullets, mortar bombs, artillery shells, guided and unguided rockets, anti-tank, surface-to-air and air-to-surface missiles, helicopters and fixed-wing aircraft from both sides will make life extremely hazardous for all helicopter crews. It is obvious that neither Soviet nor NATO helicopters can fly in front of their own gun, rocket or air defence positions or mortar baseplates without risk. Therefore they must avoid these areas or the weapons must stop firing temporarily. In either case free-flowing operations will be inhibited. Some form of control, be it radar or procedural (times, routes and heights to fly etc), is essential. And all pilots and ground troops must be aware of the minute-by-minute policy for opening fire on helicopters to minimise their own losses.

Good aircraft and helicopter identification is vital. Fleeting glimpses of low flying machines, often in poor visibility, make recognition and identification extremely difficult even for professional soldiers. For a conscript army, such as the Soviet, it is an almost insuperable problem without the help of an effective identification (IFF) system which is deployed at least down to individual anti-aircraft weapon systems and installed in every aircraft.

Logistic support for helicopters

Nothing could be worse than for a successful advance having to halt for lack of fuel and ammunition. Helicopters will play their part in consuming vast quantities of both commodities. Great care will be necessary in siting fuel and ammunition dumps. In recent years supply procedures have been refined, ammunition loads frequently palletised and a pipeline system for fuel built directly to airfields. But with helicopters often operating from field sites fuel will have to be transferred from storage tanks to vehicle bowsers which can deliver direct. Helicopters may themselves be press-ganged into carrying emergency supplies of fuel and ammunition, the Hook and Halo being particularly suitable for internal or external carriage. It will be for the divisional or higher commander to allocate the priorities for the use of the helicopters assigned to him; on occasion the resupply of an advancing tank division may take priority. Stocks now in the GSFG are enormous and strenuous efforts are continually being made to speed the delivery of all supplies from rear to forward units. While a decade ago it was thought in NATO that the Warsaw Pact supply system was the weak link in the chain, there can be no doubt now that it matches up well to the quality of the fighting troops.

Afghanistan

A discussion of helicopter tactics would not be complete without a reference to the operations in Afghanistan. Arguably, the helicopter has proved to be the single most effective piece of combat equipment used against the Mujahideen and the Hind is probably the most feared. Without helicopters the Russians would certainly not have been able to prosecute the war as successfully as they have.

In the first stages the Mujahideen did not have the right weapons or ideas to provide an effective counter to helicopters. Gradually, however, different kinds of weapon systems were acquired while tactics and techniques were put to trial (and error). Although the number of Soviet and Afghan helicopters deployed is not known there is no doubt that a sizeable number, running probably to well over 100, has succumbed to machine gun and missile fire. When the guerrilla leader Abdul Haq met Mrs Thatcher in London in March 1986 he emphasized, according to some British newspapers, the paramount need for SAMs despite the fact that the Russians had equipped their Hinds with flares to decoy heat-seeking missiles some years before. These measures do not seem to have been completely successful against the US Stinger missile. The humble machine gun, however, should not be overlooked as, in the view of most Soviet crews, its fire is, apparently, good reason to take evasive action; attack profiles are thus degraded.

A number of articles has appeared in the Soviet press describing the employment of helicopters in Afghanistan. Fast-moving fixed-wing aircraft find it extremely difficult to operate in mountainous terrain for obvious reasons and so the brunt of close air support has been borne by the Hind; indeed, not only has it substituted for aircraft but also for tanks and artillery which, in conventional warfare, would have been expected to provide much of the supporting fire for the infantry.

Early tactics revealed a certain contempt by helicopter crews for the Mujahideen as Hinds fired from the hover or made steep diving attacks. Within 12–15 months a more healthy regard for Mujahideen tenacity and weapon skills forced a change in tactics, driving the Hinds down to lower levels, making them open fire at greater ranges and bringing in other helicopters to carry out reconnaissance and target acquisition. Forward air controllers (FAC) were introduced, flying in Hoplites, Hounds or Hinds, to designate targets with smoke or white phosphorous rockets. Operating in pairs or threes, one helicopter now sometimes flies high to attract fire while the other(s) lie in wait, ready to engage any enemy positions which open fire. Hinds have been used for the bombing of villages, irrigation systems and crops and other types for the indiscriminate mining of roads, tracks and paths with PFM-1 butterfly and other mines.

Convoy escort has been a continual and necessary task. Sometimes it has been thought advisable to have Hinds circling overhead while Hips land troops to secure the high ground on both sides of the route ahead of the convoy in very much the same way that the British Army did, mainly without the assistance of helicopters, during its campaigns in similar territory up to 1967. As soon as the convoy has passed safely the troops are lifted onto the next heights in a leapfrogging action. Search and destroy missions have been carried out frequently but the large cordon and search operations of the early days seem to have given way to commando-type raids with Mujahideen HQ as priority targets. Helicopters, particularly Hips and Hooks for troop and equipment lift and Hinds for close air support, have been crucial to the success of these operations.

In the words of Abdul Haq air assault operations worry him the most: "Generally speaking, I believe that heliborne paratroop operations could be described as the most effective Soviet tactics." Airborne and air assault units are often lifted into remote Mujahideen sanctuaries to capture leaders, attack assembly areas, destroy installations, disrupt supply routes and seal off selected areas before the Mujahideen can reinforce or evacuate them. Inserted by helicopter, they are also used to act as an anvil to the hammer of mechanised ground forces; the Panjshir Valley has experienced a number of such operations.

One role that has not received much publicity is that of casualty evacuation. But with ever increasing sensitivity towards the impact at home of casualty figures helicopters are regularly used in this role. Taking a leaf out of the American book, they are also employed to recover other downed helicopters, a technique pioneered in Vietnam. Unsurprisingly, much of the helicopter effort is devoted to resupply, particularly to units located in remote or inaccessible places.

The war has undoubtedly pointed up the weaknesses and shortcomings in helicopter tactics against guerrilla forces, in tactical air control, in the lack of initiative shown by individual crews and flight commanders and in mountain flying techniques. The combat experience gained and the lessons learned have been invaluable but care will no doubt be taken in trying to transfer them across to a European battlefield. Despite the major impact that helicopters have had on the war in terms of providing tactical mobility and mobile firepower, Afghanistan is a 'bleeding wound' according to Mikhail Gorbachev in a speech he made to the Communist Party Congress on 25 February 1986. But without helicopters the patient by now might have bled to death. With the Soviet withdrawal under way an even greater burden is likely to fall on Soviet and Afghan helicopters.

Conclusion

Throughout the 1960s and 1970s the debate raged between Soviet military theoreticians as to the uses of helicopters on the battlefield. The American experience in Vietnam proved highly influential even though some pessimists pointed to the vulnerability of helicopters in combat. But the view prevailed that they have an important place in the combined arms concept and with this decision no efforts have been spared to build up a most formidable array of combat helicopters. Despite certain misgivings Colonel Savkin summed it all up in 1972: "The armed helicopter may turn out to be a means of fundamental change in the nature of ground combat. Although the helicopter is not ideally suited to this role, nevertheless it possesses those characteristics which most ensure superiority in mobility." He believed that helicopter units could be used for tasks that had been carried out by tanks in the Second World War, namely, for the development of success and as a mobile reserve. Now, 16 years later, helicopters enjoy a new and more prominent position in the Soviet order of battle. The potential of the latest versions of the Hind, the Havoc and the Hokum, and the Halo seems to be well appreciated at all levels within the ground forces – and not just by the aviators. Imagination and vision have been applied to the employment doctrine of helicopters and consequently they have been given both a tactical and an operational role.

The 1987, and most recent, edition of *Taktika* (Tactics) by Lieutenant General Reznichenko brings us up to date: "Fire support helicopters . . . are designed for combat with armoured enemy targets, the destruction of nuclear attack means, field artillery, suppression of air defence in tactical depth, and disruption of command and control and logistics systems. Besides this, fire support helicopters can be deployed for the direct support of one's own forces in the course of inflicting strikes on personnel and enemy firing points." It is quite clear therefore that operations across the FLOT are considered to be standard practice despite the risks involved.

The attack helicopters are not given the title attack for nothing: unlike NATO which seems to prefer to call its armed helicopters anti-armour helicopters and thus, by definition, confine them to a tactical role only, the Russians seem keen to exploit the speed, combat radius and flexibility of helicopters. By using them in considerable numbers they can make a devastating impact on a given situation.

There are still weaknesses. The Russians believe that they still do not have enough helicopters, that their crews are inadequately trained and lack versatility, that their helicopters are not properly equipped for night operations, that they remain vulnerable to most kinds of enemy fire and that their logistic support is poorly organised; furthermore, they appear dissatisfied with their attempts to integrate and control all elements of fire support, in particular from rotary and fixed-wing aircraft and artillery. The Russians are clearly committed, though, to the use of helicopters and considerable resources are being poured into their development and the elimination or reduction of their shortcomings.

The dramatic expansion of the Soviet Navy in recent years has captured the headlines but more attention is now at last being paid to the capabilities of Soviet helicopters. Their development in terms of equipment sophistication, organisation, employment doctrine and sheer numbers has been equally dramatic – if less publicly obvious – and has resulted in a helicopter force second to none. Indeed, the Russians could almost be said to be standing at the threshold of a new military era: one in which the helicopter, from Hoplite to Halo, threatens to become the Front Commander's prime means for rapid manoeuvre warfare.

Notes

1. The other types of operation which contribute to the strategic offensive are airborne, amphibious and naval.

2. The Soviet terms *takticheskii* (tactical) refers to operations up to divisional level; the term *operativnyi* (operational) describes action by an army or Front; and *strategicheskii* (strategic) is applied at the highest level. A corps is a tactical formation even if it has a role of operational significance.

3. The transformation to a genuine dual nuclear-conventional capability for the Ground Forces was first unveiled in this exercise which was in a conventional setting. The colour films released depicted large-scale airmobile operations.

4. A book, written by Colonels I. S. Lyutov and P. T. Sagaydak and entitled *Motostrelkovyi Batalon v Takticheskom Vozdushnom Desante* (The Motorised Rifle Battalion in a Tactical Airborne Landing) was published in Moscow in 1969. It refers to US airmobile forces, conditions of employment and how to load equipment and troops. It emphasises that motor rifle troops should be accompanied by their APCs.

5. The MRB has some 500 officers and men and consists of three motor rifle companies, each of three platoons, a mortar battery with eight 120 mm mortars, and various other elements. Some MRBs have about 35 BMP infantry fighting vehicles while others are equipped with the wheeled BTR 60 or 70. The MRB is not a unit in its own right like a NATO infantry battalion but is rather a sub-unit of the larger Motor Rifle Regiment. The MRB is usually commanded by a senior captain or a junior major.

6. Airmobile in this context is taken to include both troop lift helicopters in the air assault role and armed or attack helicopters. A heliborne force, on the other hand, denotes a force, usually infantry with some specialist support, carried into battle by helicopter.

7. The new generation of helicopters is much less restricted by these limitations.

Biographies

It was a very small and close-knit group of Soviet aircraft and engine designers that dominated the Soviet aircraft industry for almost half a century from the mid-1920s to the early 1970s. The sub-group of rotary-wing designers was astonishingly small, a mere four men only having led design bureaux which have succeeded in designing, building and actually flying a Soviet helicopter: Bratukhin, Kamov, Mil and Yakovlev. Since the deaths of Kamov and Mil, Mikheyev and Tishchenko have taken over their bureaux respectively. Kuznetsov and Skrzhinsky, among others, built a few short-lived autogiros but cannot claim to be in the original group. Of these, Kamov and Mil were predominant as helicopter designers, Yakovlev being much better known as a fixed-wing designer.

The lives and characters of these men are generally obscure. Little has been written about them and, with one exception, they have revealed little of themselves. Yakovlev, however, has written a most interesting book entitled *Tsel Zhizni* (The Aim of a Lifetime), an autobiography of sorts in which he has described the development of Soviet aviation since the 1930s and his part in it. It is a selective account with much omitted and some dates at best suspect. Sergei Ilyushin has written of this book: "While describing his own activities as a designer and public figure, the author gives a truthful and profoundly informed account of the main and most characteristic phases of the development of Soviet aviation . . . . Written in a simple and lively manner and abounding in exciting episodes handled with convincing veracity, this book will doubtlessly appeal to the widest range of readers."

Yakovlev apart, we know more about the designers' products than we do of themselves. To accuse them of lack of personality, as some do, is less than fair. Whatever else, they have been men of vision and great influence, and their work has been recognised by many prestigious awards. In the early days, at the turn of the century and up to 1930, they relied heavily on the pioneering work of Nikolai Zhukovsky and Boris Yuriev in particular and for this reason I have also included a few notes on these two men. I have excluded Igor Sikorsky because, although he was the greatest pioneer of them all, he made little impact on the rotary scene while living in Russia.

Nikolai Zhukovsky

The man dubbed by Lenin as the 'Father of Russian Aviation', Nikolai Yegorovich Zhukovsky was born on 5 January 1847 in the small village of Orekhovo in Central Russia, the son of an engineer. In 1858 he was sent to Moscow for his schooling. He entered Moscow University and at the age of 21 took a degree in applied mathematics. The subject of his master's thesis was liquid kinematics. In 1870 he began to teach physics in a Moscow girls school before becoming a Professor of Mathematics at the Moscow Higher Technical School (*Vysshee Tekhnicheskoe Uchilishche* – MVTU) in 1872. Here he lectured on mechanical analysis while also working as an instructor in mechanics at the Academy of Commercial Sciences. In 1876 he began to investigate hydrodynamics which was one step away from aerodynamics. In 1882 Zhukovsky received a doctorate in applied mathematics and four years later became a Professor of Theoretical Mechanics at Moscow University. At about this time he turned his attention, although not exclusively, to specifically aeronautical matters; in 1890 in a work entitled *K Teorii Letaniya* (On the Theory of Flying), he considered an elementary rotor and obtained the formulae for its thrust and power.

In 1899 Zhukovsky set up the first aerodynamic laboratory in Russia as part of the MVTU and in 1902 added a wind tunnel – one of the first in the world. Although somewhat crude it had a rectangular section of almost 1.5 m × 0.3 m (5 ft × 1 ft). Two years later, with Zhukovsky's help, the Institute of Aerodynamics was established at Kuchino, a village some 19 km (12 miles) out of Moscow. This was possible mainly due to the generosity of a very wealthy amateur enthusiast, one Ryabushinsky, who provided certain research facilities, including a more sophisticated wind tunnel, on his estate. Much time was given over to the study of problems associated with helicopters, particularly with regard to the air stream created by propellers, vertical and horizontal.

On 22 January, 1904 Zhukovsky published his paper *On the Useful Load Lifted by a Helicopter* in which he set out to prove the feasibility of heavy loads being lifted by helicopters with single and multi rotors. He wrote: "On the basis of all that has gone before it must be concluded that, given the present proportionate weight of the engine, a twin-propeller helicopter cannot lift into the air more than a definite useful load; as concerns multi-propeller helicopters, it is clear that with an inceasing number of propellers, they can lift any load. Moreover, multi-propeller helicopters designed for the same proportionate engine weight and the same useful load give lighter weight aircraft with less powerful engines than do twin-propeller helicopters."

In 1906 Zhukovsky's well-known work *O Prisoedinennykh Vikhryakh* (About Connected Vortices) was published and a year later *Grebnoy Vint s Bolshim Chislom Lopastei* (A Multi-Bladed Propeller-Screw) appeared. It is claimed that both works were the first in their field and are now the basis of all applied aerodynamics. It was at

193

about this time that Zhukovsky, by means of his new wind tunnel, discovered that a thicker wing gives better results than a very thin one, a fact contrary to the beliefs of virtually all aeronautical designers of that time. Zhukovsky began to lecture at the MVTU in 1909 on the 'Theoretical Principles of Aeronautics'. During this year he also investigated the theory of the effect of a helicopter's horizontal flight speed on the operation of its rotor; his paper was entitled *Opyt Teoreticheskogo Opredeleniya Effekta Vetra, Duyushchego v Ploskosti Grebnogo Vinta* (Experiments on the Theoretical Determination of the Effect of the Airflow on the Surface of a Propeller). This paper revealed that three forces and three tilting moments act on a propeller – and implied that to balance and control a helicopter would be beyond the ability of most mortals!

An evident glutton for work, Zhukovsky encouraged his students, who included Bothezat (later to emigrate to the USA), Sabinin, Sorokomovsky, Vetchinkin and Yuriev, to put his helicopter theories to practical test. In 1910 they set to work to build a helicopter, led by Yuriev. By the end of that year Zhukovsky had succeeded in establishing three aerodynamic laboratories in or near Moscow: the Kuchinsky Aerodynamic Institute just outside Moscow, a laboratory at Moscow University and the laboratory at the MVTU. It was claimed by Yuriev that the latter was the leading laboratory in the field of aerodynamic research in the world. Some familiar names apart from those already mentioned worked there: Arkhangelsky, Cheremukhin, Myasishchev and Tupolev. It is interesting to note that Igor Sikorsky, also very active at this time, is not included among them in Soviet literature.

It was at about this time that Russian factories began to build aircraft and engines in small numbers. These were mainly French and assembled from parts bought abroad. Only one plant, the Russo-Baltic Railway Carriage Plant in St. Petersburg (later Leningrad), was devoted to building Russian designs, specifically Sikorsky's four-engined *Ilya Muromets*, the world's first four-engined aircraft.

As the First World War approached Zhukovsky was busily engaged upon research into lifting capacity, propellers, hydraulics, hydrodynamics and wing shapes, all in addition to guiding his students in their studies. During the war his clinical and searching mind was almost fully occupied with the techniques of bombing and navigation. By 1916 Zhukovsky's students had established a number of schools for the instruction of military pilots in aviation matters, including the principles of flight. In July of that year Zhukovsky and Vetchinkin founded at the MVTU aerodynamic laboratory an Evaluation and Test Bureau, the *Raschetno-Ispytatelnoe Biuro* – the first aviation scientific research centre to help designers by putting research on a systematic footing. It was hardly established, however, before the March 1917 Revolution brought about its temporary demise. Within 20 months it was nevertheless to form the basis of TsAGI.

Despite the turmoil in Russia as Bolshevik power was challenged from within and by the Western Allies, Lenin gave his strong support to Zhukovsky in the establishment of TsAGI in December 1918. He was able to collect together a small group of about 30 experienced aeronautical enthusiasts with whom he had already worked. They were charged with research and development, and the building and testing of experimental aircraft and engines. Zhukovsky was the Director. In 1919 the MVTU was renamed the Moscow Aviation Technical School. A year later it was expanded and renamed the Institute for Engineers of the Red Air Fleet. After Zhukovsky's death on 17 March, 1921 at the age of 74 this Institute was renamed once more, becoming the N. Ye. Zhukovsky Military Aviation (Engineering) Academy in 1922. It was transferred to Sverdlovsk in July 1941, remaining there until the end of the Second World War. It is now housed in what was once the Petrovsky Palace on Leningradsky Avenue.

Zhukovsky was truly a man of immense intellectual stature and physical energy. He published over 200 scientific papers of which more than 50 were pioneering works on aeronautical subjects. In this he was helped by the German, Otto Lilienthal, the first man to launch himself into the air and fly (in 1891). The two men corresponded and Lilienthal even gave Zhukovsky one of his 1894-type gliders. Although many designers, including Igor Sikorsky, emigrated after the Revolution, Zhukovsky and some of his colleagues remained, together with their research facilities, intact in Moscow. Zhukovsky's influence on the Russian aeronautical scene can be traced down to the present day. His work and his institutions left a legacy that played no small part in the development of Soviet aviation. In 1920 the Council of Peoples' Commissars gave Zhukovsky an address commending his work over the last 50 years; it created also an annual prize in his name for the best work in mathematics and mechanics.

Boris Yuriev

Of Zhukovsky's three most prominent rotary-wing students, Yuriev, Sabinin and Vetchinkin, Boris Nikolaevich Yuriev came to be the best known. His association with the helicopter began in Tsarist times, eight years before the Revolution, and continued until after Stalin's death in 1953. He is sometimes referred to as the 'Patriarch of Soviet helicopter engineering'.

Yuriev was born in Smolensk on 10 November, 1889. Little is known of his first twenty years. In 1909 he attended Zhukovsky's course on the 'Theoretical Principles of Aeronautics' at the MVTU. The following year with his fellow student Sabinin, he developed propeller theory for helicopter rotors and proposed his 'coupling equation' which accounted for the velocity of inflow air of the propeller. Zhukovsky was impressed by this work and encouraged his students to put theory into practice. A group, headed by Yuriev, was created to get on with this project. The group's first design was of a helicopter with a single main rotor and two anti-torque rotors. This invention was patented and on 26 September, 1910 Patent Certificate No. 45,212 was issued. Yuriev, however, continued to work on the design and soon dispensed with one of the anti-torque rotors, putting the other at the tail end of the fuselage – a revolutionary concept at that time. Drag and weight were saved. An amended patent was issued on 23 February, 1911.

That same year Yuriev claimed that he invented what he called an automatic pitch control mechanism – the decisive and final step in completing his single rotor design. On 12 April, 1911 he gave a presentation entitled 'A Discusssion of the Earlier Helicopter Systems and a Description of a New Type of Helicopter of the Author's Design' to the First All-Russian Aeronautical Congress.

In 1912 Yuriev's group felt sufficiently confident to begin the construction of an actual helicopter. It incorporated a 25 hp Anzani engine but not Yuriev's cyclic control; his sponsors had insufficient money for such refinements. It did, however, employ a single main rotor and a small anti-torque rotor. The machine was exhibited at the International Aeronautical and Automobile Exposition in Moscow and, according to Yuriev, attracted much attention. The group who had built it gave explanations as to how it worked to interested visitors and distributed lithographed leaflets. Yuriev was awarded a Gold Medal by the organisers of the Exposition. The Second All-Russian Aeronautical Congress was scheduled to take place at the same time. Among the reports was one by Yuriev on 'A Helicopter of My Own Construction.' During the course of the ground tests begun after the Exposition, the main rotor drive shaft failed as a result of the very uneven running of the engine. No money was available to continue the programme. The group now investigated the problems associated with multi-rotor helicopters but the outbreak of the First World War put paid to further activities of this nature.

Yuriev has written contemptuously of the lack of support given to him and his group by officials of the Military Engineering Administration before the First World War. They had proposed buying foreign aircraft and engines, rejecting out of hand the work of Russian designers. After the "Great October Socialist Revolution", wrote Yuriev, "a completely different picture was to be seen. From the first days that the Soviet authorities were established, Professor Zhukovsky and his numerous pupils began to work on the creation of native aviation. In all these undertakings they received complete support. However, they did not become occupied with the helicopter problem at once. It was first necessary to create a scientific foundation and prepare cadres of air engineers and researchers. Without this it was impossible to create the powerful air forces necessary for the defence of our Homeland." Indeed, serious helicopter work did not begin again until 1925 when Yuriev was put in charge of the Vertical Flight Section of TsAGI.

Before this, nonetheless, he had become an instructor at the MVTU, having finished his course there as a student of Zhukovsky in 1919. He continued instructing there on and off for ten years, becoming a Professor in 1925. He joined TsAGI in 1920 and in the same year also started teaching at the Zhukovsky Military Aviation Academy. Only in 1949 did he retire from his post. Before being appointed to head the Vertical Flight Section, Yuriev turned his attention to the design of a jet-driven rotor helicopter. Fuel jets were located near the blade tips. He took out patent No. 761 in 1924. In the same year he obtained patent No. 1,526 for a multi-rotor helicopter; each rotor was to be driven by a separate engine mounted on the fuselage frame.

From 1925 to 1928 Yuriev and others (notably Bunkin, Bratukhin, Cheremukhin, Izakson, Leymer and Vinogradov) built many models and tested them in wind tunnels. In 1928 clearance was given to build a first experimental helicopter, the 1-EA, based on Yuriev's principle of a single main rotor and two anti-torque rotors. It was the first Soviet helicopter to leave the ground, in 1930, although Yuriev had left the Helicopter Section two years earlier when it was renamed the 'Section of Special Constructions'.

In 1930, while still actively engaged in helicopter research, Yuriev became an instructor, to add to his other teaching posts, at the Ordzhonikidze Aviation Institute in Moscow.

By 1938 Yuriev was a man of considerable influence in the aeronautical world, holding such titles as Chief of the Aircraft Circle, Meritorious Figure of Science and Technology, Doctor of Technological Sciences, Professor and Brigade Engineer. It was in that year that he was consulted and supported the appointment of Colonel Grigori Tokaev to head the Zhukovsky Aerodynamics Laboratory. Nothing exceptional in this but Yuriev spoke out strongly in favour of Tokaev when he was sacked in February 1941. Tokaev subsequently led a team which designed an experimental tail-first light aircraft with swept-back wings for the MiG design bureau. Tokaev, however, achieved greater notoriety by defecting to the West in 1948 and writing a book, *Comrade X*, about his experiences. In this he pays handsome tribute to Yuriev's loyal support.

In 1943 Yuriev became a Member of the Academy of Sciences of the USSR and a year later joined, for the next six years, the Commission of Historical Technology within the Academy. It is not known when Yuriev was first given an honorary military rank but by 1944 he was being referred to as a lieutenant general.

Yuriev was still working hard in 1950 on applied aerodynamics in the Institute of Mechanics in the Academy of Sciences. Some time after this he began work on a textbook for aviation schools entitled *The Aerodynamic Design of Helicopters*. He died in Moscow on 14 March, 1957 at the age of 67. During his life he had received international recognition and many awards, the most prized being two Orders of Lenin.

Academician Yuriev's contribution to the development of the helicopter should not be underestimated although he has been somewhat eclipsed by the men who came later, Mil and Kamov in particular, who actually built successful helicopters. Yuriev was a man who feared none and was not afraid to speak his mind even in times of potential danger such as the late 1930s and when the Establishment was later gunning for Tokaev. He was very much a patriot, blindly loyal to the Soviet Union as evidenced by this extract from an article he wrote for *Ogonyok*: "In 1925 Koschel . . . copied in the most unscrupulous manner the designs of a Russian helicopter developed fifteen years before and stole all our calculations. Sometime earlier, in Holland a similar lack of restraint distinguished one Baumhauer (who built and flew the first single rotor helicopter) and a year later a Frenchman, Oehmichen. In later years Sikorsky, Piasecki, Hiller, Bristol, Bell and others 'appropriated' the former labours of Russian designers." In his textbook he wrote: "Our country is therefore rightfully considered the birthplace of helicopter construction."

Nikolai Kamov

Nikolai Ilyich Kamov was born on 14 September, 1902 in Irkutsk, Siberia. Little has been revealed of his early life but at the age of 21 he graduated from the Tomsk Technical Institute. Although qualified in locomotive design he started work as an aircraft fitter in Moscow, subsequently moving to the workshops of Dobrolet (the forerunner of Aeroflot). By 1926 he had moved on to GAZ No. 23 in Leningrad to work under Dmitri P. Grigorovich. He qualified as a pilot. This factory, named the Experimental Floatplane and Flying Boat Design Section (*Otdel Morskogo Opytnogo Samoletostroeniya* – OMOS), worked for two years until 1928 but was unable to produce any successful flying boats at all. To compensate for this failure foreign designers had to be brought in to replace the disgraced Grigorovich (who was imprisoned for 'sabotage') and German and Italian aircraft imported. Kamov went to work for a Frenchman, Paul Richard, for a short time.

Teaming up with Nikolai Skrzhinsky, Kamov turned his attention next to autogiros. The news of the success of the Spaniard, Juan de la Cierva, who had flown his first autogiro in January 1923, had spread to the Soviet Union. With the help of *Osoaviakhim* (*Obshchestvo sodeistviya oborone, aviatsionnomu i khimicheskomu stroitelstvu*, Society for the Support of Defence and of Aviation and Chemical Construction) funds and using the fuselage of an Avro 504K and a Gnome-Rhône engine, the two engineers built what came to be known as the KaSkr-1 or *Krasnyi Inzhener* (Red Engineer). It made a number of successful flights from Moscow Central Airport in 1929 and 1930. A newer model with a more powerful engine, the KaSkr-II, later made 90 flights.

In 1931 Kamov was placed in charge of Autogiro Brigade No. 3 of the Section of Special Constructions (*Otdel Osobykh Konstrukstsii* – OOK) of TsAGI, then under the leadership of Aleksandr M. Izakson. Other Brigades were led by Vyacheslav Kuznetsov, Nikolai Skrzhinsky and Mikhail Mil; Ivan Bratukhin and V. Lapisov led the helicopter Brigades. In 1934 Kamov's A-7 autogiro appeared. Flight trials indicated a certain lack of stability and a modified version was produced. In 1939 Kamov left his Brigade to set up an A-7 production line in Smolensk and a year later, in February 1941, one example was taken to the Tyan-Shan mountains to participate in a geographical and geological expedition.

As a result of the purges OOK lost its director, Izakson, his deputy, Cheremukhin, and a number of other key personnel. In January 1941 the staff still intact were divided between helicopter development led by Bratukhin at the Moscow Aviation Institute and autogiro development led by Kamov. He now designed his AK autogiro but because of the advancing Germans he had to stop work in July 1941 and move east to the area of Lake Baikal; work resumed in 1942 but in 1943 his team was disbanded. It was at this time that Kamov became a member of the Communist Party.

In 1945 Kamov was permitted to establish his own Design Office (which became an OKB in 1948) at which time he began the design of his famous Ka-8, an ultra light helicopter with two co-axial rotors, a layout to be adopted by all but one of his subsequent helicopters. These have all been relatively small and production runs have been generally modest. As a designer and builder of helicopters Kamov has of course been overshadowed by Mikhail Mil and his OKB. Indeed it is quite legitimate to wonder why Kamov and his OBK ever survived and in fact prospered. Perhaps he had friends in high places; perhaps it was believed that to give the Mil OKB a monopoly on helicopter development would be unwise. Nevertheless nearly all Kamov's types have found favour with the Soviet Navy and his Ka-25 Hormone has appeared in over 20 versions. Kamov's Ka-22 Hoop compound helicopter which caused a sensation at the Tushino Air Display in 1961 was quite out of keeping with all his other designs, before and after. This design may have had its origins in the Bratukhin design bureau, disbanded in 1951.

In 1962 Kamov became a Doctor of Technical Sciences and ten years later a Hero of Socialist Labour. He was twice awarded the Order of Lenin in addition to other medals and honours. On 24 November, 1973 Kamov died, his aeronautical career having spanned six decades.

Ivan Bratukhin

The life and works of Ivan Bratukhin are a good deal more obscure than most of the Soviet helicopter designers. Perhaps the major reason for this is that, although a pioneer in his field, he was unlucky to be at the peak of his career – in the 1940s – at a time when resources available for the design and construction of helicopters were at a low ebb. It was rather fighters and assault aircraft that received the highest priority throughout the decade. Furthermore, Stalin was concerned to exploit the wealth of German aviation technology that his troops captured during their drive through Eastern Europe at the end of the Second World War; technology that was confined almost entirely to fixed-wing aircraft. Aviation factories were stripped bare; presses, machine-tools and drawings were transported bodily back to the Soviet Union. But Bratukhin hardly benefited and his efforts received little more than occasional official acknowledgement.

Ivan Pavlovich Bratukhin was born on 25 February, 1903 in the village of Yashchera in what is now Kirov Region. At the age of 17 he joined the Communist Party at a time when Bolsheviks were still engaged in trying to win complete control of the country. In 1925 TsAGI set up a helicopter research section under Boris Yuriev. Bratukhin joined it in 1926 but left shortly after to attend the Bauman Technical School in Moscow from which he graduated in 1930. He returned to the Section of Special Constructions at TsAGI.

TsAGI's first helicopter, the 1-EA, crashed in June 1932 and Bratukhin was appointed head of the inquiry into the cause of the accident. By this time he was already leader of the Helicopter Construction Brigade which built and tested the TsAGI 5-EA, a modified 3-EA.

It was not a particularly successful machine, and both Bratukhin, Kamov and their teams redoubled their efforts to produce a truly efficient helicopter capable of vertical take-off. In 1936 Bratukhin succeeded in producing the 11-EA but static tests indicated that modifications were needed. Before further work could proceed Stalin unleashed his purges. Bratukhin was one of the aircraft designers fortunate to survive although his general lack of obvious success could well have been put down to sabotage, as it was with a hapless few. Indeed, his test pilot, Aleksei Cheremukhin, was arrested and imprisoned together with other members of the bureau. Helicopter development was stopped.

In 1938 Bratukhin was allowed to recommence development and modification of his 11-EA which subsequently became the 11-EA PV; it flew for the first time in October 1940. This was, however, after the Bratukhin design team had been reconstituted as the OKB-3 in the Moscow Aviation Institute. Boris Yuriev was the director for a mere three months until Bratukhin took over in March 1940.

In July 1940 the OKB-3 received approval to go ahead with an opposed twin-rotor helicopter designed by Bratukhin after the fashion of the German Focke-Achgelis Fa 61. Bratukhin's 2 MG Omega, however, had two engines mounted on outriggers below the rotors. For the next ten years Bratukhin stuck to this layout; it may have been this lack of imagination that was his undoing for although it was perhaps suitable in 1941 it was clearly out of date ten years later by which time the Mi-1 Hare had already entered service. Bratukhin's OKB was therefore disbanded.

Despite little official encouragement Bratukhin's work was recognised by Stalin in 1946 with the award of a Stalin Prize. He was later to be awarded the Order of Lenin, the Order of the Red Banner and various other decorations. He became a Professor in 1954 while still working at the Moscow Aviation Institute and in 1962 a Doctor of Technology. Two years later he was given the title of Honoured Scientist and Engineer. Little has been heard of Bratukhin since although he was credited with editing the helicopter section of a magazine called *Krylya Rodiny* (Wings of the Motherland) in 1969.

Aleksandr Yakovlev

Aleksandr Sergeyevich Yakovlev was born in Moscow on 19 March, 1906, the son of a clerk. It was not long before he began to show a flair for engineering. Having completed secondary school at the age of 17, he made up his mind to study aircraft design. To further his aims he took a job as a labourer in the carpentry shop at the Zhukovsky Military Aviation Academy in Moscow in 1924. It was here that Yakovlev built his Pegas glider which flew the same year. While all this was a step in the right direction Yakovlev had no actual contact with aeroplanes. The following year he managed to get accepted as a mechanic's helper in the Academy's flying training unit, a part of the Red Air Force. He was soon promoted to engine mechanic.

By this time several small groups of amateur enthusiasts were building their own sports planes. In 1927 Yakovlev, with the help of *Osoaviakhim* funds, followed suit, designing his two-seat AIR-1 biplane powered by an imported de Havilland Cirrus engine. This aircraft made its first flight on 12 May, 1927. So successful was the AIR-1 that on 12 June Yakovlev and his pilot were able to fly the 1,530 km (950 miles) from Moscow to Sevastopol (with a stop in Kharkov) in $10\frac{1}{2}$ hours; the pilot flew back alone non-stop in $15\frac{1}{2}$ hours. These feats more or less gained Yakovlev's admission to the Zhukovsky Academy as a student in the same year. He studied engineering there for the next four years until 1931.

Having finished his course Yakovlev went to the Menzhinsky Works, GAZ No. 39, where he joined the design team of Dmitri Grigorovich and Nikolai Polikarpov. They were involved with light military aircraft and ran the only design bureau apart from TsAGI, now headed by Tupolev. In addition to his official duties, Yakovlev continued to work on light sports aircraft. His monoplane, the AIR-7, having achieved over 290 kph (180 mph) in late 1932 suffered damage as a result of poor design, the starboard aileron becoming detached during a test flight. An accident inquiry recommended "Yakovlev to be barred from aircraft construction . . . ." Although this recommendation was not accepted Yakovlev and his team were ordered off the premises. Eventually the Head of the Aircraft Industry Division allowed him to move into a bed factory on the Leningrad Highway near Moscow. In due course the manufacture of beds was transferred elsewhere; Yakovlev succumbed to a bout of euphoria. Shortly after he was named as the Director of the Light Plane Factory which was rebuilt in 1935. The AIR-9, AIR-9*bis* and AIR-10 were all built in this factory, the AIR-9*bis* leading to the AIR-10 which was the prototype for the famous UT-2 trainer. Nevertheless Yakovlev was only rescued from this relative obscurity when his training aircraft came to Stalin's notice. From that time on he enjoyed the dictator's special confidence.

In 1934 Yakovlev went abroad for the first time, flying in a four-engined Tupolev

TB-3 to Italy in company with a group of pilots and engineers. He was back the following year to visit the Milan Air Salon in September together with Sukhoi, Tupolev and Polikarpov. In 1936 he was sent to France to negotiate the purchase of some Caudron sports aircraft from Renault. While the negotiations continued Yakovlev and some others went to England to see the Air Show at Hendon, London. During this visit Yakovlev saw the Hurricane and the first Spitfire prototype. He came away impressed.

In 1938 Yakovlev became a member of the Communist Party.

Early in 1939 Stalin convened a meeting of aircraft designers and engineers in the Kremlin. Also present were Molotov, Voroshilov and Kaganovich, the People's Commissars of Foreign Affairs, Defence and the Aircraft Industry respectively. The aim of the conference was for each designer to describe his current work and his plans for the future. Yakovlev, as a light sports aircraft designer, was invited. He was able to describe a twin-engined long-range reconnaissance aircraft, capable of 570 kph (350 mph), that he was currently testing. It was his first non-sports plane. At the military's insistence, however, the aircraft was modified as a short-range bomber and designated the BB-22 (*Blizhnii Bombardirovshchik*, Short-range Bomber). It went into production in April 1939 when Yakovlev was summoned to Stalin, congratulated on the BB-22's performance, awarded the Order of Lenin, a ZIS car and 100,000 roubles. It was redesignated the Yak-2 and later the Yak-4 after modifications but it was never worthy of the praise heaped upon it.

Another meeting was called later the same year, at which the designers were encouraged to build a fighter incorporating Klimov's M-105 engine and Shpitalny's 20 mm cannon. As his entry for the competition was nearing completion, Yakovlev was nominated as a member of a delegation to visit Germany in October 1939. He protested but was overruled. The delegation stayed in Germany a month, escorted by Ernst Udet (Goering's deputy) who showed the Russians the latest Luftwaffe machines. A Fieseler Storch was presented to the leader of the delegation; negotiations took place to buy various Dornier, Heinkel, Junkers and Messerschmitt aircraft.

Yakovlev's fighter, the I-26, later designated Yak-1, was the first to be completed. It was rolled out on 1 January, 1940. It flew early in March, to be followed by Lavochkin's I-22, later the LaGG-1 (first flight on 30 March, 1940) and Mikoyan's I-220, later the MiG-1 (first flight on 5 April, 1940). All three aircraft were put into mass production. Some 60% of all Soviet single-seat fighters built during the Great Patriotic War were products of Yakovlev's bureau and stemmed from the Yak-1.

On 9 January, 1940 Yakovlev was again summoned to the Kremlin. There he was informed by Stalin that he, Stalin, had relieved Kaganovich of his duties as People's Commissar of the Aircraft Industry and replaced him with Aleksei Shakhurin. Yakovlev was to be Shakhurin's deputy, taking over from Sergei Ilyushin and responsible for scientific research and experimental development. Yakovlev had serious misgivings about this appointment but eventually consented to accept it. History does not relate what might have befallen him if he had refused! He was given the honorary rank of Major General in the Red Air Force. And he was still only 33. In October he was awarded the title of Hero of Socialist Labour for the first time.

On 22 June, 1941 the Germans invaded the Soviet Union and within a month were carrying out air raids against Moscow. Their advance towards the capital was rapid, so rapid in fact that by July the evacuation of industrial plants east to Siberia had already begun. Although Yakovlev does not mention the place in his book *Tsel Zhizni* (The Aim of a Lifetime), he in fact arrived in Novosibirsk at the end of October. Conditions, to say the least, were difficult and Yakovlev had to share the assembly line at GAZ No. 153 with Lavochkin's LaGG-3 fighters. The plant was jammed with unfinished fighters. More were parked outside, some not being seen until the snow melted the following spring.

In mid-November 1941 the Germans launched their attack on Moscow, penetrating to within 20 km (12.5 miles) by early December. On 5 December the first of a series of Soviet attacks to relieve Moscow began and the Germans started to withdraw. Quite soon the city was comparatively safe and on 3 March, 1942 Yakovlev returned from Siberia. Six months later, however, he was sent back with orders to step up radically the output of fighter aircraft. Within a month he was able to return to Moscow and report that 20 examples of his new fighter, the Yak-9, were being produced each day.

In early 1943 Yakovlev's design bureau returned to Moscow, leaving behind only a small staff to supervise the production of the Yak-9. Oleg Antonov became his deputy director, going to Novosibirsk and remaining there until 1946 when he established his own OKB. By April 1943 Yakovlev could report that a new design, the Yak-3, had been built and tested. He was promoted to lieutenant general six months later.

The remaining war years were spent by Yakovlev in refining and modifying his fighter aircraft. Even during the war, however, his thoughts were turning to jet aircraft. In February 1945 a requirement for a fighter airframe to utilise German gas turbine engines was issued. By October of that year the Mikoyan, Lavochkin, Sukhoi and Yakovlev design bureaux had presented their projects to Stalin. The first two, the MiG-9 and the Yak-15, a Yak-3 with a Jumo 004B, flew for the first time on the same day, 24 April, 1946. Yakovlev had been very much against the idea of using a German Me 262 jet fighter as an example and building a Soviet version on the grounds that he thought that Soviet designers should be allowed free expression rather than be condemned to copying German types. In May 1947 the Yak-15 entered service with the Red Air Force.

In the same year Yakovlev's first helicopter flew. Design of a two-seat, co-axial rotor helicopter had been begun in 1944. Unfortunately Yakovlev does not explain in his book why he embarked on building helicopters. Nevertheless he had a certain success with this venture although he relied heavily on Skrzhinsky, Yerlikh and others.

In 1948 Yakovlev, by now a colonel general, relinquished his duties as Deputy Minister of the Aircraft Industry. This move freed him to concentrate on the design of the Yak-25 Flashlight, the first all-weather, jet-powered interceptor to be built in series. It eventually entered production in early 1955. It also gave him more time to devote to the Yak-100, his second helicopter and his entry in the competition for a two/three-seat communications helicopter, subsequently won by the Mil Mi-1 Hare. Yakovlev's third and only other helicopter, the Yak-24 Horse, was designed in the main by Skrzhinsky and flew for the first time in July 1952. At that time it was the biggest helicopter in the world.

Since that time Yakovlev has continued his work on fighters, notably the Yak-28 Brewer/Firebar and the VTOL Yak-38 Forger operating from the decks of the ASW cruisers; transport aircraft such as the very successful Yak-40 Codling and the larger and newer Yak-42 Clobber; and even small aerobatic aircraft like the Yak-18 Max and its successor the Yak-50, both highly successful in World Aerobatic Championships over the years and the primary training aircraft in most of the Warsaw Pact air forces.

In 1957 Yakovlev had his first book *Notes of an Aircraft Designer* published and in 1972 the second edition of the more voluminous *The Aim of a Lifetime*. The latter is an eminently readable book and an interesting account of the development of Soviet aviation from the 1930s onwards. It deals with the establishment of the aircraft industry, with the First Five Year Plan, the war years and the transition to the jet age, not to mention his relationship with Stalin.

Aleksandr Yakovlev was the youngest of the more important wartime aircraft designers and his unexpected appointment as Deputy People's Commissar of the Aircraft Industry was not well received by some of his contemporaries. Nevertheless

Yakovlev survived this experience and the purges of the 1930s during which some of his superiors became victims. Through the strength of his personality and his obvious talents Yakovlev has maintained his eminent position in Soviet aviation for over 40 years. He has been awarded the Stalin Prize six times, the Order of Lenin seven times, twice the title of Hero of Socialist Labour and the French Legion of Honour. The headquarters of his OKB is still on the site of his old bed factory but Yakovlev himself has long since handed over his major responsibilities to his deputies – which included his son Sergei.

Mikhail Mil

Mikhail Leontevich Mil was born in Irkutsk on 22 November, 1909, the son of an office worker. He became interested in aviation when he was very young. At the age of 12 he took part in a model aeroplane competition and won a prize. When he was 17, in 1926, he entered the Technological Institute in Tomsk. The work that he was involved in there had no connection with aviation and he soon lost interest. He transferred to the Aviation Institute at Novocherkassk. Rotary-wing machines fired his imagination now and, while still a student, he spent time with *Osoaviakhim* which assisted Kamov and Skrzhinsky to build the first Soviet autogiro, the KaSkr-1, in 1929.

Mikhail Mil graduated from the Novocherkassk Aviation Insitute in 1931 and joined TsAGI. He worked in the rotary-wing section which was engaged in research into helicopter aerodynamics. Mil was particularly concerned with stability and the design of rotor blades. On the practical level he was part of the team which designed and built the A-12 and A-15 autogiros. As an engineer in the latter half of the 1930s, Mil became Kamov's deputy designer.

When the war started Mil was appointed as Senior Engineer to the First Autogiro Artillery Communications Squadron which was equipped wiuh the A-7*bis* autogiro. This squadron took part in the battles on the Western Front while the Red Army withdrew in disarray in the face of the German onslaught.

In 1943 Mil returned to TsAGI and more or less at the same time became a member of the Communist Party. For a time he was divorced from rotary-wing work, researching instead the stability and control of fighter aircraft. In 1945 Mil received his Doctorate of Technology and a year later was appointed Head of TsAGI's Rotating Wing Scientific Research Laboratory. Under his direction experimental research into rotor aerodynamics was carried out and a wind tunnel model of a helicopter assembled.

In December 1947 Mil was given new instructions: he was to become the Chief Designer of a newly created experimental design bureau for helicopters. This bureau was the last of the helicopter bureaux to be established to meet the requirement for a two/three seat communications helicopter. Bratukhin and Yakovlev had already been working on helicopters of their own designs. Mil's previous theoretical and practical work, his engineering talents and his undoubted leadership all combined to enable his OKB to design, build and roll out a helicopter, the GM-1 (later designated the Mi-1 Hare), to meet this requirement within the very short space of nine months. The Mi-1 was a sensational success and the first Soviet helicopter to go into quantity production.

In October 1951 the famous meeting of aircraft and helicopter designers took place in the Kremlin. The outcome of this meeting was the development of the Yak-24 Horse and the Mi-4 Hound, a helicopter arguably even more successful than the Mi-1. Since that time Mil's OKB has designed bigger and better helicopters. These have ranged from the comparatively small Mi-2 Hoplite to the largest helicopters in the world, the Mi-26 Halo and the Mi-12 Homer. His various helicopter types over the years have established nearly 70 official world records.

In 1971 Mil's champion weight-lifter, the Mi-12, startled the world when it appeared in public at the Paris Air Show although Mil was not there to see it: he died in Moscow from cancer on 31 January, 1970. His OKB was taken over by Marat Tishchenko.

Mikhail Mil's achievements as a helicopter designer were lavishly rewarded. Three times he was awarded the Order of Lenin; he also received the Orders of the Great Patriotic War, second class, the Order of the Red Banner and the Red Star. He was given a Lenin Prize in 1958 for the design of the Mi-4 and the State Prize for his Mi-6 and Mi-10 in 1968. In 1966 he was awarded the title of Hero of Socialist Labour.

Of the two main helicopter design bureaux Mil's has proved to be the more successful, on the single criterion of numbers of Kamov and Mil helicopters built. His range of helicopter types has also been much wider. Mil's early devotion to theory stood him in good stead; despite other configurations favoured by his contemporaries, he elected to build his first helicopter with a single main rotor and a single anti-torque rotor – a layout his OKB has retained in all subsequent designs but one. Indeed, he paid particular attention to Yuriev's theoretical work and was adept at putting much of it into practice. Certainly up to the design of the Mi-6 the influence of Yuriev can be seen quite clearly. Despite the bureaucratic constraints of the Soviet system Mil excelled as a manager and leader in addition to his eminence as a practical engineer.

Not a typically cautious Soviet technocrat, he was never short of ideas and always keen to put them forward. It was a measure of the system that he was only occasionally successful in such initiatives. He had the foresight to appreciate at an early stage that if helicopters could operate efficiently as transports then they would have a secure future. He saw that he had to demonstrate that helicopters were economically competitive with short range surface and fixed-wing aircraft transport. Rolling, as opposed to vertical, take-offs would assist in this demonstration by allowing heavier payloads. The ability to take-off vertically would be a bonus.

Mil's name will always be associated with the birth, growing pains and maturity of Soviet helicopter development. His most prominent position in the Soviet Union's development of helicopters, like that of Sikorsky's in the USA, is unlikely ever to be eclipsed.

Appendix 1
SOVIET ROTARY-WING AIRCRAFT

First Flight	Designer	Designation	Engine	Remarks
	Sikorsky		25 hp Anzani	1909; did not fly
	Sikorsky		25 hp Anzani	1910; did not fly
	Yuriev		25 hp Anzani	1912; did not fly
1929	Kamov/ Skrzhinsky	KaSkr-1	110 hp Gnome-Rhône	Autogiro
1930	Yuriev/ Sabinin	TsAGI 1-EA	120 hp M-2 (2)	
1930	Kamov/ Skrzhinsky	KaSkr-2	230 hp Gnome-Rhône	Autogiro
1931	Kuznetsov	TsAGI 2-EA	230 hp Gnome-Rhône	Autogiro
1932	Kuznetsov	TsAGI 4-EA (A-4)	300 hp M-26	Autogiro
1933	Yuriev/ Izakson	TsAGI 3-EA	120 hp M-2 (2)	Tethered only
1933	Bratukhin	TsAGI 5-EA	120 hp M-2 (2)	
1933	Kuznetsov	TsAGI A-6	100 hp M-11	Autogiro
1934	Kamov	TsAGI A-7	480 hp M-22	Autogiro
1934	Kuznetsov	TsAGI A-8	100 hp M-11	Autogiro
1935	Kuznetsov	TsAGI A-14	100 hp M-11	Autogiro
	Isacco	Isacco-4	120 hp DH Gipsy III (4) 300 hp Wright J-5	1935; did not fly
1936	Kuznetsov	TsAGI A-13	100 hp M-11	Autogiro
1936	Skrzhinsky	TsAGI A-12	670 hp Wright-Cyclone (M-25)	Autogiro
	Mil	TsAGI A-15	750 hp M-25V	1936 autogiro; did not fly
1936	Bratukhin	TsAGI 11-EA	630 hp Curtiss Conqueror	Tethered only
1940	Bratukhin	TsAGI 11-EA PV	630 hp Curtiss Conqueror	Compound helicopter
	Kamov	AK	220 hp MV-6	1940 autogiro; did not fly
1941	Bratukhin	2 MG Omega	220 hp MV-6 (2)	
1944	Bratukhin	Omega II	350 hp MG-31F (2)	
1945	Bratukhin	G-3	450 hp P&W R-985-AN-1 (2)	

First flight	Designer	Designation	NATO reporting name	Engine	Remarks
1947	Bratukhin	G-4		500 hp AI-26GR (2)	
1947	Bratukhin	B-5		550 hp AI-26GR(F) (2)	
	Bratukhin	B-9		550 hp AI-26GR(F) (2);	did not fly
1947	Bratukhin	B-10		575 hp AI-26GVF (2)	
1947	Yakovlev	EG		140 hp M-11FR-1;	prototype only (PO)
1947	Kamov	Ka-8		44.8 hp M-76	PO
1948	Bratukhin	B-11		575 hp AI-26GVF (2)	PO
1948	Mil	Mi-1	Hare	575 hp AI-26V	
1948	Yakovlev	Yak-100		575 hp AI-26GRFL	PO
1949	Kamov	Ka-10	Hat	55 hp AI-4V	PO
1950	Zherebtsov	?		Blade tip ramjets;	research only
1952	Mil	Mi-4	Hound	1,700 hp ASh-82V	
1952	Yakovlev	Yak-24	Horse	1,700 ASh-82V (2)	
1952	Kamov	Ka-15	Hen	275 hp AI-14VF	
1957	Kamov	Ka-18	Hog	275 hp AI-14VF	
1957	Mil	Mi-6	Hook	5,500 shp D-25V (2)	
1960	Mil	Mi-10	Harke-A	5,500 shp D-25V (2)	
1960	Kamov	Ka-20	Harp	900 shp GTD-3 (2)	PO
1960?	Kamov	Ka-22	Hoop	5,700 shp AI-20V (2);	compound helicopter; PO
1961	Mil	Mi-8	Hip	1,700 shp TV2-117A (2)	
1961	Mil	Mi-2	Hoplite	400 shp GTD-350 (2);	built in Poland
1963?	Kamov	Ka-25	Hormone	990 shp GTD-3BM (2)	
1965	Kamov	Ka-26	Hoodlum-A	325 hp M-14V-26 (2)	
1965	Mil	Mi-10K	Harke-B	5,500 shp D-25V (2)	
1968	Mil	Mi-12	Homer	6,500 shp D-25VF (4)	PO
1969?	Mil	Mi-24	Hind	2,200 shp TV3-117 (2)	
1973	Mil	Mi-14	Haze	1,900 shp TV3-117 (2)?	
1976?	Kamov	Ka-27/32	Helix	2,225 shp TV3-117V (2)	
1976?	Mil	Mi-18		1,900 shp TV3-117 (2)?	PO
1977	Mil	Mi-26	Halo	11,400 shp D-136 (2)	
1979	Mil	Mi-17	Hip-H	1,900 shp TV3-117MT (2)	
1982?	Mil	Mi-28	Havoc	? (2)	
1983?	Kamov	?	Hokum	2,225 shp TV3-117V? (2)	
1986	Kamov	Ka-126	Hoodlum-B	720 shp TVD-100	Production to be in Romania
1986	Mil	Mi-34	Hermit	325 hp M-14V-26	

Notes

1. In addition to the above list a number of very small helicopters and autogiros has been built in recent years by, for example, the Kharkov and Kuibyshev Aviation Institutes.

2. In 1975 eight records were set by a female crew in a Mil helicopter designated the A-10. This type is in fact a Mi-24.

3. In some cases improved or different engines have been installed during the service of the helicopter. The final type is given above.

4. Until the first Mil and third Kamov helicopters only the A-4 and A-7 autogiros had entered production. Prototype only (PO) indicates that the types thereafter did not enter production.

5. The Mi-25/35 and Ka-28 are export versions of the Mi-24 and Ka-27 respectively and are therefore not included.

Appendix 2
SOVIET ROTARY-WING TYPES

Designation	NATO reporting name	Description
KaSkr-I		Two-seat autogiro
TsAGI 1-EA		First Soviet helicopter; 2 engines, main rotors with 4 blades, 4 anti-torque rotors
KaSkr-II		Improved version of KaSkr-I
TsAGI 2-EA		Two-seat autogiro; operational
TsAGI 4-EA (A-4)		Larger and more powerful version of 2-EA; operational
TsAGI 3-EA		Improved version of 1-EA
TsAGI 5-EA		Improved version of 3-EA with 6 main rotor blades
TsAGI A-6		Lighter and more sophisticated version of A-4.
TsAGI A-7		Two-seat military autogiro, armed with 2 MGs; operational
TsAGI A-8		Similar to A-6 but with hydraulic shock absorbers
TsAGI A-14		A-6 without wings.
Isacco-4		Five passenger machine with 4 blade tip engines and one propulsion engine; did not fly.
TsAGI A-13		Lighter version of A-8
TsAGI A-12		Single-seat wingless autogiro-fighter
TsAGI A-15		Two-seat wingless autogiro-fighter; did not fly
TsAGI 11-EA		Single-engined, larger version of 5-EA with 2 anti-torque propellers
TsAGI 11-EA PV		Improved version of 11-EA; compound helicopter
TsAGI AK		Two-seat wingless autogiro; not completed
2 MG Omega		Two-seat experimental helicopter
Omega II		Up-engined version of 2 MG Omega
G-3		Up-engined version of Omega II
G-4		Up-engined version of G-3 cleared for production
B-5		First of new breed of 'aerodynamic' helicopters; crew of 2 plus 6 passengers
B-9		Air ambulance; not completed
B-10		Military reconnaissance and observation
Yakovlev EG		Two-seat co-axial; not operational
B-11		Experimental 3-seat communications
Ka-8		Experimental 'flying motorcycle'
Mi-1	*Hare*	Utility; pilot plus 2/3 passengers; some armed

Designation	NATO reporting name	Description
Mi-1U, T, UT		Dual control trainer
-1NKh		Civil multi-purpose
-1P		Amphibious version with pontoons
-1S		Casualty evacuation; wrongly designated Mi-3 for a time
-1 *Moskvich*		VIP transport
SM-1		Polish-built Mi-1
-1W		Improved version with metal rotor blades
-1WS		Casualty evacuation with 2 external stretcher pods
-1SZ		Dual control trainer
SM-2		Polish development of SM-1 with modified forward fuselage for pilot and 4 passengers
Yak-100		Two versions of single main/tail rotor type: 2-seat trainer and 3-seat communications; not operational
Ka-10	Hat	Stretched Ka-8; not operational
-10M		Improved version with better engine
Zherebtsov		Single seat; tip jet driven; for research only
Mi-4	Hound-A	12–16 passenger/utility; some armed
	-B	ASW; shore-based
	-C	Communications jammer
-4L		6-passenger de luxe
-4P		8–10 passenger with square windows
-4S		Civil multi-purpose
-4V		High altitude, multi-purpose
Yak-24	Horse	Twin-engined, tandem rotor, 24 troops
-24U		37–40 troops
-24A		Civil 30-seater; not operational
-24K		8-seat VIP; not operational
Ka-15	Hen	Navy reconnaissance/utility
-15M		Multi-purpose
-15U		Dual control trainer
Ka-18	Hog	Stretched Ka-15; mainly for civil use
Mi-6	Hook-A	Military lift for 65 troops or heavy/bulky equipment
	-B	Airborne command post
-6P		90-seat civil passenger/general utility
Mi-10	Harke-A	Heavy lift crane with tall undercarriage
-10K	-B	Short-legged variant with gondola cockpit
Ka-20	Harp	Prototype for Ka-25
Ka-22	Hoop	Experimental convertiplane
Mi-8	Hip-A	Prototype with single 2,700 shp engine and 4-bladed main rotor
	-B	Modified Hip-A with 2 × 1,400 shp engines
	-C	Production model with 2 × 1,500 shp engines and 5-bladed main rotor; utility; some armed
	-D	Command and control, radio relay
	-E	Assault helicopter with nose MG, rockets and 4 Swatter ATGM
	-F	Export version of Hip-E but with 6 Sagger ATGM
	-G	Airborne command post
	-H	See Mi-17
	-J	Radar jammer
	-K	Communications jammer

Designation	NATO reporting name	Description
-8P		28-seat civil passenger
-8 Salon		9–11-seat de luxe
-8T		Civil utility, passenger and load carrier
Mi-2	Hoplite	Polish-built, Soviet-designed civil and military multi-role
-2M		11-seater
-2B		Improved avionics
Ka-25	Hormone-A	ASW; ship-based
	-B	Ship-to-ship missile guidance
	-C	SAR, utility, vertical replenishment
-25K		Crane; not operational
Ka-26	Hoodlum-A	Civil multi-purpose
Ka-126	Hoodlum-B	Single turbine-powered development of Ka-26
Mi-12	Homer	Heavy lift; not operational
Mi-24	Hind-A	Armed assault with anhedral wings for rockets, Swatter ATGM; MG in nose
	-B	As Hind-A but no anhedral or ATGM rails; not operational
	-C	Trainer; none with ATGM rails
	-D	Attack helicopter with redesigned forward fuselage, under nose gun turret and improved sensors
	-E	As Hind-D but with Spiral ATGM
	-F	As Hind-E but with fixed twin-barrelled 30 mm cannon on starboard side instead of gun turret
	-G	Missiles removed; unidentified devices on wing tips
Mi-25	Hind	Export version of Hind-D
Mi-35	Hind	Export version of Hind-E?
Mi-14	Haze-A	ASW; shore-based
	-B	Mine countermeasures; shore-based
	-C	SAR
Ka-27	Helix-A	ASW; ship-based
	-B	Naval assault helicopter; without radar; some armed
	-C	Utility
	-D	SAR
Ka-28	Helix	Export version of Ka-27 Helix-A
Ka-32S	Helix	Ice patrol, offshore oil support; with search radar; civil version of Helix-A
-32T	Helix-C	Civil utility
Mi-18		Prototype for Mi-17
Mi-26	Halo	Civil/military heavy lift
Mi-26T		Civil heavy lift for extreme weather conditions
Mi-17	Hip-H	Improved and more powerful version of Mi-8/Hip-C
Mi-28	Havoc	Tandem 2-seat attack helicopter; not yet operational
Ka-?	Hokum	Tandem 2-seat attack helicopter; not yet operational
Mi-34	Hermit	Training and sports helicopter; not yet operational

Notes

1. This list includes only those rotary-wing aircraft known to have been built or partially built.

2. Neither KaSkr, TsAGI nor Bratukhin aircraft became operational except where indicated.

Appendix 3
WORLD RECORDS

International sporting authority

The Fédération Aéronautique Internationale (FAI) is the sole international sporting body to make and enforce rules to encourage and control sporting events and records in the fields of both aeronautics and astronautics.

FAI classifications

All aircraft and apparatus recognised by the FAI are divided into classes and sub-classes for the purposes of sporting meetings and records. There are two categories for each of these sub-classes:

General category: the best performance achieved.

Feminine category: the best performance achieved by a woman or a female crew

Rotorcraft are designated Class E and sub-classes are as follows:

E.1	Helicopter
E.1.a	Helicopter weighing less than 500 kg (1,102 lb)
E.1.b	Helicopter weighing from 500 kg to less than 1,000 kg (2,205 lb)
E.1.c	Helicopter weighing from 1,000 kg to less than 1,750 kg (3,858 lb)
E.1.d	Helicopter weighing from 1,750 kg to less than 3,000 kg (6,614 lb)
E.1.e	Helicopter weighing from 3,000 kg to less than 4,500 kg (9,921 lb)
E.1.f	Helicopter weighing from 4,500 kg to less than 6,000 kg (13,228 lb)
E.1.g	Helicopter weighing from 6,000 kg to less than 10,000 kg (22,046 lb)
E.1.h	Helicopter weighing from 10,000 kg to less than 20,000 kg (44,092 lb)
E.2	Convertiplane
E.2.a	Convertiplane weighing less than 500 kg
E.2.b	Convertiplane weighing from 500 kg to less than 1,000 kg
E.2.c	Convertiplane weighing from 1,000 kg to less than 1,750 kg
E.2.d	Convertiplane weighing from 1,750 kg to less than 3,000 kg
E.3	Autogiro
E.3.a	Autogiro weighing less than 500 kg
E.3.b	Autogiro weighing from 500 kg to less than 1,000 kg
E.3.c	Autogiro weighing from 1,000 kg to less than 1,750 kg
E.3.d	Autogiro weighing from 1,750 kg to less than 3,000 kg

Establishment of records

A new record must constitute an improvement over the preceding one of at least:

1% in distance records
3% in altitude records
1% in speed records

A record established with an aircraft carrying a payload is broken in its category when an aircraft carrying an equal or superior payload accomplishes a better performance, in accordance with the conditions set forth in the paragraph above.

Soviet rotorcraft records

The list below comprises all FAI-recognised records set by Soviet rotorcraft. Also detailed are the current records in those categories in which a Soviet pilot has at one time set a record.

Name	Country	Date of record	Aircraft		
CLASS E.1					
Distance in a closed circuit				**km**	**miles**
V. Koloshenko	USSR	19.04.64	Mi-8	2,465.74	1,532.13
J. Schweibold	USA	26.03.66	YOH-6A	2,800.2	1,739.96
Altitude with 1,000 kg (2,205 lb) load				**metres**	**feet**
V. Vinitsky	USSR	26.04.56	Mi-4	6,048	19,843
G. Alferov	USSR	26.03.60	Mi-4	7,465	24,491
B. Blackwell	USA	26.10.71	CH-54B	9,499	31,165
Altitude with 2,000 kg (4,409 lb) load					
G. Tinyakov	USSR	17.12.55	Yak-24	5,082	16,673
R. Kaprelyan	USSR	25.04.56	Mi-4	6,018	19,744
K. Chernobrovkin	USSR	12.03.65	Mi-4	6,369	20,896
E. Price	USA	29.10.71	CH-54B	9,595	31,480
Altitude with 5,000 kg (11,023 lb) load					
S. Brovtsev	USSR	16.04.59	Mi-6	5,584	18,320
V. Koloshenko	USSR	26.05.65	Mi-10K	7,151	23,461
E. Price	USA	27.10.71	CH-54B	7,778	25.518
Altitude with 10,000 kg (22,046 lb) load					
R. Kaprelyan	USSR	30.10.57	Mi-6	2,432	7,979
R. Kaprelyan	USSR	16.04.59	Mi-6	4,885	16,027
G. Karapetyan	USSR	2.02.82	Mi-26	6,400	20,997
Altitude with 15,000 kg (33,070 lb) load					
G. Alferov	USSR	23.09.61	Mi-10	2.326	7,631
R. Kaprelyan	USSR	13.09.62	Mi-6	2,738	8,983
G. Alferov	USSR	28.05.65	Mi-10K	2,840	9,318
V. Koloshenko	USSR	22.02.69	Mi-12	2,951	9,682
S. Petrov	USSR	4.02.82	Mi-26	5,600	18,373
Altitude with 20,000 kg (44,092 lb) load					
R. Kaprelyan	USSR	13.09.62	Mi-6	2,738	8,983
G. Alferov	USSR	28.05.65	Mi-10K	2,840	9,318
V. Koloshenko	USSR	22.02.69	Mi-12	2,951	9,682
A. Kholupov	USSR	4.02.82	Mi-26	4,600	15,092
Altitude with 25,000 kg (55,115 lb) load					
G. Alferov	USSR	28.05.65	Mi-10K	2,840	9,318
V. Koloshenko	USSR	22.02.69	Mi-12	2,951	9,682
G. Alferov	USSR	3.02.82	Mi-26	4,100	13,451
Altitude with 30,000 kg (66,139 lb) load					
V. Koloshenko	USSR	22.02.69	Mi-12	2,951	9,682
Altitude with 35,000 kg (77,162 lb) load					
V. Koloshenko	USSR	6.08.69	Mi-12	2,255	7,398
Altitude with 40,000 kg (88,185 lb) load					
V. Koloshenko	USSR	6.08.69	Mi-12	2,255	7,398

Name	Country	Date of record	Aircraft		
Speed over a 15/25 km (9.32/15.53 miles) course				**kph**	**mph**
N. Liochin	USSR	21.09.61	Mi-6	320.0	198.83
G. Karapetyan	USSR	21.09.78	A-10(1)	368.4	228.9
Speed over a closed circuit of 100 km (62.14 miles)					
B. Zemskov	USSR	21.11.59	Mi-6	268.92	167.09
B. Galitsky	USSR	26.08.64	Mi-6	340.15	211.36
J. Egginton	UK	11.05.86	Lynx	400.87	249.1
Speed over a closed circuit of 500 km (310.68 miles)					
B. Zemskov	USSR	29.04.56	Mi-4	187.25	116.35
B, Galitsky	USSR	15.09.62	Mi-6	315.66	196.14
G. Rastorgueva	USSR	1.08.75	A-10(1)	331.02	205.69
T. Doyle	USA	8.02.82	S-76	345.74	214.83
Speed over a closed circuit of 1,000 km (621.37 miles)					
B. Galitsky	USSR	15.09.62	Mi-6	300.38	186.65
G. Rastorgueva	USSR	13.08.75	A-10(1)	332.65	206.69
Speed over a closed circuit of 2,000 km (1,242.74 miles)					
V. Koloshenko	USSR	19.04.64	Mi-8	201.83	125.41
I. Kopets	USSR	14.09.67	Mi-8	235.12	146.09
Speed over a closed circuit of 1,000 km with a 1,000 kg load					
B. Galitsky	USSR	15.09.62	Mi-6	300.38	186.65
Speed over a closed circuit of 1,000 km with a 2,000 kg load					
B. Galitsky	USSR	15.09.62	Mi-6	300.38	186.65
Speed over a closed circuit of 1,000 km with a 5,000 kg load					
V. Koloshenko	USSR	11.09.62	Mi-6	282.35	175.45
Greatest load carried to an altitude of 2,000 m (6,562 ft)				**kg**	**lb**
Ye. Miliutichev	USSR	17.12.55	Yak-24	4,000	8,818
R. Kaprelyan	USSR	30.10.57	Mi-6	12,004	26.464
G. Alferov	USSR	23.09.61	Mi-10	15,103	33,296
R. Kaprelyan	USSR	13.09.62	Mi-6	20,117	44,350
G. Alferov	USSR	28.05.65	Mi-10K	25,105	55,347
V. Koloshenko	USSR	22.02.69	Mi-12	31,030	68,409
V. Koloshenko	USSR	6.08.69	Mi-12	40,204.5	88,636
Greatest mass lifted to an altitude of 2,000 m				**kg**	**lb**
G. Alferov	USSR	3.02.82	Mi-26	56,768.8	125,154
Time to climb to an altitude of 3,000 m (9,843 ft)				**mins**	**secs**
R. Witowski	Poland	5.04.57	SM-1	7	48
S. Gajewski	Poland	11.09.57	SM-1	6	45.6
J. Henderson	USA	12.04.72	CH-54B	1	22.2

CLASS E.1(Female)

Name	Country	Date of record	Aircraft		
Distance in a closed circuit				**km**	**miles**
I. Kopets	USSR	14.09.67	Mi-8	2,082.2	1,293.8
Distance in a straight line					
V. Larina	USSR	11.09.67	Mi-1	1,654.6	1,028.1
I. Kopets	USSR	15.08.69	Mi-8	2,232.2	1,387
Altitude without payload				**metres**	**feet**
T. Russiyan	USSR	27.03.59	Mi-1	4,140	13,583
T. Russiyan	USSR	12.01.65	Mi-4	7,534	24,718
T. Zueva	USSR	29.01.85	Ka-32	8,250	27,067

Name	Country	Date of record	Aircraft	metres	feet
Altitude in horizontal flight				metres	feet
T. Zueva	USSR	11.03.82	Ka-26	5,602	18,379
T. Zueva	USSR	11.05.83	Ka-32	6,552	21,496
T. Zueva	USSR	29.01.85	Ka-32	8,215	26,952
Altitude with a 1,000 kg load					
I. Kopets	USSR	1.12.82	Mi-26	5,750	18,865
N. Yeremina	USSR	29.01.85	Ka-32	7,305	23,967
Altitude with a 2,000 kg load					
I. Kopets	USSR	1.12.82	Mi-26	5,750	18,865
N. Yeremina	USSR	29.01 85	Ka-32	6,400	20,997
Altitude with a 5,000 kg load					
I. Kopets	USSR	1.12.82	Mi-26	5,750	18,865
Altitude with a 10,000 kg load					
I. Kopets	USSR	1.12.82	Mi-26	5,750	18,865
Altitude with a 15,000 kg load					
I. Kopets	USSR	2.12.82	Mi-26	4,800	15,748
Altitude with a 20,000 kg load					
I. Kopets	USSR	3.12.82	Mi-26	4,050	13,287
Altitude with a 25,000 kg load					
I. Kopets	USSR	3.12.82	Mi-26	3,750	12,303
Greatest load carried to an altitude of 2,000 m				kg	lb
I. Kopets	USSR	3.12.82	Mi-26	25,110	55,357
Greatest mass lifted to an altitude of 2,000 m					
I. Kopets	USSR	3.12.82	Mi-26	56,520	124,603
Speed over a 15/25 km course				kph	mph
G. Rastorgueva	USSR	16.07.75	A-10(1)	341.32	212.09
Speed over a closed circuit of 100 km					
I. Gurova	USSR	28.03.58	Mi-1	175.46	109.03
A. Geppener	USSR	22.06.61	Mi-1	196.67	122.2
T. Russiyan	USSR	10.06.65	Mi-2	269.38	167.38
G. Rastorgueva	USSR	18.07.75	A-10(1)	334.46	207.82
Speed over a closed circuit of 500 km					
T. Russiyan	USSR	18.06.60	Mi-1	142.64	88.63
S. Kotova	USSR	21.07.65	Mi-4	195.45	121.45
I. Kopets	USSR	28.08.67	Mi-8	273.51	169.95
G. Rastorgueva	USSR	1.08.75	A-10(1)	331.02	205.68
Speed over a closed circuit of 1,000 km					
T. Larina	USSR	2.09.66	Mi-1	137.38	85.36
I. Issaeva	USSR	28.08.67	Mi-8	258.67	160.73
G. Rastorgueva	USSR	13.08.75	A-10(1)	332.65	206.69
Speed over a closed circuit of 2,000 km					
I. Kopets	USSR	14.09.67	Mi-8	235.12	146.09
Time to climb to an altitude of 3,000 m				mins	secs
G. Rastorgueva	USSR	8.08.75	A-10(1)	2	33.5
N. Yeremina	USSR	12.05.83	Ka-32	2	11.1

Name	Country	Date of record	Aircraft		

Time to climb to an altitude of 6,000 m (19,685 ft) — mins / secs

				mins	secs
G. Rastorgueva	USSR	26.08.75	A-10(1)	7	43
T. Zueva	USSR	11.05.83	Ka-32	4	46.5

SUB-CLASSES E.1.a and E.1.b
No records set by Soviet helicopters

SUB-CLASS E.1.c

Speed over a closed circuit of 100 km — kph / mph

				kph	mph
V. Vinitsky	USSR	29.05.58	Ka-15	162.78	101.15
D. Prost	France	13.05.71	SA 341	296.0	183.92

Speed over a closed circuit of 500 km

V. Vinitsky	USSR	6.05.59	Ka-15	170.44	105.91
D. Kyle	USA	12.03.71	OH-6A	249.85	155.25

SUB-CLASS E.1.d

Distance in a closed circuit — km / miles

				km	miles
V. Riakhovsky	USSR	24.03.58	Mi-1	555.38	345.09
F. Belushkin	USSR	24.06.60	Mi-1	1,006.6	625.47
A. Lutsenko	USSR	15.05.63	Mi-1	1,188.52	738.51
A. Anossov	USSR	23.09.66	Mi-1	1,270.08	789.19
A. Gorbatchev	USSR	27.04.67	Mi-1	1,400.63	870.31
A. Anossov	USSR	17.04.68	Mi-1	1,528.77	949.93

Distance in a straight line

F. Belushkin	USSR	19.03.58	Mi-1	794.92	493.94
F. Belushkin	USSR	21.09.60	Mi-1	1,224.76	761.03
A. Anossov	USSR	10.09.66	Mi-1	1,504.5	934.85
S. Hoffman	USA	20.04.74	Bo-105	1,714.84	1,065.5

Altitude without payload — metres / feet

				metres	feet
S. Gajewski	Poland	11.09.57	SM-1	6,394	20,978
F. Belushkin	USSR	12.03.59	Mi-1	6,700	21,982
E. Sampson	USA	11.12.64	UH-1D	10,713	35,148

Altitude in horizontal flight

A. Sherstyuk	USSR	17.06.80	Ka-26	5,330	17,487
B. Graham	USA	5.02.82	S-76A	7,940	26,050

Time to climb to an altitude of 3,000 m — mins / secs

				mins	secs
A. Sherstyuk	USSR	8.04.80	Ka-26	8	51.2
M. Jot	France	15.09.87	SA 365M	2	54

Speed over a closed circuit of 100 km — kph / mph

				kph	mph
A. Avidzba	USSR	5.03.58	Mi-1	176.65	109.77
V. Riakhovsky	USSR	7.02.59	Mi-1	189.32	117.64
V. Vinitsky	USSR	21.05.59	Mi-1	210.53	130.82
B. Anopov	USSR	14.05.63	Mi-2	253.82	157.72
D. Wright	USA	6.02.82	S-76	331.2	205.8

Speed over a closed circuit of 500 km

V. Vinitsky	USSR	19.05.59	Mi-1	196.45	122.06
B. Odneal	USA	23.11.64	UH-1D	286.83	178.23

Speed over a closed circuit of 1,000 km

F. Belushkin	USSR	24.06.60	Mi-1	141.39	87.86
J. Johnston	USA	15.09.64	UH-1D	235.1	146.08

Name	Country	Date of record	Aircraft		

SUB-CLASS E.1.d (Female)

Distance in a straight line				**km**	**miles**
V. Larina	USSR	11.09.67	Mi-1	1,654.6	1,028.1
Altitude in horizontal flight				**metres**	**feet**
T. Zueva	USSR	11.03.82	Ka-26	5,602	18,379
Altitude without payload					
T. Zueva	USSR	11.03.82	Ka-26	5,626	18,458
Time to climb to an altitude of 3,000 m				**mins**	**secs**
N. Yeremina	USSR	11.03.82	Ka-26	8	19.3

SUB-CLASSES E. 1.e, f, g and h
No records set by Soviet helicopters

CLASS E.2

Altitude without payload				**metres**	**feet**
D. Yefremov	USSR	24.11.61	Ka-22	2,588	8,491
Altitude with a 1,000 kg load					
D. Yefremov	USSR	24.11.61	Ka-22	2,588	8,491
Altitude with a 2,000 kg load					
D. Yefremov	USSR	24.11.61	Ka-22	2,588	8,491
Altitude with a 5,000 kg load					
D. Yefremov	USSR	24.11.61	Ka-22	2,588	8,491
Altitude with a 10,000 kg load					
D. Yefremov	USSR	24.11.61	Ka-22	2,588	8,491
Altitude with a 15,000 kg load					
D. Yefremov	USSR	24.11.61	Ka-22	2,588	8,491
Speed over a 15/25 km course				**kph**	**mph**
D. Yefremov	USSR	7.10.61	Ka-22	356.3	221.4
Greatest load carried to an altitude of 2,000 m				**kg**	**lb**
D. Yefremov	USSR	24.11.61	Ka-22	16,485	36,343

Note

1. The A-10 is a version of the Mi-24.

Appendix 4
FOREIGN USERS

This Appendix lists those countries thought to have received Soviet helicopters during the last four decades. The figures in brackets indicate the number of helicopters believed to be in the military service of the countries shown in 1987. These figures have been extracted in the main from the 1987/88 edition of the *Military Balance* with the kind permission of the International Institute for Strategic Studies.

A (?) denotes that this type is in military service now but the number is not known. Where there is no figure nor (?) the type is only in civil service or has been withdrawn from service altogether.

In the fighting between Chad and Libya the Chadians captured three Mi-24/25 Hinds; other Hinds have been flown to Pakistan by defecting Afghan pilots. Some of these have probably been passed on to France and the USA but these countries are not shown as possessing them in the list below.

Mi-1 Hare　　　Afghanistan, Albania, Algeria, Bangladesh, China, Cuba, Czechoslovakia (20), East Germany, Egypt, Finland, Hungary, Iraq, Mongolia, North Korea, North Yemen, Poland, Romania, Somalia, Sudan, Syria, Vietnam, Yugoslavia

Mi-2 Hoplite　　Bulgaria (?), Czechoslovakia (55), Denmark, East Germany (?), Egypt, Finland, Hungary (15), Indonesia, Iran, Iraq, Libya (20), Nicaragua (4), Nigeria, Poland (130), Romania, Somalia, Syria (10), Sudan, Sweden, UK, USA, Yugoslavia (?)

Mi-4 Hound　　Afghanistan (12), Albania (29), Algeria (40), Austria, Bangladesh, Bulgaria (?), Cameroun, China (50+), Cuba (60), Czechoslovakia (60), East Germany, Egypt, Finland, Ghana, Hungary, India, Indonesia, Iraq (20), Kampuchea, Laos, Mali (2), Mongolia, North Korea (20), North Yemen, Pakistan, Poland (20), Romania (14), Somalia (6), South Yemen, Syria, Vietnam, Yugoslavia

Mi-6 Hook　　Algeria (4), Bulgaria, Egypt, Ethiopia, Indonesia, Iraq (10), Laos (2), Libya, Peru (6), Poland, Syria, Vietnam (15)

Mi-8 Hip　　　Afghanistan (25), Algeria (29), Angola (50), Anguilla, Bangladesh (12), Bulgaria (?), China, Cuba (40), Czechoslovakia (65), East Germany (101), Egypt (27), Ethiopia (22), Finland (13), Guinea-Bissau (1), Guyana (3), Hungary (25), India (?), Iraq (100), Japan, Kampuchea (6), Laos (10), Libya (?), Madagascar (6), Mali (1), Mongolia (?), Mozambique (10), Nicaragua (?), North Korea (?), North Yemen (23), Pakistan (16), Peru (5), Poland (30), Romania (15), Somalia (4), South Yemen (30), Sudan, Syria (?), USA, Vietnam (36), Yugoslavia (90), Zambia (7)

Mi-10 Harke　　Iraq, Pakistan, USA

Mi-14 Haze　　Bulgaria (12), Cuba (4), East Germany (13), Libya (25), North Korea (?), Poland (15), Romania (?), Syria (34), Yugoslavia (?)

Mi-17 Hip	Angola (13), Cuba (?), India (?), Nicaragua (?), North Korea (?), Peru, Syria (30)
Mi-24/25/35 Hind	Afghanistan (13), Algeria (45), Angola (21), Bulgaria (35), Czechoslovakia (40), Cuba (18), East Germany (30), Ethiopia (22), Hungary (30), India (12), Iraq (40?), Libya (27), Mozambique (12), Nicaragua (12), North Korea (50), Poland (30), South Yemen (15), Syria (50), Vietnam (30)
Mi-26 Halo	India (10?)
Ka-25 Hormone	India (?), Syria (8), Vietnam (17), Yugoslavia (10)
Ka-26 Hoodlum	Bulgaria, East Germany, Hungary (25), India, Japan, Romania, Sri Lanka, Sweden, West Germany, Yugoslavia
Ka-28 Helix	India (?), Yugoslavia (?)

GLOSSARY

AA	Anti-aircraft
ADF	Automatic direction finder
Advancing blade	The rotor blade that is moving forward into the relative airflow
Aerofoil	A surface shaped to produce lift when driven through the air, eg a rotor blade
AGL	Above ground level
Angle of attack	The acute angle between the chord line of a rotor blade and the relative airflow
Angle of incidence	The acute angle between the chord line and the horizontal or longitudinal axis of the helicopter
Anhedral	The slope downwards, relative to the horizontal, of the wings from root to tip
APC	Armoured personnel carrier
APU	Auxiliary power unit
Articulated rotor system	A rotor system in which individual blades are free to flap, drag and feather (change pitch) by means of hinges connecting them to the rotor hub
ASW	Anti-submarine warfare
Autogiro	A rotorcraft which derives most or all of its lift from a rotor which turns freely in flight under the single influence of the air flowing through the blades – like a windmill
Autorotation	When autorotating a helicopter descends under control but without power from the engine. The rotor blades continue to rotate, now freely, at the same speed because of the upward flow of air through the rotor disc
Avgas	Aviation gasoline; used in piston-engined aircraft
AV-MF	*Aviatsiya Voenno-Morskogo Flota* – Naval Aviation
Chord	The distance between the leading edge and trailing edge of an aerofoil section
Co-axial, contra-rotating rotor system	Two sets of main rotor blades, mounted on a common axis, but turning in opposite directions. The torques cancel each other out and therefore no tail rotor is required
Collective lever	On the pilot's left hand side, this lever has the effect of changing pitch on all the main rotor blades simultaneously. It is used to make the helicopter climb or descend
C³	Command, control and communications
Compound helicopter	A helicopter which also has wings and/or propellers to assist the main rotor system to provide lift and/or propulsion

222

Convertiplane	A rotorcraft which in flight can change from getting lift from its rotor blades to getting it from wings and vice versa
Cyclic stick	The pilot's 'control column' by means of which he can make the helicopter go forwards, backwards and to each side. His movements are transmitted to the rotor blades so that each blade can change pitch individually
Derated	Engine restricted to power less than the theoretical maximum available
Dihedral	The slope upwards, relative to the horizontal, of the wings from root to tip
Disc loading	The ratio of gross weight of the helicopter to the rotor disc area, ie. divide the weight by the disc area
DOSAAF	*Dobrovolnoe Obshchestvo Sodeistviya Armii, Aviatsii i Flotu* – Voluntary Society for Assistance to the Army, Air Force and Navy
Drag damper	A hydraulic or friction system, usually installed between the rotor hub and blades, to reduce the amount of blade drag
EA	*Eksperimentalnyi Apparat* – Experimental Apparatus
ECM	Electronic countermeasures
EW	Electronic warfare
FA	*Frontovaya Aviatsiya* – Frontal Aviation
FAI	Fédération Aéronautique Internationale
FEBA	Forward edge of the battle area
Fire and forget	A missile which does not require either the target to be tracked, or itself to be guided, by any operator
FLOT	Forward line of own troops. No troops are ahead of this line while a few, for example reconnaissance and screen forces, will be between the FLOT and FEBA which delineates the main battle area
Free turbine	An extra turbine positioned at the rear of a gas turbine engine and connected to the transmission but not to the engine. The flow of gas rotates this disc and thus the transmission
FROG	Free (flight) rocket over ground; a surface-to-surface rocket
Gas turbine	An engine which takes in air, compresses it and then mixes it with fuel to form a combustible gas. This gas is then fed through to a varying number of turbine discs which convert the kinetic energy of the burnt gas into mechanical energy to drive the output shaft to the main rotor gearbox and ultimately the rotor system
GAZ	*Gosudarstvennyi Aviatsionnyi Zavod* – State Aircraft Factory
GOF	Group of Forces
Governor	A device that automatically controls the fuel flow to the engine to maintain rotor rpm irrespective of pitch changes made by the pilot
Ground effect	Also ground cushion. It is caused by the downwash of air from the rotor being reflected back upwards from the ground to produce a 'cushion' of air beneath the helicopter. It follows that less power is required to hover in ground effect than to hover out of ground effect. The depth of the ground cushion is approximately equivalent to the length of the helicopter's main rotor blade
Ground resonance	Violent rocking of the helicopter on the ground. If not checked the helicopter will destroy itself
GSFG	Group of Soviet Forces Germany
HEAT	High explosive anti-tank
HF	High frequency

Hinges	An articulated rotor has hinges to allow the blades to flap, drag and feather. Feathering may be achieved by pitch change bearings
'Hot and high'	The adverse combination of high ambient temperatures and high altitude
hp	Horse power
ICBM	Intercontinental ballistic missile
IERAT	*Institut Ekspluatatsii i Remonta Aviatsionnoy Tekhniki* – Institute of Aviation Equipment Operation and Maintenance
IFF	Identification friend or foe – a secondary radar system designed to provide a positive identification of friendly aircraft. It has an interrogator which transmits a coded signal to a transponder in the helicopter. A valid response identifies the helicopter as friendly; an incorrect response or none at all as hostile. The current Soviet second generation system is the SRO-2
IFV	Infantry fighting vehicle
IR	Infra-red
KGB	*Komitet Gosudarstvennoi Bezopasnosti* – State Security Committee
km	Kilometres
kph	Kilometres per hour
Laser designator	A laser beam or stream of pulses illuminates the target. The laser spot on the target is detected by a receiver in the missile head which directs the missile towards it
LII	*Letno-issledovatelskii Institut* – Flight Research Institute
m	Metres
mm	Millimetres
MAD	Magnetic anomaly detection. The package is towed on a cable and the equipment is able to detect very small disturbances in the Earth's magnetic field caused by the magnetic material of a submerged submarine
MAI	Ministry of Aviation Industry
mph	Miles per hour
MRB	Motor rifle battalion
MVTU	*Moskovskoe Vysshee Tekhnicheskoe Uchilishche* – Moscow Higher Technical School
Night Vision Systems	In simple terms these consist of: *Active IR*: This involves the use of an IR light source such as a special searchlight whose beam is invisible to the naked eye. The beam illuminates the target and surrounding area; a device sensitive to this light converts it into a visual display for the crew. The range is limited *Image Intensification (II)*: The enhancement of available light. Whatever light there is is reflected by the target, amplified by an intensifier and displayed. It is used in night vision goggles *Thermal Imaging (TI)*: All objects emit energy depending on their temperature and those that radiate differently from their surroundings present a thermal contrast which can be detected and displayed. Greater range than active IR. Complements day sights and can see through conventional smoke, camouflage nets, bushes etc
NII	*Nauchno-issledovatelskii Institut* – Scientific Research Institute
NKVD	*Narodnyi Komissariat Vnutrennikh Del* – People's Commissariat for Internal Affairs (until 1943)
OKB	*Opytno Konstruktorskoe Biuro* – Experimental Design Bureau
OMG	Operational Manoeuvre Group
OOK	*Otdel Osobykh Konstruktsii* – Section of Special Constructions

224

Osoaviakhim	*Obshchestvo sodeistviya oborone, aviatsionnomu i khimicheskomu stroitelstvu* – Society for the support of Defence and of Aviation and Chemical Construction
Parasite drag	Drag caused by the shape of the helicopter. The undercarriage, weapon pylons, antennae etc also help to cause drag
Pitch	The acute angle between the chord line of a rotor blade and the plane of rotation of the main rotor, normal to the rotor shaft
Radar warning receiver	A device in the cockpit that warns the crew that a radar has illuminated, and perhaps locked onto, their aircraft; up to four external antennae give 360° coverage
Radial engine	A piston engine where the cylinders are arranged like the spokes of a wheel. To achieve good balance there is always an odd number of cylinders. The pistons are all connected to a single crank-pin
Reduction gear	One or more gears in a gearbox which reduce the rpm of the rotor compared to the engine rpm. In the Mi-4, for example, the main rotor turns at 178 rpm while the engine rpm are 2,400
R and D	Research and Development
Rigid rotor system	A rotor system which allows the blades to change pitch but which is as rigid as possible in other respects; the main blades do not droop when stationary
Rotor hub (or head)	The top part of the rotor system, incorporating the hinges, to which the rotor blades are attached
Rotor downwash	The air forced downwards by the movement of the blades
rpm	Revolutions per minute
SAM	Surface-to-air missile
SAR	Search and rescue
Semi-monocoque	A type of construction where the skin, ie. of the fuselage, is relieved of the full load by longitudinal girder-members and transverse frames to which the skin is rivetted
Semi-rigid rotor system	A rotor system whose blade roots permit flexing in the flapping and dragging planes
Service ceiling	The maximum height at which the helicopter is ever likely to be used. It is defined as that height at which the rate of climb has become reduced to 30.5 m (100 ft) per minute
ShKAS	*Shpitalny-Komaritsky Aviatsionnyi Skorostrelnyi* – Shpitalny-Komaritsky rapid-firing aviation machine gun
shp	Shaft horse power
Skin friction drag	Drag caused by the slowing down of air passing over a surface
Stabiliser	Tailplane
STOL	Short take-off and landing
Swashplate	The device on the rotor shaft which permits pitch changes to be made to the rotor blades
Tail skid (or bumper)	A device to prevent the tail rotor striking the ground in the event of an excessively high nose attitude close to the ground
Tandem rotor	A twin rotor system, fore and aft, in which the torques cancel each other out
Taper	An increasing reduction in chord towards the rotor blade tips
TBO	Time between overhauls
Torque	A 'twisting moment', the turning effect of force. When under power the fuselage of a helicopter tends to turn in the opposite direction to the rotation of the single main rotor. A tail rotor is therefore installed to counter this torque reaction and help provide directional control

TsAGI	*Tsentralnyi Aero-gidrodinamicheskii Institut* – Central Aero- and Hydrodynamic Institute
TsIAM	*Tsentralnyi Institut Aviatsionnogo Motorostroeniya* – Central Aeroengine Institute
TsKB	*Tsentralnoe Konstruktorskoe Biuro* – Central Design Bureau
Turboshaft engine	A 'conventional' gas turbine engine, having a common shaft which drives the compressors and transmission
UHF	Ultra high frequency
VHF	Very high frequency
Vertolet	The Russian word for helicopter, specially coined after the Second World War – possibly by Kamov – to replace the non-Russian word '*gelikopter*' (there is no letter 'h' in Russian). Some types, eg. Mi-2, Mi-8, Mi-12 and Mi-14, were originally designated V-2, V-8, V-12 and V-14
VIAM	*Vsesoyuznyi Institut Aviatsionnykh Materialov* – All-Union Institute for Aviation Materials
VILS	*Vsesoyuznyi Institut Legkikh Splavov* – All-Union Institute for Light Alloys
Vortex ring	This is usually encountered during a steep and fast descent with power on. The rotor is forcing air downwards and the helicopter then descends through this turbulent and downwards moving air. The result is a yet higher rate of descent, vibration and a partial loss of control
V-TA	*Voenno-Transportnaya Aviatsiya* – Transport Aviation
VTOL	Vertical take-off and landing
V-VS	*Voenno-Vozdushnye Sily* – Military Air Force
WSK-PZL	*Wytwornia Sprzetu Komunikacyjnego-Polskie Zaklady Lotnicze* – Transport Equipment Plant-Polish Aviation Works
Yaw	Motion round the normal axis. The normal axis passes through the centre of gravity and is vertical when the aircraft is flying straight and level.

BIBLIOGRAPHY

Alexander, Arthur *Decision Making in Soviet Weapons Procurement*, Adelphi Papers 147/48. IISS 1978

Alexander, Jean *Russian Aircraft Since 1940*, Putnam, London 1975

Baylis, John and Segal, Gerald *Soviet Strategy*, Croom Helm, London 1981

Boyd, Alexander *The Soviet Air Force Since 1918*, Macdonald & Jane's, London 1977

Chaiko, Lev *Helicopter Construction in the USSR*, Delphic Associates Inc, Falls Church, Virginia, 1986

Duz, P. D. *History of Aeronautics and Aviation in the USSR*, Moscow, 1960

Gablehouse, Charles *Helicopters and Autogiros: A Chronicle of Rotating-Wing Aircraft*, Muller, 1967

Gibbs-Smith, Charles *Flight Through the Ages*, Thomas Y. Crowell Company Inc, 1974

Gunston, Bill *Aircraft of the Soviet Union*, Osprey, London 1983

Higham, Robin and Kipp, Jacob *Soviet Aviation and Air Power*, Brassey's, London 1978

Hubler, Richard *Straight Up*, Duell, Sloan & Pearce, New York

Izakson, Aleksandr *Sovetskoe Vertoletostroenie*, (Soviet Rotary-Wing Aircraft Design) Moscow, 1964

Kehoe, Capt J. W. and Brower, K. S. *US and Soviet Weapon System Design Practices*, 1981

Lyutov, Col I. S. and Sagaydak, Col P. T. *Motostrelkovyi Batalon v Takticheskom Vozdushnom Desante* (The Motorised Rifle Battalion in a Tactical Airborne Landing), Moscow, 1969

Mil, M. L. *Helicopters: Calculation and Design. Vol 1. Aerodynamics*

Moore, Capt John *Warships of the Soviet Navy*, Jane's, London 1981

Munson, Kenneth *Helicopters and Other Rotorcraft Since 1907*, Blandford Press Ltd, London 1973

Němeček, Vaclav *The History of Soviet Aircraft Since 1918*, Collins, London 1986

Nowarra, Heinz and Duval, G. R. *'Russian Civil and Military Aircraft 1884–1969*, Fountain Press, London 1971

Savkin, Col V. Ye. *The Basic Principles of Operational Art and Tactics*, Moscow, 1972

Scott, Harriet Fast and Scott, William *The Armed Forces of the USSR*, Arms & Armour Press, London 1981

Shavrov, V. B. *Istoriya Konstruktsii Samolëtov v SSSR do 1938* (A History of Aircraft Design in the USSR to 1938), Moscow 1969

Sweetman, Bill and Gunston, Bill *Soviet Air Power*, Salamander Books Ltd, London 1978

Sikorsky, Igor *The Story of the Winged-S*, Dodd, Mead & Company, New York 1967

Weinstein, Valery *Advanced Alloys in the Soviet Aviation Industry*, Delphic Associates Inc, Falls Church, Virginia 1986

Yakovlev, Aleksandr *The Aim of a Lifetime*, Moscow 1972

Yakovlev, Aleksandr *Notes of an Aircraft Designer*, Arno Press, 1972

Yuriev, Boris *The Aerodynamic Design of Helicopters*, Moscow 1956

The Military Balance 1987–88, International Institute for Strategic Studies, London 1987

Jane's All The World's Aircraft, Jane's, London

Soviet Military Power, US DoD, Washington

Index

Personalities

Alferov, G. 91
Alksnis, Gen Yakov I. 14
Antonov, D. I. 12
Antonov, Konstantin A. 3
Antonov, Oleg K. 205
Antonov OKB 205
Arkhangelsky, A. A. 194

Baikalov, M. K. 20, 30
Baranov, Pyotr I. 6
Baranovsky, Vladimir 35, 45
Baumhauer, A. G. von 198
Belov, Maj Gen M. 178, 179, 183, 186
Beria, Lavrenty 69
Bothezat, G. A. 194
Braginsky, J. S. 25
Bratukhin, Ivan P. 12, 13, 14, 19, 20, 22, 23, 25, 39, 192, 197, 199, 201–202, 207
Bratukhin OKB (OKB-3) 18, 19, 23, 25, 200, 201, 202
Breguet, Louis 18, 34
Brovtsev, Sergei G. 30, 71
Bunkin, K. A. 12, 197
Buryan, F. S. 5
Bykov, I. 2

Cameron, Capt J. A. 99
Chaiko, Lev 124, 148, 158
Chekalov, Lev 31
Cheremukhin, Aleksei M. 6, 10, 12, 13, 194, 197, 201
Chernavin, Adm Vladimir 67
Chernavsky, A. P. 8, 9, 10
Chernov, D. K. 2
Chernyshov, Col Yuri 181
Cierva, Juan de la 5, 8, 199
Crocco, G. A. 14

d'Ascanio 34
Dorand, Rene 18, 34

Fedotov, A. P. 5
Frunze, M. V. 174

Gagarin, Yuri A. 86
Gagen, I. S. 14
Galitsky, Boris 84

Gallai, M. L. 30
Gareyev, Col Gen M. A. 174
Garnayev, Yuri A. 72, 87
Goering, Hermann 204
Gorbachev, Mikhail 158, 171, 190
Gorshkov, Adm Sergei 58, 60, 67
Grechko, Marshal Andrei A. 135, 175
Grigorovich, Dmitri P. 199, 203
Gurov, Mikhail 35

Haq, Abdul 189
Hitler, Adolf 18

Ilyushin, Sergei V. 68, 192, 204
Isacco, Vittorio 15
Ivanov, I. D. 10
Ivchenko, A. G. 22
Izakson, Aleksandr M. 10, 12, 13, 197, 199

Johnson, President Lyndon 60

Kaganovich, Lazar M. 204
Kamov, Nikolai I. 5, 8, 9, 34, 35, 37, 39, 41, 47, 68, 192, 198, 199–200, 201, 207
Kamov OKB 34, 35, 39, 41, 45, 47, 50, 153, 154, 157, 159, 160, 161, 165, 169, 200
Kapralov, Aleks 34
Kaprelyan, R. 84
Karapetyan, Gurgen R. 136
Kasyanikov, Veniamin 49
Koloshenko, Vasily P. 112, 116
Korzinshchikov, A. S. 4
Korzinshchikov, K. A. 6, 7, 8
Koschel 198
Koshits, D. A. 6, 8, 13
Kozyrev, Ivan 8, 9
Kuznetsov, Vyacheslav A. 6, 7, 8, 192, 199

Lapisov, V. P. 12, 199
Lavochkin OKB 205
Lenin, Vladimir I. 14, 15, 193, 194
Leymer, A. L. 197
Lilienthal, Otto 195
Lodygin, A. N. 1, 2
Lomonosov, Mikhail V. 1, 14
Loutzky, Boris 4
Lyutov, Col I. S. 191

228

Aircraft types

Aero engines

Weapons and Equipment

Warships

Military formations

General